Black African Voices

Uche Okeke, Beautiful Nza (Nigeria), 1958. Pen and ink.

Black
African
Voices

JAMES E. MILLER, JR.
Professor of English, University
of Chicago. Awarded Fulbright to Italy, 1958–1959.
Author of *Quests Surd and Absurd: Essays in American
Literature,* and other works.

ROBERT O'NEAL
Professor and Chairman of the English
Department, San Antonio College. Author of *Teachers'
Guide to World Literature for the High School* and con-
tributor of articles to professional publications.

HELEN M. McDONNELL
Chairman, English Department,
Ocean Township High School, Oakhurst, New Jersey.
Contributor of articles to professional publications.

Introductory Essay
Africa of My Grandmother's Singing: Curving Rhythms
by Wilfred G. O. Cartey

SCOTT, FORESMAN AND COMPANY

Editorial Direction / LEO B. KNEER

Development / MARGARET RAUSCH
with Ghia Brenner, Dorothy Koeber, Fitzgerald Higgins, and
Susan Green
Design / ROBERT AMFT

The authors and editors of *Black African Voices*
wish to express their appreciation to the following teachers.
Acting as reader-consultants, they chose from the many
selections submitted to them those that they believed were most
relevant to the interests and needs of today's youth. They tested
their opinions against classroom use and contributed ideas
that evolved during the give-and-take of class discussion.

SISTER EUGENE FOX, S.C.
Seton High School
Cincinnati, Ohio

MR. THOMAS GAGE
Concord High School
Concord, California

MRS. JEANNE LUCKETT
Provine High School
Jackson, Mississippi

MR. RONALD MIDKIFF
Rome City Schools
Rome, Georgia

MR. ELMER E. MOORE, JR.
Dobbs Ferry High School
Dobbs Ferry, New York

MR. ROBERT ROMANO
Concord–Carlisle High School
Concord, Massachusetts

MRS. ELIZABETH DRUM McDOWELL
Highland Heights High School
Nashville, Tennessee

COVER: Jimoh Buraimoh: Bead Work on Cloth (Oshogbo). Courtesy of Pall Mall Press, London.

CONTENTS

AFRICA OF MY GRANDMOTHER'S SINGING: CURVING RHYTHMS

Wilfred G. O. Cartey

We cannot pigeonhole the voices of the black continent of Africa, voices which recall the past, pulsate with the present, and are tremulous with the future. Mabel Segun of Nigeria wonders:

> *. . . which part of me will be supreme—*
> *the old and tested one, the present*
> *or the future unknown.*
> *Sometimes all three have equal power*
> *and then*
> *how I long for a pigeon-hole.*[1]

And like her, we may want to pigeonhole the various voices which speak in this anthology, but we dare not. For how can we pigeonhole a gourd full of wisdom scattered all over the earth of Africa? Each person must take his own bit of wisdom from the earth of Africa, wisdom scattered generously by a folk hero, Anansi:

An internationally known authority on African and Caribbean literature and culture, Wilfred Cartey has published numerous studies and works on Africa, including an anthology of African literature, a two-volume reader on African history, culture, and politics, and most recently, Whispers From A Continent: The Literature of Contemporary Black Africa. *Cartey, who is himself a poet, is at present Literary Editor of* African Forum *and Associate Professor of African Literature at Columbia University.*

---

1. The authors and selections from which the quotations in this essay are taken, together with the pages on which the quotations may be found, are listed at the end of the essay in the order in which they are mentioned.

> *"My son, you are right: but your words show to me*
> *that it is better for many people to have wisdom*
> *rather than one. . . ." So speaking, he opened the*
> *gourd and scattered the wisdom all over the ground*
> *so that he who may want it can gather what he will.*

Wisdom comes from many voices: from the folk voices of Africa where reside the oral traditions of the Continent, and from the voices of those who speak to us now from Senegal and Nigeria, from Ghana and Sierra Leone in the west of the continent, from across the Sudan to Ethiopia in the east and down through Tanzania to South Africa at the southern end of the continent.

So let us accept the call of one of these voices, Léopold Sédar Senghor of Senegal:

> *Let the rhythmic silence cradle us.*
> *Let us listen to its song, let us listen to the*
> *   beat of our dark blood, let us listen*
> *To the deep pulse of Africa beating in the midst*
> *   of forgotten villages.*

But the villages of Africa are not forgotten, for their pulse beat is so strong that both animate and inanimate things are vital. The whole landscape through which we travel in these selections is animated. The spirit world is alive and gives life to the living: The essential ontology of Africa linking and curving through ancestor and offspring, man and nature, beast and trees, sea and fires . . . nothing is dead, no voice is still:

> *Hear the fire's voice,*
> *Hear the voice of water.*
> *In the wind hear the sobbing of the trees,*
> *It is our forefathers breathing.*
>
> *The dead are not gone forever. . . .*
> *They are in the rustling tree,*
> *In the murmuring wood,*

> *In the still water,*
> *In the flowing water,*
> *In the lonely place, in the crowd. . . .*
> *They are in a woman's breast,*
> *A child's crying, a glowing ember.*

An essential continuity is preserved between earth-mother and child, earth-mother whose breast provides sustenance to son, son who is son of all Africa, son through whom dead father lives and is reborn. So the Sudanese mother sings as she rocks through time:

> *Clutching my breast with your hand,*
> *So strong and firm for all its littleness. . . .*
> *Whose spirit is it that is in you, little warrior?*

For through the little child, life flows; and even though there is no shadow to the father, life is sweet at Kumansenu where:

> *The sea and the wet sand to one side of it;*
> *green tropical forest on the other; above it the*
> *slow tumbling clouds. The clean round blinding*
> *disc of sun and the blue sky, covered and sur-*
> *rounded the small African village, Kameni.*

and where only a little child can unlock her dead father's trinket. In African belief, the child is close to the ancestors and it is Asi who can communicate with the spirit of her father or with the spirit of her father's father. So it is that sometimes the past and present and future merge and "sometimes all three have equal power."

In the play *Edufa* by Efua T. Sutherland, Ampoma, fated to die, bridging past, present, and future, wails to her mother a lament for her children:

> *. . . Children! My children! If I could cross this*
> *water, I would pluck you back from the mountain-*
> *side. . . . Children! . . . And . . . Mother . . . Mother.*

Edufa, the son, will turn back to Kankam, his father, for solace:

> *If you see my father, call him back that I may*
> *weep on his shoulder.*

And Abena, Edufa's sister, grieves for the child of Ama, for Ampoma's dying:

> *O child of Ama,*
> *Child of Ama in the night*
> *Is wandering,*
> *Crying, "Mm-m-m-m,*
> *How my mother's pondering."*
> *O child of Ama,*
> *Why is she wandering,*
> *Why wandering,*
> *Why wandering in the night*
> *Like the dying?*
> *Meewuo!*

So the play of daughter-father, daughter-mother, of son-father, of the African child, unfolds before us in many of these selections.

Camara Laye tells us of his early childhood in Guinea, of totemic traditions, of his father's craft wisdom, and of his father's creative genius inspired by the guardian spirit of the little black snake. He tells too of his mother's careful nurturing and of his grandmother's pampering. From all of these he garners his wisdom. He also gathers his wisdom from oral tradition, from the folk tales.

Like Camara Laye's mother, concerned about her husband's largess and his wasting his powers in the creating of gold trinkets, the wife in an anonymous Ethiopian folk tale is equally concerned about her husband's squandering his powers on other women and not on her. As in so many of the folk tales and selections, where mediation, counseling, and judgment play a large part, the woman here turns to a mediator for advice. His counsel is sage and natural—the cat is wild, sweeten him.

At times the mediator's judgment elicits a chuckle and wry commentary from the plaintiffs and the bystanders:

> *"Ah, how good it is!" they said to each other.*
> *"How did we ever get along before justice was*
> *given to us?"*

For here, in the humorously told folk tale "Justice" the judge is not only blind but deaf. The anonymous "Talking Skull," "Talk," and "Anansi's Fishing Expedition" are all humorously told. In "Talking Skull" the humor is macabre; in "Talk" the humor stems from the natural animation of landscape and matter; yams talk, dogs talk, trees talk, branches talk, stones talk, fish traps talk, cloths talk, and rivers talk. Using an incremental repetition, this folk tale comes full circle with the final parody of a pompous chief:

> *The chief listened to them patiently, but he*
> *couldn't refrain from scowling. . . . So the men went*
> *away, and the chief shook his head and mumbled to*
> *himself, "Nonsense like that upsets the community."*
> *"Fantastic, isn't it?" his stool said. "Imagine,*
> *a talking yam!"*

However, even when parodied, the general counseling and mediation by elders—chiefs, witch doctors, judges—represents the lore in action serving as a basis for morality, a directive to behavior, a carrier of traditional wisdom.

But the essence of the folk tale is its easy narrative element, its story-telling, yarn-spinning quality which makes of disbelief belief and wonder. Many African writers attempt to capture the fluidity of traditional tales in their stories, adding, of course, their own personal stamp to their creation.

There is an easy lyrical note singing through Fagunwa's "Forest of the Lord" where

> *". . . The birds there speak with human voices and*
> *the animals buy and sell with each other. Many*
> *of the trees there have no roots, yet their wood*
> *is fresh and their leaves are glossy and green.*
> *A mouse in the Forest of the Lord is bigger than*
> *an ordinary bush-rat and a snail is bigger than a*

> *tortoise. Powerful sprites and grim hobgoblins*
> *are in league there and all sorts of bold snakes*
> *cast fear on hunters, for it is there that the*
> *chief snake of all the world lives, whose name*
> *is 'Angry Python'."*

Peopling his forest with snakes and animals and sprites, this Nigerian writer evokes a whole spirit world which can be charmed by the sound of an ancestral flute played by a brave man, father to the story teller:

> *My father. . . . took this flute and began to blow it and*
> *the sound of this flute filled the whole place. . . . and*
> *the songs were echoed throughout the forest. Now this*
> *flute was sweeter than a king's flute and as the song*
> *of the flute was a lament it could not fail to enter*
> *the recesses of the sprite's brain. . . . The little crea-*
> *ture . . . spoke, saying . . . "I thank you for the lament*
> *which you sang, a song full of wisdom. . . ."*

The ancestral flute had charmed the forest; in Ghana the traditional drums boom out to pay homage to the spirit of the sea, the whale, in Blay's essay "Funeral of a Whale" when

> *. . . bound by tradition, the fishermen must bear the*
> *unhappy tidings to the ruler of the town. . . . The*
> *state drums boom out the warning of great calamity.*
> *. . . The funeral ceremony being declared open, the*
> *women like minstrels tell the story of the whale*
> *in parables. . . . The young men keep order and play*
> *native instruments, while the old correct any de-*
> *parture from the traditional funeral procedure.*

And a single drum roll also heralds another death when Stanley meets Mutesa [2]:

---

2. Henry Morton Stanley, an American journalist, led an expedition to the court of King Mutesa of Buganda, a region northwest of Lake Victoria, in 1875.

> *Only a few silent nods from aged faces*
> *And one rumbling drum roll*
> *To summon Mutesa's court to parley*
> *For the country was not sure.*
>
> *The gate of reeds is flung open,*
> *There is silence . . .*
> *The tall black king steps forward,*
> *He towers over the thin bearded white man*
> *Then grabbing his lean white hand*
> *Manages to whisper*
> *"Mtu mweupe karibu"*
> *White man you are welcome.*
> *The gate of polished reed closes behind them*
> *And the West is let in.*

Many conflicts ensued from the opening of that gate to the West. The many traditions questioned and abused, the many doubts aroused, the many allegiances shaken trouble Mabel Segun to identify the world, the culture to which she really belongs:

> *poised between two civilisations. . . .*
> *I'm tired of hanging in the middle way—*
> *but where can I go?*

The encounter of these two civilizations brought not only tiredness but also death to the people of the African continent, to the people so fertile in humanity that Bernard Dadié of the Ivory Coast sings:

> *I would sing to you*
> *You who hold heaven within reach. . . .*
> *You who like to hear a woman laugh,*
> *You who like to watch a child play,*
> *You who like to offer your hand*
> *To form a chain*
>
> *Bullets still behead the roses*
> *in the mornings of dreams.*

And now, the conscripted warrior, thinking of his love and of his child, dies fighting to regain his land from Stanley and the West:

> *He went there*
> *Involuntarily*
> *He went there*
> *And the courage was not his own*
> *And the hate was not his own. . . .*
> *There was his wife*
> *There were his children his mother a letter*
> *There was so much*
> *But all crumbled away*
> *All*
> *In the treacherous cackling*
> *Of the grenades*
> *With yellow beaks*
> *And red tails . . .*

Yet even though others flee their homeland, going into exile like Peter Abrahams to tell freedom, or are jailed in South Africa without raising a hand of protest, the song to the African earth continues. The song to the earth which nourishes its children is told in many lyric and epic passages, like this in Richard Rive's "African Song."

> *And then everyone was standing and Muti watched fasci-*
> *natedly as the people sang . . . . And already this one*
> *was led away because he had no pass . . . . one must not*
> *lift the hand in protest. And still the people sang . . . .*
> *God bless Africa. God bless the sun-scorched Karoo*
> *and the green of the Valley of a Thousand Hills . . . .*
> *the mountain streams that chatter impudently . . . . the*
> *mighty waters that hurl themselves against her shores.*
> *. . . the cataracts that taunt the solemn rocks, and the*
> *African sky that spits blood in the evening . . . . the*
> *timeless hills . . . . this Africa of heat and cold, and*
> *laughter and tears, and deep joy and bitter sorrow.*
> *. . . this Africa of blue skies and brown veld . . . .*

The earth of Africa, sung of in many of these selections, is reassuring, revitalizing its children, promising new beginnings. Lenrie Peters of Gambia sings in "Parachute":

> *As the warm earth*
> *Reaches out to you,*
> *Reassures you*
> *The vibrating interim is over . . . .*
> *Earth has nowhere to go:*
> *You are at the starting point . . . .*
> *We are always at the starting point.*

And David Diop of Senegal accepts the message of these beginnings, hears the singing of the rebirth of his continent:

> *Africa of my grandmother's singing*
> *Along the banks of her far-off river . . . .*
> *Africa tell me Africa*
> *Is it you . . . .*
>
> *Then gravely a voice answered me:*
> *Impetuous son, that young and robust tree*
> *That tree over there*
> *Splendidly alone midst white faded flowers*
> *It is Africa your Africa that springs up again*
> *Springs up patiently obstinately*
> *And whose fruits ripen with*
> *The bitter flavor of freedom.*

Now Soyinka's appeal for rain

> *O it must rain*
> *These closures on the mind, binding us*
> *In strange despairs, teaching*
> *Purity of sadness*

no longer goes unanswered. Now the fertilizing rain pounds through the land and the continent bringing rest and freedom, and Clark says:

> *So let us roll over on our back*
> *And again roll to the beat*
> *Of drumming all over the land*
> *And under its ample soothing hand*
> *Joined to that of the sea*
> *We will settle to sleep of the innocent and free.*

Now the splendid vision opens out, the vision of freedom, liberation and the regrouping of black comrades. The vision extends beyond the shores of Africa, outwards, to the Americas. And as before, time—past, present, and future—merged, so too here, distant geographies where the black man lives flow together. Diop can exhort:

> *For there rings out higher than my sorrows*
> *Purer than the morning where the wild beast wakes*
> *The cry of a hundred people smashing their cells*
> *And my blood long held in exile*
> *The blood they hoped to snare in a circle of words*
> *Rediscovers the fervour that scatters the mists*
> *Listen comrades of the struggling centuries*
> *To the keen clamour of the Negro from Africa to the*
> *   Americas*
> *It is the sign of the dawn*
> *The sign of brotherhood which comes to nourish the*
> *   dreams of men.*

And with the awakening, with the rediscovery, with the vigilant returning, with the shedding of the foreigner's suit, the comrades can

> *Walk in peace, walk alone, walk tall,*
> *walk free, walk naked*

as the Ethiopian poet Medhen sings out:

> *Let the roots of your motherland caress your body,*
> *Let the naked skin absorb the home-sun and shine*
> *   ebony.*

PASSAGES QUOTED IN THE ESSAY

Mabel Segun, "The Pigeon-Hole," page 322
Anonymous, "The Gourd Full of Wisdom," page 82
Léopold Sédar Senghor, "Night of Sine," page 325
Birago Diop, "Forefathers," page 105
Anonymous, "Song of a Mother to Her First-born," page 60
Abioseh Nicol, "Life is Sweet at Kumansenu," page 276
Efua T. Sutherland, *Edufa,* pages 339, 382, 333
Anonymous, "Justice," page 64
Anonymous, "Talk," page 67
D. O. Fagunwa, "The Forest of the Lord," pages 161, 171
J. Benibengor Blay, "Funeral of a Whale," page 87
James D. Rubadiri, "Stanley Meets Mutesa," page 320
Mabel Segun, "Conflict," page 322
Bernard Dadié, "Men of All Continents," page 94
Rui Nogar, "Poem of the Conscripted Warrior," page 285
Richard Rive, "African Song," page 301
Lenrie Peters, "Parachute," page 298
David Diop, "Africa," page 107
Wole Soyinka, "I Think It Rains," page 330
J. P. Clark, "Night Rain," page 91
David Diop, "Listen Comrades," page 108
Tsegaye Gabre Medhen, "Home-Coming Son," pages 252, 253

Peter Abrahams / *South Africa*
(1919–   )

THE BLACKS

IT WAS a hot, humid, oppressive August day in Accra, capital of the Gold Coast that was to become Ghana.[1] The air had the stillness of death. I walked down toward the sea front. Perhaps there would be the hint of a breeze there. As I neared the sea front I was assailed by a potent stench of the sea with strong overtones of rotting fish.

The houses were drab, run-down wooden structures or made of corrugated iron, put together any way you please. The streets were wide and tarred, and each street had an open drainage system. . . . I have seen women empty chamber pots into these drains in the early morning. The fierce sun takes care of the germs, but God help you if smells make you sick.

In about eight minutes of walking, some fifteen "taxis" pulled up beside me: "Hi, massa! Taxi, massa! Me go anywhere you go cheap!" They are all private taxis with no meters and driven by strapping young men with flashing teeth. The place is full of taxi drivers willing to go anywhere and do anything cheap.

The street traders here are women. "Mammy traders," they are called. They trade in everything. They sell cigarettes, one at a time; round loaves of bread and hunks of cooked meat on which the big West African flies make sport. They love bargaining and

---

"The Blacks" by Peter Abrahams, originally from *Holiday Magazine* (1959). Copyright © 1959 by Perfect Publishing Co. Reprinted by permission of Curtis Brown, Ltd.

1. *the Gold Coast . . . Ghana.* The Gold Coast, upon gaining its independence from Britain in 1957, took the name of the ancient West African kingdom of Ghana.

haggling. They are a powerful economic factor in the life of the country. The more prosperous ones own their own trucks, some own fleets of trucks. These "mammy trucks" are the principal carriers of the country. They carry passengers as well as produce and go hurtling across the countryside with little regard for life or limb. Each truck has its own distinctive slogan, such as: *Repent for Death is Round the Corner*, or *Enter Without Hope*, or *The Last Ride* or *If it Must it Will*. My own favorite—and I traveled in this particular truck—pleaded *Not Today O Lord Not Today*.

I passed many mammy traders, many mammy trucks, before I reached the sea front. I crossed a street, jumped over an open drain, and there was the sea. But there was no breeze, and no shade from the terrible sun. In the end I gave in to the idea of "taxi, massa, taxi" and looked about for one. But now there was no taxi in sight. Instead, I saw suddenly a long procession of many women and a few men. The procession swung round a corner and came into full view, twenty or thirty yards long. The women wore white flowing robes and white kerchiefs on their heads. Their faces were painted into grotesque masks made with thick streaks of black, red, white and yellow paints. The heavy thud of bare feet rose above the hum of the sea.

Then, all at once, the drums burst forth and there was no other sound about me. The marching women began to jig, then dance. As the tail of the procession passed me the drums reached a frenzy. A thin, pure note from a reed rose above the drums. The whole procession became a shivering, shaking mass. The reed note held longer than seemed human. And then, dramatically, there was silence. The thudding feet faded away out of sight and sound. There was silence and a slight racing of my heartbeat and the hum of the sea, and, of course, the overpowering fishy stench.

I thought of Richard Wright,[2] with whom I had had breakfast that morning. This was his first visit to any part of Africa and

---

2. *Richard Wright* (1908–1960), prominent black American novelist.

he seemed to find it bewildering. Countee Cullen, the late American Negro poet, had speculated:

> One three centuries removed
> From the scenes his fathers loved,
> Spicy grove, cinnamon tree,
> What is Africa to me?

Wright was finding the answers and finding them disconcerting. . . . He expressed to me that morning what he later summed up in his book on the Gold Coast: "I was black and they were black but it did not help me."

What Wright did not understand, what his whole background and training had made difficult for him to understand, was that being black did not of itself qualify one for acceptance in tribal Africa. But how could he, when there are thousands of urban-bred Africans up and down the vast continent who do not themselves understand this? The more perceptive of the urban Africans are only now beginning to comprehend, but slowly.

Being black is a small matter in tribal Africa because the attitude toward color is healthy and normal. Color does not matter. Color is an act of God that neither confers privileges nor imposes handicaps on a man. A man's skin is like the day: the day is either clear or dark. There is nothing more to it until external agencies come in and invest it with special meaning and importance.

What does matter to the tribal African, what is important, is the complex pattern of his position within his own group and his relations with the other members of the group. He is no Pan-African dreaming of a greater African glory when the white man is driven into the sea. The acute race consciousness of the American Negro, or of the black South African at the receiving end of apartheid,[3] is alien to him. The important things in his life are anything but race and color—until they are forced on him. And "Mother Africa" is much too vast to inspire big continental

---

3. *apartheid* (ə pärt′hāt,-hīt), the policy of white supremacy and racial segregation pursued by the Union of South Africa.

dreams in him. She is a land of huge mountains, dark jungles and vast deserts. In her rivers and in her jungles and in her grasslands lurk creatures that are the enemies of man: the leopard and the lion, the snake and crocodile. All this makes travel, by the old African methods, extremely difficult and makes for isolation between one group of people and another. The African who is in Britain is likely to be a deal better informed on what is happening all over the continent than would be his fellow African in any of the main centers of both tribal and nontribal Africa. In terms of communications the man in the tribe lives in the Dark Ages.

Richard Wright was surprised that even educated Africans, racially conscious literate people, had not heard of him and were skeptical of a grown man earning his living by writing. They could not understand what kind of writing brought a man enough money to support a family. Wright really wanted to understand the African, but—"I found the African an oblique, a hard-to-know man."

My sympathies were all with Wright.

The heat and salty rancid fish smell had made me desperately thirsty. Across the way a mammy trader squatted beside her pile of merchandise: cooked meats, sweet potatoes—a whole host of edibles—and some bottles of opaque white liquid that could be either coconut milk or palm juice as well as the inevitable little pile of cigarettes priced at a penny apiece. I had been warned of the risks involved in eating anything sold by the street traders. But to hell with it. I was thirsty and not exactly a stranger to African germs. I crossed the street, felt the bottles and chose the one that seemed coolest and looked the least opaque.

"How much?"

"One shilling." [4] The carved ebony face looked at me with dead eyes.

I pulled the screwed-up newspaper stopper from the bottle, wiped its mouth and took a swig. I could not decide whether it was coconut milk or palm juice. It had been heavily watered

---

4. *shilling*, fourteen cents before devaluation.

down and sweetened. But it was wet and thirst-quenching. I drank half the bottle, firmly ignoring the little foreign bodies that floated in the liquid. Then I paid her and drank the rest. I put down the empty and began to move away.

"You African?" she asked in her harsh, cold, masculine voice.

I stopped, turned and looked at her face. It was as deadly cold and impersonal as before: not a flicker of feeling in her eyes. Like an African mask, I thought. But unlike Wright, I did not try to penetrate it; I knew the futility of trying. She would show feeling if and when she decided, not before.

"Yes," I said, and added, "from the south. Far, far south."

She paused for so long that I began to move again.

"You like here?" Nationalism had obviously touched her.

I turned back to her. "No," I said.

"Why you don't like?"

"I don't say I don't like."

"But you don't like?"

I showed her my teeth, African-wise, which is neither smile nor grimace but a blending of the two. "*You* like Africa?" I asked.

Now it was her turn to show me her teeth. There was a flicker of feeling in her eyes, then they went dead again. She nodded. I had established my claim. Only outsiders—white people or the Richard Wrights—liked or disliked Africa.

I left the mammy trader and carried on up the smelly and hot street. Much and little had passed between us. Out to sea some fishing boats appeared on the sky line. About me were the citizens of Accra. Some wore the cloth of the country—the men looking like pint-sized citizens of ancient Rome painted black and the women looking extraordinarily masculine—and others wore western dress.

My thoughts shifted to my forthcoming meeting with Kwame Nkrumah,[5] Ghana's first prime minister. It was well over seven

---

5. *Kwame Nkrumah* (kwä′mä nə krü′mä), (1909–   ), Ghanian nationalist who became the first president of the new Republic of Ghana in 1960. He was deposed by the army and the police in 1966.

years since I had last seen him, in London. Then he was a poor struggling student; now he was the head of a state and the spokesman for the great Pan-African dream of freedom and independence.

I remembered our past friendship and wondered what changes I would find in him. Anyway, it was now 9 A.M. and my date with him was for 9:30. I would soon know.

A few minutes later I flagged a taxi and simply said, "Kwame's office."

A pale-brown West Indian miss was the prime minister's secretary. She welcomed me as though I was a V.I.P. The prime minister had not come back from a conference yet. The tribal business was taking up a lot of his attention. She told me with indignation how members of the Ashanti tribe had to crawl on their bellies for some twenty yards into the presence of their king, the Asantehene, and how tribalism had to give way or there would be no progress. If she was any indication, then Nkrumah was very worried about the opposition the tribesmen were offering his western-style Convention Peoples Party.

A number of officials came in. The lady stopped assailing the tribes. Then there was some bustle and the prime minister arrived. In something just over five minutes he had seen and dealt with these officials and I was ushered into his office. It was a big, pleasant, cool room.

Nkrumah came round his big official desk, took my hand and led me to a settee near the window. The now famous smile lit up his face. As we exchanged greetings, felt each other out with small talk in an attempt to bridge the gap of years, my mind went back to our London days. This poised, relaxed man, with the hint of guarded reserve about him, was a far cry from the friend I had last seen nearly eight years earlier.

For me, the most striking change of all was in his eyes. They reflected an inner tranquillity which was the one thing the Nkrumah in Europe never had.

Even his name had been subtly different then. He had been our friend Francis Nkrumah, an African student recently arrived from the United States, and he had not seen Africa for a decade and more. He had quickly become a part of our African colony in London and had joined our little group, the Pan-African Federation, in our protests against colonialism.

He was much less relaxed than most of us. His eyes mirrored a burning inner conflict and tension. He seemed consumed by a restlessness that led him to evolve some of the most fantastic schemes.

The president of our federation was an East African named Johnstone Kenyatta,[6] the most relaxed, sophisticated and "westernized" of the lot of us. Kenyatta enjoyed the personal friendship of some of the most distinguished people in English political and intellectual society. He was subtle, subtle enough to attack one's principles bitterly and retain one's friendship. He fought the British as imperialists but was affectionate toward them as friends.

It was to this balanced and extremely cultured man that Francis Nkrumah proposed that we form a secret society called The Circle, and that each of us spill a few drops of our blood into a bowl and so take a blood oath of secrecy and dedication to the emancipation of Africa.

Johnstone Kenyatta laughed at the idea; he scoffed at it as childish juju. He conceived our struggle in modern, twentieth-century terms with no ritualistic blood nonsense. In the end Francis Nkrumah drifted away from us and started his own little West African group in London. We were too tame and slow for him. He was an angry man in a hurry.

Then he went back to his part of Africa, and Francis Nkrumah became Kwame Nkrumah. He set himself at the head of the largely tribal populace and dabbled in blood ritual. There was some violence, a spell in prison, and finally Nkrumah emerged as the first African prime minister in a self-governing British African territory.

Tribal myths grew up around him. He could make himself

---

6. *Johnstone Kenyatta* (1891–   ), called *Jomo*, Kenyan nationalist. He became the first president of the new Republic of Kenya in 1964. See page 190.

invisible at will. He could go without food and sleep and drink longer than ordinary mortals. He was, in fact, the reincarnation of some of the most powerful ancestral spirits. He allowed his feet to be bathed in blood.

By the time I visited the Gold Coast the uneasy alliance between Nkrumah and the tribal chiefs had begun to crack. A week or so before my arrival he had threatened that, unless they co-operated with his government in turning the Gold Coast into an efficient twentieth-century state, he would make them run so hard that they would leave their sandals behind them. This was a calculated insult to the tribal concept that a chief's bare feet must never touch the earth.

That was the beginning of the secret war. Nkrumah thought he would win it easily. He was wrong.

And the chiefs have, negatively, scored their victories too. They have pushed him to a point where his regime is, today, intolerant of opposition. The tribal society brooks no opposition. Nkrumah's government banishes its most active opponents. As a modern socialist leading a western-style government, he justifies this as a temporary expedient. But his less sophisticated ministers frankly talk the tribal language of strength, frankly express the tribal impulse to destroy those who are out of step.

There was an air of delicacy about our conversation and we were both aware of this. We touched on local politics. He let off at full blast against the tribalist. I told him I had heard that the Accra Club was still exclusively European. His eyes lit up. "You wait and see," he said. Then, in relation to nothing either of us had said, he leaned toward me and exclaimed, "This place is rich! God, man, there's so much riches here!"—as though the revelation had just been made to him.

But always, throughout our talk, I sensed a new reserve, a new caution that had not been there in the young student I had known in Europe.

As we talked in Nkrumah's cool office that hot August day in Accra, my mind kept slipping back to our mutual friend Jomo or Johnstone Kenyatta, now imprisoned in his native Kenya for leading the Mau-Mau movement.[7] Significantly, though we mentioned many friends, both Nkrumah and I avoided Kenyatta. I had decided not to mention him first. I had hoped Nkrumah would. He did not.

A year earlier, I had flown up to Kenya from South Africa and visited Kenyatta. I felt terribly depressed as I got off the plane. Things had grown so much uglier in the Union. The barricades were up in the ugly war of color. When I had left South Africa in the dim-and-distant past, there were isolated islands where black and white could meet in neutral territory. When I went back in 1952, the islands were submerged under the rising tide of color hatreds, and I was glad to quit that dark, unhappy land which yet compelled my love.

It was in this mood that I got off the plane. I had not seen my friend Jomo for years. Now there he was, just outside the airport terminal building, leaning on a heavy cane, bigger than I remembered him in Europe, paunchy, his face looking puffy. And behind him was a huge crowd of Africans.

I began to move toward him when a lean-faced, lean-hipped white colonial-administrator type suddenly appeared beside me and said: "Mr. Abrahams."

I stopped and thought, "Oh, Lord."

Kenyatta also came forward. The two men ignored each other. Lean-face introduced himself and said the Colonial Office had alerted them that I was coming to do some writing for the London *Observer* and they had drawn up a provisional schedule for me. Had I done anything about accommodations?

Before I could answer, Kenyatta said, "You are staying with me, of course." The old detachment was back in his eyes. They seemed to say, "You've got to choose, pal. Let's see how you choose."

---

7. *the Mau-Mau movement.* The Mau-Mau rebellion in the early 1950's primarily involved Kikuyu (ki kü′yü) tribesmen who wanted to drive European settlers from the fertile highlands of Kenya. A state of emergency was declared by the British government, and troops were brought in to crush the revolt. Most of the rebels had been driven into remote areas by 1956, but order was not completely restored until the end of the decade.

Lean-face said, "We've got something set up for you for tomorrow and—"

"I live in the bush," Kenyatta added.

It dawned on me that I had become, for the moment, the battlefield of that horrible animal, the racial struggle. I made up my mind, resenting both sides and yet conscious of the crowd of Africans in the background. A question of face was involved.

"I've promised to spend this weekend with Mr. Kenyatta," I said.

Lean-face was graceful about it. I promised to call the Secretariat first thing on Monday morning. He gave me a copy of the schedule that had been prepared for me and wondered, *sotto voce,* whether I knew what I was letting myself in for. Kenyatta assured me that I would be perfectly safe, that nobody was going to cut my throat. I was aware that they were talking to each other through me. I was aware that they knew I was aware, and that made me bad-tempered.

"Then I'll say good night, Mr. Abrahams," Lean-face said pointedly.

As soon as he was out of hearing Kenyatta began to curse.

"It's good to see you again, Johnstone," I gripped his hand.

"Jomo," he replied. The hint of ironic speculation was back in his eyes. A slightly sardonic, slightly bitter smile played on his lips.

"Welcome to Kenya, Peter," he said. Then, abruptly: "Come meet the leaders of my people. They've been waiting long."

We moved forward and the crowd gathered about us. Jomo made a little speech in Kikuyu,[8] then translated it for my benefit. A little old man, ancient as the hills, with huge holes in his ears, then welcomed me on behalf of the land and its people. Again Jomo translated.

After this we all bundled into the fleet of rattling old cars and set off for the Kikuyu reserve in the heart of the African bush. Kenyatta became silent and strangely remote during the journey.

We stopped at the old chief's compound, where other mem-

8. *Kikuyu* (ki kü′yü), the language of the principal people of Kenya.

bers of the tribe waited to welcome me. By this time the reception committee had grown to a few hundred. About me, pervading the air, was the stench of burning flesh; a young cow was being roasted in my honor. Before I entered the house a drink was handed to me. Another was handed to the old chief and a third to Kenyatta. The old man muttered a brief incantation and spilled half his drink on the earth as a libation. Jomo and I followed suit. Then the three of us downed our drinks and entered the house.

A general feasting and drinking then commenced, both inside and outside the house. I was getting a full ceremonial tribal welcome. The important dignitaries of the tribe slipped into the room in twos and threes, spoke to me through Kenyatta for a few moments, and then went away, making room for others.

"Africa doesn't seem to change," Kenyatta murmured between dignitaries. There was a terrible undercurrent of bitterness behind the softly murmured words. I was startled by it and looked at his face. For a fleeting moment he looked like a trapped, caged animal.

He saw me looking at him and quickly composed his face into a slightly sardonic, humorous mask. "Don't look too closely," he said.

And still the dignitaries filed in, had a drink, spoke their welcome and went out.

The ceremonial welcome reached its high point about midnight. Huge chunks of the roasted cow were brought in to us, and we gnawed at the almost raw meat between swigs of liquor. Outside, there was muted drumming. Voices were growing louder and louder.

Suddenly, in the midst of a long-winded speech by an immensely dignified Masai [9] chief from a neighboring and friendly tribe, Kenyatta jumped up, grabbed his heavy cane and half staggered through the door.

"Come, Peter," he called.

Everybody was startled. I hesitated. He raised his cane and

9. *Masai* (mä sī′), a nomadic people of East Africa.

beckoned to me with it. I knew that this would be a dreadful breach of tribal etiquette.

"Come, man!" he snapped.

I got up, aware of the sudden silence that had descended on the huge gathering. By some strange magic everybody seemed to know that something had gone wrong.

"Jomo," I said.

"I can't stand any more," he snapped. "Come!"

I followed him to the door. I knew the discourtesy we were inflicting on the tribe. I also knew that my friend was at the breaking point. We walked through the crowd of people, got into Kenyatta's car and drove off into the night. The African moon was big and yellow, bathing the land in a soft light that almost achieved the clarity of daylight.

He took me to his home. It was a big, sprawling, empty place on the brow of a hill. Inside, it had nothing to make for comfort. There were hard wooden chairs, a few tables and only the bed in the bedroom. There were no books, none of the normal amenities of western civilization. When we arrived two women emerged from somewhere in the back and hovered about in the shadows. They brought in liquor, but I never got a clear glimpse of either of them. My friend's anguish of spirit was such that I did not want to ask questions. We sat on the veranda and drank steadily and in silence until we were both miserably, depressingly drunk.

And then Kenyatta began to speak in a low, bitter voice of his frustration and of the isolated position in which he found himself. He had no friends. There was no one in the tribe who could give him the intellectual companionship that had become so important to him in his years in Europe. The things that were important to him—consequential conversation, the drink that represented a social activity rather than the intention to get drunk, the concept of individualism, the inviolability of privacy —all these were alien to the tribesmen in whose midst he lived. So Kenyatta, the western man, was driven in on himself and was forced to assert himself in tribal terms. Only thus would the tribesmen follow him and so give him his position of power and importance as a leader.

To live without roots is to live in hell, and no man chooses voluntarily to live in hell. The people who could answer his needs as a western man had erected a barrier of color against him in spite of the fact that the taproots of their culture had become the taproots of his culture too. By denying him access to those things which complete the life of western man, they had forced him back into the tribalism from which he had so painfully freed himself over the years.

None of this was stated explicitly by either Kenyatta or myself. But it was there in his brooding bitter commentary on both the tribes and the white settlers of the land. For me, Kenyatta became that night a man who in his own life personified the terrible tragedy of Africa and the terrible secret war that rages in it. He was the victim both of tribalism and of westernism gone sick. His heart and mind and body were the battlefield of the ugly violence known as the Mau-Mau revolt long before it broke out in that beautiful land. The tragedy is that he was so rarely gifted, that he could have made such a magnificent contribution in other circumstances.

What then is tribal man? Perhaps his most important single characteristic is that he is not an individual in the western sense. Psychologically and emotionally he is the present living personification of a number of forces, among the most important of which are the ancestral dead. The dead have a powerful hold on the living. They control and regulate the lives and activities of the living from the grave. They hand out the rules and codes by which the living conduct their daily affairs. If there is a drought, if there is a famine, it is a sign that the ancestors are angry because someone has broken a rule of the tribe, a law laid down by the dead. There will be no peace, no order, no prosperity in the tribe until the ancestors are appeased.

So the chief calls the whole tribe to a meeting in which the guilty ones will be "smelled out." The procedure begins with the drums—a key factor in African life. Their insistent throbs call the people to the gathering on a placid, almost monotonous key at first, but working on the emotions. Everyone in the village will be present; no man, woman or child would think of not obeying the summons. They form a circle, with the witch doctor or medicine man and the drummers to the fore. When all the people are assembled the throbbing of the drums increases. They beat in tune to the heartbeats of the human circle.

The witch doctor is dressed in lion or leopard skin, sometimes in monkey skin. His face is painted in bold streaks of color: white, black, red. There are crisscrossing lines on his body too. He wanders about the center of the circle, almost idly at first. Every now and then he pauses and looks straight into someone's eyes and keeps on looking. For the person looked at, this is an encounter with fate. Few stare back. Their eyes slide past his face or go glazed. They fear but are not supposed to fear. They know the ancestors are just, that the innocent are never punished. To experience fear, therefore, is an acknowledgment of guilt. It is not necessary to know the nature of your guilt; if you were not guilty, there would be no fear in your mind.

The tempo of the drums increases. The witch doctor begins to dance, slowly at first. He begins to talk in a high-pitched nasal voice; spirits always talk through their noses. The drums and the incantations go on and on, getting faster and wilder, dominating the hearts and minds of all the circle. People begin to tremble and shiver. Some drop down in a trance and lie moaning on the ground. Everyone is possessed by the frenzy of the drums. The spirits of the ancestors are abroad.

Suddenly the drums stop. The witch doctor stands fixed for a dreadful moment that seems without end. Then he pounces. He grabs his victim and drags him or her into the center of the circle. The victim does not resist, does not protest. The ancestors are always just.

There may be one, there may be many victims. But once the victim or victims are "smelled out," the hypnotic spell of the drums is broken. People relax. Their hearts beat normally once more. Now the ancestors will be propitiated and the living freed of the evil which beset them. Now the famine or the drought or the plague or whatever had beset the land will depart from it. And so, while the victim or victims are put to death, the rest of the tribe celebrates the passing of the great evil.

Another key characteristic of tribal man is that his society is exclusive and not, like western society, inclusive. The lines are drawn very clearly, very sharply. Anybody not an "insider" is an enemy, actually or potentially—someone to distrust, someone to fear, someone to keep at bay. There is no choice, no volition about this. It is something ordained by the ancestral dead. The tribal society is therefore possibly the most exclusive society in the twentieth-century world. If you are not in the tribe, there is no way into it. If you are in it, there is no way out of it except death. Dissent is not recognized. To break the rules of the tribe is to court death.

Even the family, the foundation of the tribal in-group, is no simple affair. It is often a cluster of four generations. A man's family can be made up of his father, his father's first, second and third wives—there may be more—and the children of these. A man inherits the wives and children of his brothers who die before him. The wives then become his wives, the children of his brother become brothers and sisters to his own children by his own wife. Then there are the children's children. These and the old people, the grandparents, make up the immediate family, the heart of the in-group. Then there are the families related to one's family by blood ties—the families of uncles and cousins. These have the same complex structure of many wives and brothers and sisters, many of whom are inherited. A group of such blood-related families makes the clan. Clans have been known to be big enough to fill whole villages.

Another and most vital factor in the life of tribal man is his attitude to life and death. Neither life nor death is ever wholly accidental. Disease is never natural. These are brought about by the good and evil spirits all around us. The evil spirits are preoccupied with bringing disaster on the tribe, the good with protecting the tribe. To achieve their malign ends, evil spirits enter the bodies of ordinary human beings. To fight the evil spirits, good spirits enter the bodies of witch doctors. Life and death are thus out of the hands of mortal men.

The world of tribal man is so dominated by the spirits that some tribes will not eat birds because of the spirits that dwell in them, some will not eat fish, some are vegetarians and some eat meat only.

Tribal man is hemmed in, imprisoned by his ancestors. His horizons are only as wide as they permit. He is also protected by them. The rules are such that there are no orphans in the tribe, no misfits, no neurotics. And of course, the ancestral dead are hostile to change.

This, then, is the "oblique, the hard-to-know man" whom Richard Wright encountered on his first visit to Africa. He is the man who raised Nkrumah to power. He is the man whose pressures led Jomo Kenyatta to the Mau Mau and then to his lonely prison-exile in a barren and isolated spot. He, tribal man, will have a crucial say in the future of Africa.

The ancestral dead notwithstanding, change is being imposed on him. How he reacts to the change will have a powerful bearing on tomorrow's Africa.

If the men inaugurating the new ways have the sense and the patience to preserve the finer qualities of the old ways and fuse these with the new, then we can expect something magnificently new out of Africa. ▶

Jacob Afolabi
Sacrifice of Abraham
(Oshogbo),
1964. Lino-cut.

> *"And judgement is turned away backward, and justice standeth afar off: for truth is fallen in the street, and equity cannot enter."*
>
> ISAIAH.

WEDNESDAY was crackling day. On that day the children of the location [1] made the long trek to Elsburg siding for the squares of pig's rind that passed for our daily meat. We collected a double lot of cow dung [2] during the day before; a double lot of *moeroga*.[3]

I finished my breakfast and washed up. Aunt Liza was at her wash-tub in the yard. A misty, sickly sun was just showing. And on the open veld [4] the frost lay thick and white on the grass.

"Ready?" Aunt Liza called.

I went out to her. She shook the soapsuds off her swollen hands and wiped them on her apron. She lifted the apron and put her hand through the slits of the many thin cotton dresses she wore. The dress nearest the skin was the one with the pocket. From this she pulled a sixpenny piece. She tied it in a knot in the corner of a bit of coloured cloth.

"Take care of that. . . . Take the smaller piece of bread in the bin but don't eat it till you start back. You can have a small piece of crackling with it. Only a small piece, understand?"

"Yes, Aunt Liza."

"All right."

From TELL FREEDOM, by Peter Abrahams. Copyright 1954 by Peter Abrahams. Reprinted by permission of Alfred A. Knopf, Inc. and John Farquharson, Ltd.

1. *location*, the district in which nonwhites are required to live in South Africa. 2. *cow dung.* Cow dung is used for fuel in treeless areas. 3. *moeroga*, a type of wild spinach. 4. *veld*, a grassland, with scattered trees.

I got the bread and tucked it into the little canvas bag in which I would carry the crackling.

"Bye, Aunt Liza." I trotted off, one hand in my pocket, feeling the cloth where the money was. I paused at Andries's home.

"Andries!" I danced up and down while I waited. The cold was not so terrible on bare feet if one did not keep still.

Andries came trotting out of their yard. His mother's voice followed; desperate and plaintive: "I'll skin you if you lose the money!"

"Women!" Andries said bitterly.

I glimpsed the dark, skinny woman at her wash-tub as we trotted across the veld. Behind, and in front of us, other children trotted in twos and threes.

There was a sharp bite to the morning air I sucked in; it stung my nose so that tears came to my eyes; it went down my throat like an icy draught; my nose ran. I tried breathing through my mouth but this was worse. The cold went through my shirt and shorts; my skin went pimply and chilled; my fingers went numb and began to ache; my feet felt like frozen lumps that did not belong to me, yet jarred and hurt each time I put them down. I began to feel sick and desperate.

"Jesus God in heaven!" Andries cried suddenly.

I looked at him. His eyes were rimmed in red. Tears ran down his cheeks. His face was drawn and purple, a sick look on it.

"Faster," I said.

"Think it'll help?"

I nodded. We went faster. We passed two children, sobbing and moaning as they ran. We were all in the same desperate situation. We were creatures haunted and hounded by the cold. It was a cruel enemy who gave no quarter. And our means of fighting it were pitifully inadequate. In all the mornings and evenings of the winter months, young and old, big and small, were helpless victims of the bitter cold. Only towards noon and the early afternoon, when the sun sat high in the sky, was there a brief respite. For us, the children, the cold, especially the morning cold, assumed an awful and malevolent personality. We talked of "It." "It" was a half-human monster with evil thoughts, evil intentions, bent on destroying us. "It" was happiest when we were most miserable. Andries had told me how "It" had, last winter, caught and killed a boy.

Hunger was an enemy too, but one with whom we could come to terms, who had many virtues and values. Hunger gave our *pap*,[5] *moeroga,* and crackling a feast-like quality. We could, when it was not with us, think and talk kindly about it. Its memory could even give moments of laughter. But the cold of winter was with us all the time. "It" never really eased up. There were only more bearable degrees of "It" at high noon and on mild days. "It" was the real enemy. And on this Wednesday morning, as we ran across the veld, winter was more bitterly, bitingly, freezingly real than ever.

The sun climbed. The frozen earth thawed, leaving the short grass looking wet and weary. Painfully, our feet and legs came alive. The aching numbness slowly left our fingers. We ran more slowly in the more bearable cold.

In climbing, the sun lost some of its damp look and seemed a real, if cold, sun. When it was right overhead, we struck the sandy road which meant we were nearing the siding. None of the others were in sight. Andries and I were alone on the sandy road on the open veld. We slowed down to a brisk walk. We were sufficiently thawed to want to talk.

"How far?" I said.

"A few minutes," he said.

"I've got a piece of bread," I said.

"Me too," he said. "Let's eat it now."

"On the way back," I said. "With a bit of crackling."

"Good idea. . . . Race to the fork."

"All right."

"Go!" he said.

We shot off together, legs working like pistons. He soon pulled away from me. He reached the fork in the road some fifty yards ahead.

"I win!" he shouted gleefully, though his teeth still chattered.

---

5. *pap,* a porridge made with coarsely ground corn.

We pitched stones down the road, each trying to pitch further than the other. I won and wanted to go on doing it. But Andries soon grew weary with pitching. We raced again. Again he won. He wanted another race but I refused. I wanted pitching, but he refused. So, sulking with each other, we reached the pig farm.

We followed a fenced-off pathway round sprawling white buildings. Everywhere about us was the grunt of pigs. As we passed an open doorway, a huge dog came bounding out, snarling and barking at us. In our terror, we forgot it was fenced in and streaked away. Surprised, I found myself a good distance ahead of Andries. We looked back and saw a young white woman call the dog to heel.

"Damn Boer [6] dog," Andries said.

"Matter with it?" I asked.

"They teach them to go for us. Never get caught by one. My old man's got a hole in his bottom where a Boer dog got him."

I remembered I had outstripped him.

"I won!" I said.

"Only because you were frightened," he said.

"I still won."

"Scare arse," he jeered.

"Scare arse, yourself!"

"I'll knock you!"

"I'll knock you back!"

A couple of white men came down the path and ended our possible fight. We hurried past them to the distant shed where a queue had already formed. There were grown-ups and children. All the grown-ups, and some of the children, were from places other than our location.

The line moved slowly. The young white man who served us did it in leisurely fashion, with long pauses for a smoke. Occasionally he turned his back.

At last, after what seemed hours, my turn came. Andries was behind me. I took the sixpenny piece from the square of cloth and offered it to the man.

---

6. *Boer,* a South African of Dutch descent.

"Well?" he said.

"Sixpence crackling, please."

Andries nudged me in the back. The man's stare suddenly became cold and hard. Andries whispered into my ear.

"Well?" the man repeated coldly.

"Please, *baas*," [7] I said.

"What d'you want?"

"Sixpence crackling, please."

"What?"

Andries dug me in the ribs.

"Sixpence crackling, please, *baas*."

"What?"

"Sixpence crackling, please, *baas*."

"You new here?"

"Yes, *baas*." I looked at his feet while he stared at me.

At last he took the sixpenny piece from me. I held my bag open while he filled it with crackling from a huge pile on a large canvas sheet on the ground. Turning away, I stole a fleeting glance at his face. His eyes met mine, and there was amused, challenging mockery in them. I waited for Andries at the back of the queue, out of the reach of the white man's mocking eyes.

The cold day was at its mildest as we walked home along the sandy road. I took out my piece of bread and, with a small piece of greasy crackling, still warm, on it, I munched as we went along. We had not yet made our peace so Andries munched his bread and crackling on the other side of the road.

"Dumb fool!" he mocked at me for not knowing how to address the white man.

"Scare arse!" I shouted back.

Thus, hurling curses at each other, we reached the fork. Andries saw them first and moved over to my side of the road.

"White boys," he said.

There were three of them. Two of about our own size and one slightly bigger. They had school bags and were coming toward us up the road from the siding.

---

7. *baas* (bäs), master. [*Afrikaans*]

"Better run for it," Andries said.

"Why?"

"No, that'll draw them. Let's just walk along, but quickly."

"Why?" I repeated.

"Shut up," he said.

Some of his anxiety touched me. Our own scrap was forgotten. We marched side by side as fast as we could. The white boys saw us and hurried up the road. We passed the fork. Perhaps they would take the turning away from us. We dared not look back.

"Hear them?" Andries asked.

"No."

I looked over my shoulder.

"They're coming," I said.

"Walk faster," Andries said. "If they come closer, run."

"Hey, *Klipkop!*" [8]

"Don't look back," Andries said.

"Hottentot!"

We walked as fast as we could.

"Bloody kaffir!" [9]

Ahead was a bend in the road. Behind the bend were bushes. Once there, we could run without them knowing it till it was too late.

"Faster," Andries said.

They began pelting us with stones.

"Run when we get to the bushes," Andries said.

The bend and the bushes were near. We would soon be there. A clear young voice carried to us:

"Your fathers are dirty black bastards of baboons!"

"Run!" Andries called.

A violent, unreasoning anger suddenly possessed me. I stopped and turned.

"You're a liar!" I screamed it.

The foremost boy pointed at me: "An ugly black baboon!"

In a fog of rage I went towards him.

---

8. *Klipkop,* literally, stone-head. [*Afrikaans*] **9.** *Hottentot* . . . *kaffir,* abusive terms for a black South African.

"Liar!" I shouted. "My father was better than your father!"

I neared them. The bigger boy stepped between me and the one I was after.

"My father was better than your father! Liar!"

The big boy struck me a mighty clout on the side of the face. I staggered, righted myself, and leapt at the boy who had insulted my father. I struck him on the face, hard. A heavy blow on the back of my head nearly stunned me. I grabbed at the boy in front of me. We went down together.

"Liar!" I said through clenched teeth, hitting him with all my might.

Blows rained on me, on my head, my neck, the side of my face, my mouth, but my enemy was under me and I pounded him fiercely, all the time repeating: "Liar! Liar! Liar!"

Suddenly, stars exploded in my head. Then there was darkness.

I emerged from the darkness to find Andries kneeling beside me.

"God, man! I thought they'd killed you."

I sat up. The white boys were nowhere to be seen. Like Andries, they'd probably thought me dead and run off in panic. The inside of my mouth felt sore and swollen. My nose was tender to the touch. The back of my head ached. A trickle of blood dripped from my nose. I stemmed it with the square of coloured cloth. The greatest damage was to my shirt. It was ripped in many places. I remembered the crackling. I looked anxiously about. It was safe, a little off the road on the grass. I relaxed. I got up and brushed my clothes. I picked up the crackling.

"God, you're dumb!" Andries said. "You're going to get it! Dumb arse!"

I was too depressed to retort. Besides, I knew he was right. I was dumb. I should have run when he told me to.

"Come on," I said.

One of many small groups of children, each child carrying his little bag of crackling, we trod the long road home in the cold winter afternoon.

There was tension in the house that night. When I got back Aunt Liza had listened to the story in silence. The beating or scolding I expected did not come. But Aunt Liza changed while she listened, became remote and withdrawn. When Uncle Sam came home she told him what had happened. He, too, just looked at me and became more remote and withdrawn than usual. They were waiting for something; their tension reached out to me, and I waited with them, anxious, apprehensive.

The thing we waited for came while we were having our supper. We heard a trap pull up outside.

"Here it is," Uncle Sam said and got up.

Aunt Liza leaned back from the table and put her hands in her lap, fingers intertwined, a cold, unseeing look in her eyes.

Before Uncle Sam reached it, the door burst open. A tall, broad, white man strode in. Behind him came the three boys. The one I had attacked had swollen lips and a puffy left eye.

"Evening, *baas!*" Uncle Sam murmured.

"That's him," the bigger boy said, pointing at me.

The white man stared till I lowered my eyes.

"Well?" he said.

"He's sorry, *baas,*" Uncle Sam said quickly. "I've given him a hiding he won't forget soon. You know how it is, *baas.* He's new here, the child of a relative in Johannesburg and they don't all know how to behave there. You know how it is in the big towns, *baas.*" The plea in Uncle Sam's voice had grown more pronounced as he went on. He turned to me. "Tell the *baas* and young *basies* how sorry you are, Lee."

I looked at Aunt Liza and something in her lifelessness made me stubborn in spite of my fear.

"He insulted my father," I said.

The white man smiled.

"See, Sam, your hiding couldn't have been good."

There was a flicker of life in Aunt Liza's eyes. For a brief moment she saw me, looked at me, warmly, lovingly, then her eyes went dead again.

"He's only a child, *baas,*" Uncle Sam murmured.

"You stubborn too, Sam?"

"No, *baas.*"

"Good. . . . Then teach him, Sam. If you and he are to live here, you must teach him. Well. . . . ?"

"Yes, *baas.*"

Uncle Sam went into the other room and returned with a thick leather thong. He wound it once round his hand and advanced on me. The man and boys leaned against the door, watching. I looked at Aunt Liza's face. Though there was no sign of life or feeling on it, I knew suddenly, instinctively, that she wanted me not to cry.

Bitterly, Uncle Sam said: "You must never lift your hand to a white person. No matter what happens, you must never lift your hand to a white person . . ."

He lifted the strap and brought it down on my back. I clenched my teeth and stared at Aunt Liza. I did not cry with the first three strokes. Then, suddenly, Aunt Liza went limp. Tears showed in her eyes. The thong came down on my back, again and again. I screamed and begged for mercy. I grovelled at Uncle Sam's feet, begging him to stop, promising never to lift my hand to any white person. . . .

At last, the white man's voice said: "All right, Sam."

Uncle Sam stopped. I lay whimpering on the floor. Aunt Liza sat like one in a trance.

"Is he still stubborn, Sam?"

"Tell the *baas* and *basies* you are sorry."

"I'm sorry," I said.

"Bet his father is one of those who believe in equality."

"His father is dead," Aunt Liza said.

"Good night, Sam."

"Good night, *baas.* Sorry about this."

"All right, Sam." He opened the door. The boys went out first, then he followed. "Good night, Liza."

Aunt Liza did not answer. The door shut behind the white folk, and soon we heard their trap moving away. Uncle Sam flung the thong viciously against the door, slumped down on the bench, folded his arms on the table, and buried his head on his arms. Aunt Liza moved away from him, came on the floor beside me and lifted me into her large lap. She sat rocking my body. Uncle Sam began to sob softly. After some time, he raised his head and looked at us.

"Explain to the child, Liza," he said.

"You explain," Aunt Liza said bitterly. "You are the man. You did the beating. You are the head of the family. This is a man's world. You do the explaining."

"Please, Liza. . . ."

"You should be happy. The whites are satisfied. We can go on now."

With me in her arms, Aunt Liza got up. She carried me into the other room. The food on the table remained half eaten. She laid me on the bed on my stomach, smeared fat on my back, then covered me with the blankets. She undressed and got into bed beside me. She cuddled me close, warmed me with her own body. With her big hand on my cheek, she rocked me, first to silence, then to sleep.

For the only time of my stay there, I slept on a bed in Elsburg.

When I woke next morning Uncle Sam had gone. Aunt Liza only once referred to the beating he had given me. It was in the late afternoon, when I returned with the day's cow dung.

"It hurt him," she said. "You'll understand one day."

That night, Uncle Sam brought me an orange, a bag of boiled sweets, and a dirty old picture book. He smiled as he gave them to me, rather anxiously. When I smiled back at him, he seemed to relax. He put his hand on my head, started to say something, then changed his mind and took his seat by the fire.

Aunt Liza looked up from the floor where she dished out the food.

"It's all right, old man," she murmured.

"One day. . . ." Uncle Sam said.

"It's all right," Aunt Liza repeated insistently.

The long winter passed. Slowly, day by day, the world of Elsburg became a warmer place. The cracks in my feet began to heal. The spells of bearable, noonday cold gave way to warmth. The noise of the veld at night became a din. The freezing nights changed, became bearable; changed again, became warm. Warm nights and hot days!

Summer had come, and with its coming the world became a softer, kindlier, more beautiful place. Sunflowers began blooming in people's yards. And people themselves began to relax and laugh. When, one evening, as I came in with some washing from the line, I heard Uncle Sam's voice raised in laughter, and saw him and Aunt Liza playing, I knew the summer had really come. Later that same evening he went into the other room and returned with a guitar. Aunt Liza beamed.

"Open the door?"

Uncle Sam nodded. He played. Soon people from the other houses came, in ones and twos, till our little room was crowded. Someone sang with his arms on his wife's shoulders, a love song:

> *I'll be your sweetheart,*
> *If you will be mine . . . .*

Summer had come indeed.

In the long summer afternoons, after my day's work, I went down to the river. Sometimes Andries and some of the other children went with me. Often I went alone.

Often, with others, or alone, I climbed the short willows with their long drooping branches. The touch of willow leaf on the cheek gives a feeling of cool wonder. Often I jumped from stone to stone on the broad bed of the shallow, clear, fast-flowing river. Sometimes I found little pools of idle water, walled off by stones from the flow. I tickled long-tailed tadpoles in these. The sun on the water touched their bodies with myriad colours. Sometimes I watched the *springhaas*—the wild rabbit of the veld—go leaping across the land, almost faster than my eye could follow. And sometimes I lay on my back, on the green grass; on the bank of the river, and looked up at the distant sky, watching thin fleecy white clouds form and re-form and trying to associate the shapes with people and things I knew. I loved being alone by the river. It became my special world.

Each day I explored a little more of the river, going further up or downstream, extending the frontiers of my world. One day, going further downstream than I had been before, I came upon a boy. He was on the bank on the other side from me. We saw each other at the same time and stared. He was completely naked. He carried two finely carved sticks of equal size and shape, both about his own height. He was not light brown, like the other children of our location, but dark brown, almost black. I moved almost to the edge of the river. He called out in a strange language.

"Hello!" I shouted.

He called out again, and again I could not understand. I searched for a place with stones, then bounded across. I approached him slowly. As I drew near, he gripped his sticks more firmly. I stopped.

He spoke harshly, flung one stick on the ground at my feet, and held the other ready as though to fight.

"Don't want to fight," I said.

I reached down to pick up the stick and return it to him. He took a step forward and raised the one in his hand. I moved back quickly. He stepped back and pointed at the stick on the ground. I shook my head.

"Don't want to fight."

I pushed the stick towards him with my foot, ready to run at the first sign of attack. I showed my new, stubby teeth in a tentative smile. He said something that sounded less aggressive. I nodded, smiling more broadly. He relaxed, picked up the stick, and transferred both to his left hand. He smacked his chest.

"Joseph! Zulu!" [10]

I smacked my own chest.

"Lee. . . ." But I didn't know what I was apart from that.

He held out his hand. We shook. His face lit up in a sunny smile. He said something and pointed downstream. Then he took my arm and led me down.

---

10. *Zulu*, a Bantu-speaking people of South Africa, who in the first half of the nineteenth century conquered all of Natal province in southeastern South Africa.

Far downstream, where the river skirted a hillside, hidden by a cluster of willows, we came on a large clear pool. Joseph flung his sticks on the ground and dived in. He shot through the water like a tadpole. He went down and came up. He shouted and beckoned me to come in. I undressed and went in more tentatively. Laughing, he pulled me under. I came up gasping and spluttering, my belly filled with water. He smacked me on the back and the water shot out of my mouth in a rush. When he realized I could not swim he became more careful. We spent the afternoon with Joseph teaching me to swim. At home, that evening, I stood beside Aunt Liza's wash-tub.

"Aunt Liza. . . ."

"Yes?"

"What am I?"

"What are you talking about?"

"I met a boy at the river. He said he was Zulu."

She laughed.

"You are Coloured. There are three kinds of people: white people, Coloured people and black people. The white people come first, then the Coloured people, then the black people."

"Why?"

"Because it is so."

Next day, when I met Joseph, I smacked my chest and said: "Lee Coloured!"

He clapped his hands and laughed.

Joseph and I spent most of the long summer afternoons together. He learnt some Afrikaans [11] from me; I learnt some Zulu from him. Our days were full.

There was the river to explore.

There were my swimming lessons, and others.

I learnt to fight with sticks; to weave a green hat of young willow wands and leaves; to catch frogs and tadpoles with my hands; to set a trap for the *springhaas;* to make the sounds of the river birds.

There was the hot sun to comfort us. . . .

---

11. *Afrikaans,* the Dutch dialect spoken in South Africa.

There was the green grass to dry our bodies. . . .

There was the soft clay with which to build. . . .

There was the fine sand with which to fight. . . .

There were our giant grasshoppers to race. . . .

There were the locust swarms when the skies turned black and we caught them by the hundreds. . . .

There was the rare taste of crisp, brown-baked, salted locusts. . . .

There was the voice of the wind in the willows. . . .

There was the voice of the heaven in the thunderstorms. . . .

There were the voices of two children in laughter, ours. . . .

There were Joseph's tales of black kings who lived in days before the white man. . . .

At home, I said: "Aunt Liza. . . ."

"Yes?"

"Did we have Coloured kings before the white man?"

"No."

"Then where did we come from? Joseph and his mother come from the black kings who were before the white man."

And laughing, and ruffling my head, she said: "You talk too much. . . . Go'n wash up."

And to Joseph, next day, I said: "We didn't have Coloured kings before the white man."

And he comforted me and said: "It is of no moment. You are my brother. Now my kings will be your kings. Come: I have promised the mother to bring you home. She awaits you. I will race you to the hill."

From the top of the hill I looked into a long valley where cattle grazed. To the right, on the sloping land, nestled a cluster of mud huts. Round each hut was a wall built of mud.

"That is my home." Joseph pointed.

We veered right and went down to it. From a distance, we saw a woman at the gate of one of the huts.

"There is the mother!" He walked faster.

She was barefooted. She wore a slight skirt that came above her knees. A child was strapped to her back. The upper part of her body was naked except for the cloth across her chest that supported the child. Round her neck, arms, and legs were strings of white beads. As we drew near, I saw that she was young. And her broad, round face was beautiful. Her black eyes were liquid soft. She called out a greeting and smiled. Joseph pushed me forward.

"This is my brother, Lee of the Coloureds, little mother."

"Greetings, Mother," I said.

"I greet you, my son," she said softly, a twinkle in her eyes. "As the man of my house has told you, food awaits. Come."

"See!" Joseph puffed out his chest. To his mother he said, "He would not believe when I told him I was the man in our house."

"He is indeed," she said.

Circling the hut was a raised platform. We sat on this while she brought us the food; salted fried locusts and corn on the cob. She sat nearby and watched us eating.

"Show the mother," Joseph said, and took another bite at the *mielies*.[12] "Show the mother you are not circumcised yet."

I showed her.

"This is strange," she said. "Have you no initiation schools?"

"No!" Joseph said.

"Then when do you enter manhood?"

"He does not know."

"Is it true?" She looked at me.

I nodded.

"He's still a child!" Joseph cried. "So big and a child!"

Christmas came and it was a feast of eating and laughter. I spent half my time at home with Aunt Liza and Uncle Sam and the other half with Joseph and the little mother.

My sixth birthday came. Joseph and the little mother and I celebrated it by the river.

Then, early one morning, just as the first cold touches crept into the morning air, Joseph came to our location.

I was washing up when I heard young voices shouting: "Look at the naked kaffir! Lee's kaffir!"

I rushed out. Joseph came gravely to me.

---

12. *mielies* (mē′lēs), corn. [*Afrikaans*]

"I come to take leave, my brother. My father has died in the mines so we go back to our land."

He stood straight and stern, not heeding the shouts of the children about. He was a man. This was the burden of his manhood. I had learned much from him, so I said equally coldly: "I must take leave of the little mother."

"She is a woman. She weeps."

We ran all the way there. . . .

When the little cart had taken them away, I climbed the hill and went down to the river. I carried Joseph's two sticks with me. These were his parting gift to his brother.

"Defend yourself," he had said. "I will make others."

I walked along the river that had been our kingdom. Now it was a desolate place. Joseph had been here with me; now Joseph had gone. Before I realized it, my tears flowed fast. There had been much between us.

So the summer passed. The autumn came. The leaves went brown on the willows by the river. They fluttered to the ground and turned to mould. The long days shortened suddenly. The cold came. Winter had come to torture us again. ▶

PROVERBS

The number of different languages spoken by the peoples of Africa is enormous—estimates have placed it as high as 800. Nearly all of these languages—and their literatures—remained unwritten until the arrival of missionaries and later, linguists who studied and recorded them in the orthography of the European languages. Much of this oral tradition is in the form of proverbs. They represent a large and ever growing body of literature. A sampling of proverbs from different parts of the continent is given below.

As a general rule in the pronunciation of African languages, all syllables are open, i.e., they end in a vowel or diphthong; vowels are pronounced much as in Italian, i.e., *a* as in *father*, *e* as *ay* in *day*, *i* as in *machine*, *o* as in *go*, *u* as in *rule*; consonants are pronounced much as in English. In some East African languages, like Kikuyu or Swahili, *m* and *n* appear as syllables in themselves. Pronounce them as if they were followed by a schwa.

Gutiri muthenya ukiaga ta ungi.
No day dawns like another. *Kikuyu* [1] (*Kenya*)

Jalele sainou ane na sainou guissetil dara, tey mague dieki thy soufe guissa yope.
The child looks everywhere and often sees nought; but the old man, sitting on the ground, sees everything. *Wolof* [2] (*Senegal*)

Julu life lisekana ifoso.
Two tortoises laughing at each other's shell.
Mongo [3] (*Dem. Rep. of the Congo*)

Mbaara ti ucuru.
War is not porridge. *Kikuyu* [1]

Akundlovu yasindwa umboko wayo.
No elephant ever found its trunk too heavy.

Zulu [4] (*South Africa*)

Mmea se, "Wo ho ye fe," a, ene ka.
When the women say to you, "You are a handsome fellow," that
means you are going to run into debt.   *Twi* [5] (*Ghana*)

Akamo ekun o ni iyonnu.
It is difficult to encompass a leopard.   *Yoruba* [2] (*Nigeria*)

Msitukane wakunga na uzazi ungalipo.
Do not abuse midwives while child-bearing continues.

Swahili [6] (*Tanzania*)

Kwa mwendwo gutiri irima.
On the way to one's beloved there are no hills.   *Kikuyu* [1]

Aya yo ni ijokan, o ni ki aka on li ehin okankan.
The monkey, having one day eaten to the full, desires that his
fore-teeth may be drawn.   *Yoruba* [2]

Didime na yi bronni nansin adi.
A feast uncovers a European's wooden leg.   *Oji* [2] (*Ghana*)

Ba don tsawo a kan ga wata ba.
Not through height does one see the moon.   *Hausa* [7] (*Nigeria*)

---

1. From *1,000 Kikuyu Proverbs,* by G. Barra. London: Macmillan and
Co., Ltd. 1960. **2.** From *Wit and Wisdom from West Africa,* compiled by
Richard F. Burton. London: Tinsley Brothers, 1865. **3.** From *Mongo
Proverbs and Fables,* collected and compiled by E. A. Ruskin. Bogandanga:
Congo Balolo Mission Press, 1921. **4.** From *Zulu Proverbs,* by C. L.
Sibusiso Nyembezi. Johannesburg: Witwatersrand University Press, 1963.
5. From *Ashanti Proverbs,* by R. Sutherland Rattray. London: Oxford
University Press, 1916. **6.** From *Swahili Sayings from Zanzibar,* by S. S.
Farsi. Dar Es Salaam: East African Literature Bureau, 1958. **7.** From
Hausa and Fulani Proverbs, by C. E. J. Whitting. Lagos: The Government
Printer, 1940.

Assoi Adiko / *Ivory Coast* (20th cent.)

THE DANCER

The fire of the tom-tom
in his veins
The fire of the tom-tom
in his heart.

5 His chest inclined
And short of breath
He streams with sweat
He shudders with frenzy
He is overcome
10 Masked by terrors.

Bells on his black
And agile feet
Shake in unison
With beating drums.
15 He leaps, he wheels,
He shudders, he quivers.

It is the dance,
And of the dance,
He is the Phoenix [1]
20 And the Giant.

"The Dancer" (le danseur) by Assoi Adiko from POESIE VIVANTE.
Reprinted by permission of *Poesie Vivante*.
1. *the Phoenix.* The Phoenix is a mythical bird, reputed to live five hundred years, then to burn itself to ashes on a pyre of its own construction and be reborn from the ashes.

Anonymous / *Ghana*

ANANSI'S FISHING EXPEDITION

Anansi the Spider is the hero of a huge body of folk tales which spread from their West African origin to the West Indies and other parts of the New World as a result of the slave trade. His name changes slightly from people to people, but his role is always that of the clever trickster who lives by his wits.

IN THE COUNTRY OF ASHANTI,[1] not far from the edge of the great West African forest, there was a man named Anansi, who was known to all the people for miles around. Anansi was not a great hunter, or a great worker, or a great warrior. His specialty was being clever. He liked to outwit people. He liked to live well, and to have other people do things for him. But because all the people of the country knew about Anansi and had had trouble with him, he had to keep thinking of new ways to get something for nothing.

One day Anansi was sitting in the village when a man named Osansa came along.

"I have an idea," Anansi said. "Why don't we go and set fish traps together? Then we shall sell the fish and be quite rich."

But Osansa knew Anansi's reputation very well, and so he said: "No, I have as much food as I can eat or sell. I am rich enough. Why don't you set your fish traps by yourself?"

"Ha! Fish alone? Then I'd have to do all the work!" Anansi said. "What I need is a fool for a partner."

---

1. *Ashanti,* a region in the northern part of Ghana.

Osansa went away, and after a while another man named Anene came along. "I have an idea," Anansi said. "Why don't the two of us go and set fish traps together? Then we shall sell the fish and be quite rich."

Anene knew Anansi very well too, but he seemed to listen thoughtfully. "That sounds like a fine idea," he said. "Two people can catch more fish than one. Yes, I'll do it."

The news went rapidly around the village that Anansi and Anene were going on a fishing expedition together. Osansa met Anene in the market and said: "We hear you are going to trap fish with Anansi. Don't you know he is trying to make a fool of you? He has told every one that he needs a fool to go fishing with him. He wants someone to set the fish traps and do all the work, while he gets all the money for the fish."

"Don't worry, friend Osansa, I won't be Anansi's fool," Anene said.

Early the next morning Anansi and Anene went into the woods to cut palm branches to make their fish traps.

Anansi was busy thinking how he could make Anene do most of the work. But when they came to the place where the palm trees grew, Anene said to Anansi: "Give me the knife, Anansi. I shall cut the branches for the traps. We are partners. We share everything. My part of the work will be to cut branches, your part of the work will be to get tired for me."

"Just a minute, let me think," Anansi said. "Why should I be the one to get tired?"

"Well, when there's work to be done someone must get tired," Anene said. "That's the way it is. So if I cut the branches, the least you can do is to get tired for me."

"Hah, you take me for a fool?" Anansi said. "Give me the knife. I shall cut the branches and you get tired for me!"

So Anansi took the knife and began cutting the branches from the trees. Every time he chopped, Anene grunted. Anene sat down in the shade and groaned from weariness, while Anansi chopped and hacked and sweated. Finally the wood for the fish traps was cut. Anansi tied it up into a big bundle. Anene got up from the ground, holding his back and moaning.

"Anansi, let me carry the bundle of wood now, and you can get tired for me," Anene said.

"Oh, no, my friend Anene," Anansi said, "I am not that simple-minded. I'll carry the wood myself, and you can take the weariness for me."

So he hoisted the bundle to the top of his head and the two of them started back to the village. Anene groaned all the way.

"Oh, oh!" he moaned. "Take it easy, Anansi! Oh, oh!"

When they came to the village Anene said: "Let me make the fish traps, Anansi, and you just sit down and get tired for me."

"Oh, no," Anansi said. "You just keep on as you are." And he made the fish traps while Anene lay on his back in the shade with his eyes closed, moaning and groaning.

And while he was making the traps, working in the heat with perspiration running down his face and chest, Anansi looked at Anene lying there taking all his weariness and sore muscles for him, and he shook his head and clucked his tongue. "Anene thinks he is intelligent," he said to himself. "Yet look at him moaning and groaning there, practically dying from weariness!"

When the fish traps were done Anene climbed to his feet and said, "Anansi, my friend, now let me carry the fish traps to the water, and you can get tired for me."

"Oh, no," Anansi said. "You just come along and do your share. I'll do the carrying, you do the getting tired."

So they went down to the water, Anansi carrying and Anene moaning. When they arrived, Anene said to Anansi: "Now wait a minute, Anansi, we ought to think things over here. There are sharks in this water. Some one is apt to get hurt. So let me go in and set the traps, and should a shark bite me, then you can die for me."

"Wah!" Anansi howled. "Listen to that! What do you take me for? I'll go in the water and set the traps myself, and if I am bitten, then you can die for me!" So he took the fish traps out into the water and set them and then the two of them went back to the village.

The next morning when they went down to inspect the traps they found just four fish. Anene spoke first.

"Anansi, there are only four fish here. You take them. To-morrow there will probably be more, and then I'll take my turn."

"Now, what do you take me for?" Anansi said indignantly. "Do you think I am simple-minded? Oh, no, Anene, you take the four fish and I'll take my turn to-morrow."

So Anene took the four fish and carried them to town and sold them.

Next day when they came down to the fish traps, Anene said: "Look, there are only eight fish here. I'm glad it's your turn, because to-morrow there doubtless will be more."

"Just a minute," Anansi said. "You want me to take to-day's fish so that to-morrow you get a bigger catch? Oh, no, these are all yours, partner; to-morrow I'll take my share."

So Anene took the eight fish and carried them to town and sold them.

Next day when they came to look in the traps they found sixteen fish. "Anansi," Anene said, "take the sixteen fish. Little ones, too. I'll take my turn to-morrow."

"Of course you'll take your turn to-morrow, it's my turn to-day," Anansi said. He stopped to think. "Well, now, you are trying to make a fool out of me again! You want me to take these sixteen miserable little fish so that you can get the big catch to-morrow; don't you? Well, it's a good thing I'm alert! You take the sixteen to-day and I'll take the big catch to-morrow!"

So Anene carried the sixteen fish to the market and sold them.

Next day they came to the traps and took the fish out. But by this time the traps had rotted in the water.

"Well, it's certainly your turn to-day," Anene said. "And I'm very glad of that. Look, the fish traps are rotten and worn out. We can't use them any more. I'll tell you what—you take the fish to town and sell them, and I'll take the rotten fish traps and sell them. The fish traps will bring an excellent price. What a wonderful idea!"

"Hm," Anansi said. "Just a moment, don't be in such a hurry. I'll take the fish traps and sell them myself. If there's such a good price to be had, why shouldn't I get it instead of you? Oh, no, you take the fish, my friend."

Anansi hoisted the rotten fish traps up on his head and started off for town. Anene followed him, carrying the fish. When they arrived in the town Anene sold his fish in the market, while Anansi walked back and forth singing loudly: "I am selling rotten fish traps! I am selling wonderful rotten fish traps!"

But no one wanted rotten fish traps, and the townspeople were angry that Anansi thought they were so stupid they would buy them. All day long Anansi wandered through the town singing: "Get your rotten fish traps here! I am selling wonderful rotten fish traps!"

Finally the head man of the town heard about the affair. He, too, became very angry, and he sent messengers for Anansi. When they brought Anansi to him he asked indignantly: "What do you think you are doing, anyway? What kind of nonsense is this you are trying to put over the people of the town?"

"I'm selling rotten fish traps," Anansi said, "very excellent rotten fish traps."

"Now what do you take us for?" the chief of the town said. "Do you think we are ignorant people? Your friend Anene came and sold good fish, which the people want, but you come trying to sell something that isn't good for anything and just smell the town up with your rotten fish traps. It's an outrage. You insult us."

The head man turned to the townspeople who stood near by, listening.

"Take him away and whip him," he said.

The men took Anansi out to the town gate and beat him with sticks. Anansi shouted and yelled and made a great noise. When at last they turned him loose, Anene said to him: "Anansi, this ought to be a lesson to you. You wanted a fool to go fishing with you, but you didn't have to look so hard to find one. You were a fool yourself."

Anansi nodded his head.

"Yes," he said thoughtfully, rubbing his back and his legs where they had beaten him. And he looked reproachfully at Anene. "But what kind of partner are you? At least you could have taken the pain while I took the beating." ▶

Anonymous / *Sudan*

SONG OF A MOTHER
TO HER FIRST-BORN

Translated by
Jack H. Driberg

Speak to me, child of my heart.
Speak to me with your eyes, your round laughing eyes,
Wet and shining as Lupeyo's bull-calf.

Speak to me little one,
5 Clutching my breast with your hand,
So strong and firm for all its littleness.
It will be the hand of a warrior, my son,
A hand that will gladden your father.
See how eagerly it fastens on me:
10 It thinks already of a spear.
O son, you will have a warrior's name and be a leader of men.
And your sons, and your sons' sons, will remember you long
     after you have slipped into darkness.
But I, I shall always remember your hand clutching me so.
I shall recall how you lay in my arms,
15 And looked at me so, and so,
And how your tiny hands played with my bosom.
And when they name you great warrior, then will my eyes be wet
     with remembering.

"Song of a Mother to Her First-born," translated by Jack H. Driberg from
INITIATION. Reprinted by permission of A. S. Barnes & Company, Inc.

And how shall we name you, little warrior?
See, let us play at naming.
20 It will not be a name of despisal, for you are my first-born.
Not as Nawal's son is named will you be named.
Our gods will be kinder to you than theirs.
Must we call you "Insolence" or "Worthless One"?

Shall you be named, like a child of ill fortune, after the dung of
        cattle?
25 Our gods need no cheating, my child:
They wish you no ill.
They have washed your body and clothed it with beauty.
They have set a fire in your eyes.
And the little puckering ridges of your brows—
Are they not the seal of their finger-prints when they fashioned
30   you?
They have given you beauty and strength, child of my heart,
And wisdom is already shining in your eyes,
And laughter.

So how shall we name you, little one?
35 Are you your father's father, or his brother, or yet another?
Whose spirit is it that is in you, little warrior?
Whose spear-hand tightens round my breast?
Who lives in you and quickens to life, like last year's melon seed?
Are you silent, then?
But your eyes are thinking, thinking, and glowing like the eyes of
40   a leopard in a thicket.
Well, let be.
At the day of the naming you will tell us.

O my child, now indeed I am happy.
Now indeed I am a wife—
45 No more a bride, but a Mother-of-one.
Be splendid and magnificent, child of desire.
Be proud as I am proud.
Be happy as I am happy.
Be loved as now I am loved.
50 Child, child, child, love I have had from my man.
But now, only now, have I the fullness of love.
Now, only now, am I his wife and the mother of his first-born.
His soul is safe in your keeping, my child, and it was I, I, I who
  have made you.

Therefore am I loved.
55 Therefore am I happy.
Therefore am I a wife.
Therefore have I great honor.

You will tend his shrine when he is gone.
With sacrifice and oblation you will recall his name year by year.
60 He will live in your prayers, my child,
And there will be no more death for him, but everlasting life
  springing from your loins.
You are his shield and his spear, his hope and redemption from
  the dead.
Through you he will be reborn, as the saplings in the Spring.
And I, I am the mother of his first-born.
65 Sleep, child of beauty and courage and fulfilment, sleep.
I am content.

Anonymous / *Ethiopia*

JUSTICE

A WOMAN one day went out to look for her goats that had wandered away from the herd. She walked back and forth over the field for a long time without finding them. She came at last to a place by the side of the road where a deaf man sat before a fire brewing himself a cup of coffee. Not realizing he was deaf, the woman asked:

"Have you seen my herd of goats come this way?"

The deaf man thought she was asking for the water hole, so he pointed vaguely toward the river.

The woman thanked him and went to the river. And there, by coincidence, she found the goats. But a young kid had fallen among the rocks and broken its foot.

She picked it up to carry it home. As she passed the place where the deaf man sat drinking his coffee, she stopped to thank him for his help. And in gratitude she offered him the kid.

But the deaf man didn't understand a word she was saying. When she held the kid toward him he thought she was accusing him of the animal's misfortune, and he became very angry.

"I had nothing to do with it!" he shouted.

"But you pointed the way," the woman said.

"It happens all the time with goats!" the man shouted.

"I found them right where you said they would be," the woman replied.

"Go away and leave me alone, I never saw him before in my life!" the man shouted.

"Justice" from THE FIRE ON THE MOUNTAIN AND OTHER ETHIOPIAN STORIES by Harold Courlander and Wolf Leslau. Copyright 1950 by Holt, Rinehart and Winston, Inc. Reprinted by permission of Holt, Rinehart and Winston, Inc.

People who came along the road stopped to hear the argument.

The woman explained to them:

"I was looking for the goats and he pointed toward the river. Now I wish to give him this kid."

"Do not insult me in this way!" the man shouted loudly. "I am not a leg breaker!" And in his anger he struck the woman with his hand.

"Ah, did you see? He struck me with his hand!" the woman said to the people. "I will take him before the judge!"

So the woman with the kid in her arms, the deaf man, and the spectators went to the house of the judge. The judge came out before his house to listen to their complaint. First, the woman talked, then the man talked, then people in the crowd talked. The judge sat nodding his head. But that meant very little, for the judge, like the man before him, was very deaf. Moreover, he was also very near-sighted.

At last, he put up his hand and the talking stopped. He gave them his judgment.

"Such family rows are a disgrace to the Emperor and an affront to the Church," he said solemnly. He turned to the man.

"From this time forward, stop mistreating your wife," he said.

He turned to the woman with the young goat in her arms.

"As for you, do not be so lazy. Hereafter do not be late with your husband's meals."

He looked at the baby goat tenderly.

"And as for the beautiful infant, may she have a long life and grow to be a joy to you both!"

The crowd broke up and the people went their various ways.

"Ah, how good it is!" they said to each other. "How did we ever get along before justice was given to us?" ▶

Anonymous / *Ghana*

TALK

ONCE, not far from the city of Accra on the Gulf of Guinea, a countryman went out to his garden to dig up some yams to take to market. While he was digging, one of the yams said to him:

"Well, at last you're here. You never weeded me, but now you come around with your digging stick. Go away and leave me alone!"

The farmer turned around and looked at his cow in amazement. The cow was chewing her cud and looking at him.

"Did you say something?" he asked.

The cow kept on chewing and said nothing, but the man's dog spoke up.

"It wasn't the cow who spoke to you," the dog said. "It was the yam. The yam says leave him alone."

The man became angry because his dog had never talked before, and he didn't like his tone, besides. So he took his knife and cut a branch from a palm tree to whip his dog. Just then the palm tree said:

"Put that branch down!"

The man was getting very upset about the way things were going, and he started to throw the palm branch away, but the palm branch said:

"Man, put me down softly!"

He put the branch down gently on a stone, and the stone said:

"Hey, take that thing off me."

This was enough, and the frightened farmer started to run for his village. On the way he met a fisherman going the other way with a fish trap on his head.

"What's the hurry?" the fisherman asked.

"My yam said, 'Leave me alone!' Then the dog said, 'Listen to what the yam says!' When I went to whip the dog with a palm branch the tree said, 'Put that branch down!' Then the palm branch said, 'Do it softly!' Then the stone said, 'Take that thing off me!' "

"Is that all?" the man with the fish trap asked. "Is that so frightening?"

"Well," the man's fish trap said, "did he take it off the stone?"

"Wah!" the fisherman shouted. He threw the fish trap on the ground and began to run with the farmer, and on the trail they met a weaver with a bundle of cloth on his head.

"Where are you going in such a rush?" he asked them.

"My yam said, 'Leave me alone!' " the farmer said. "The dog said, 'Listen to what the yam says!' The tree said, 'Put that branch down!' The branch said, 'Do it softly!' And the stone said, 'Take that thing off me!' "

"And then," the fisherman continued, "the fish trap said, 'Did he take it off?' "

"That's nothing to get excited about," the weaver said, "no reason at all."

"Oh yes it is," his bundle of cloth said. "If it happened to you you'd run too!"

"Wah!" the weaver shouted. He threw his bundle on the trail and started running with the other men.

They came panting to the ford in the river and found a man bathing.

"Are you chasing a gazelle?" he asked them.

The first man said breathlessly:

"My yam talked to me, and it said, 'Leave me alone!' And my dog said, 'Listen to your yam!' And when I cut myself a branch the tree said, 'Put that branch down!' And the branch said, 'Do it softly!' And the stone said, 'Take that thing off me!' "

The fisherman panted:

"And my trap said, 'Did he?' "

The weaver wheezed:

"And my bundle of cloth said, 'You'd run too!' "

"Is that why you're running?" the man in the river asked.

"Well, wouldn't you run if you were in their position?" the river said.

The man jumped out of the water and began to run with the others. They ran down the main street of the village to the house of the chief. The chief's servants brought his stool out, and he came and sat on it to listen to their complaints. The men began to recite their troubles.

"I went out to my garden to dig yams," the farmer said, waving his arms. "Then everything began to talk! My yam said, 'Leave me alone!' My dog said, 'Pay attention to your yam!' The tree said, 'Put that branch down!' The branch said, 'Do it softly!' And the stone said, 'Take it off me!' "

"And my fish trap said, 'Well, did he take it off?' " the fisherman said.

"And my cloth said, 'You'd run too!' " the weaver said.

"And the river said the same," the bather said hoarsely, his eyes bulging.

The chief listened to them patiently, but he couldn't refrain from scowling.

"Now, this is really a wild story," he said at last. "You'd better all go back to your work before I punish you for disturbing the peace."

So the men went away, and the chief shook his head and mumbled to himself, "Nonsense like that upsets the community."

"Fantastic, isn't it?" his stool said. "Imagine, a talking yam!"

▶

Anonymous / *Liberia*

HOW HAWK LEARNED
OF THE SHALLOW HEARTS OF MEN

CHAMELEON HAS HIS HOME in a certain tree called the palmolin tree. Men plant these trees, in which the palm birds live, in the centre of their villages. Thus it was that Chameleon lived in a tree by a village market place. People feared this animal, for although it was quite small, it possessed surprising strength. It would spring on the backs of passing men and could not be removed until it had been frightened by lightning and thunder. Then it would fall to the ground and run back to the palmolin tree.

One day when Hawk was flying above the town he saw Chameleon on the ground and swooping down he seized the little animal in his beak and carried him into the air. The people in the village below rejoiced and sang the praises of clever Hawk.

"O Hawk!" they cried, "O greatest of all birds! You have captured the awful Chameleon, that wicked animal who has lived among us causing fear and trouble. O clever Hawk, with all our hearts we thank you!"

The people were very happy. Meanwhile, up in the air Chameleon confided to Hawk, "Brother, let me go back to my tree. Long have I lived among men and I know they have two tongues. Today they praise a man and tomorrow they speak against him, for their hearts are shallow and their minds are weak. Let me return, O brother, to my tree."

"How Hawk Learned of the Shallow Hearts of Men" from LIBERIAN FOLKLORE, compiled by Doris Banks Henries. Copyright © 1966, Doris Banks Henries. Reprinted by permission of Macmillan & Co., Ltd.

But Hawk was proud of the praises of the villagers. "The people praise and love me," he declared. "I have found great favour with them. I will eat you and they may make me Chief!"

"Unhappy bird!" Chameleon said. "Tomorrow men will curse you. Their memories are brief. Men only love themselves, as you will see."

Suddenly he grasped Hawk by the throat. So powerful was his hold that Hawk began to choke. He fell and dropped breathless in the market place. The people quickly gathered and saw that Chameleon had overpowered Hawk.

"Noble Chameleon!" they cried. "O good and clever animal! You have defeated wicked Hawk, the thief who steals our chickens. With all our hearts we thank you for ridding us of that evil bird!"

They heaped praise on Chameleon and rejoiced. The Chameleon whispered in Hawk's ear, "You see now, brother? Now do you realize how shallow are the hearts of men? They have double tongues. How short their memories are! A little time ago they praised you and cursed me! Now they curse you and heap honor on me!"

"I understand," Hawk murmured. "Forgive me, Chameleon. Let us always be friends, for I know that Man will always be our common enemy!"

Then Hawk flew up into the air and Chameleon went back to his palmolin tree. These two today are still allied in friendship against the treachery of Man. ▶

Anonymous / *Liberia*

HOW THE WORLD CHANGED

MELEKA (GOD) MADE THE WORLD and the moon and the sun. The sun shone all the time, for Meleka considered that constant light would benefit men and beasts. Therefore, there was no night. For every man there was a woman. There were no white or brown or yellow people, there was only a single race of noble and pure-black men. In those days men and animals were friends and wandered freely in the forest eating fruit and nuts and green foods. Caves and houses were not needed, for when a man or a beast was tired he simply lay down to sleep where he was. Men possessed no spears and animals had no claws.

Little children left their parents whenever they pleased, wandering for months and years in foreign places. This was a source of worry and grief to men and animals, for they loved their children well. Sometimes children wandered away and were never seen again. The mothers and fathers wept in sorrow and appealed to Meleka for aid.

Meleka then took away the sun. All the men and animals were alarmed as they could not understand what the darkness was. Families grouped together in defense against unknown terrors; children roaming far away called pitifully for their parents.

After a time, Meleka caused the sun to shine again. Everyone was happy again; children who had been returning home began to wander about again. Meleka decided to divide time into nights and days to encourage the little ones to go back home and not to stray too far from their parents. In common protection against the night, men and animals united in a single friendly clan and lived together under a giant cotton tree. This tree was the only shelter they could find. They took good care of the tree for it was the only home they had. All of the animals and men loved one another and it was a happy home.

One day the son of a man discovered a piece of fire discarded by Lightning Bug. He played with it. Being a normal child with mischief in his head, he waited until no one was watching, then carried fire to the foot of the cotton tree. The giant tree had already been badly burnt before the animals and men saw and smelled the smoke.

A great cry of despair rose up from the animals. They stood about in fear, helplessly watching fire consume their home in a roaring, smoking blaze. After many hours the tree groaned, cracked and came crashing down to earth amid a shower of bright red sparks. The men and animals fled in all directions.

"It is finished!" cried the animals. "We have been betrayed by man. We agreed to live in peace beneath the cotton tree, but man is wicked. We will not stay any longer. There is war between us!"

Most of the animals fled far into the forest where they made their homes in caves and thickets. Men built houses of mud and thatch and their tribe multiplied. A few brave or foolish animals, such as dogs, goats or cows, decided to live with them.

On the other side of a mountain there was a certain pond which Meleka had used as a painting bowl. His colours had settled to the bottom of the pond, leaving the water looking clear and sweet. A group of naughty children bathed there. Their swimming and splashing stirred up Meleka's colours and the children were astonished to see their skins change colour from lustrous black to white, brown and yellow. In great alarm they rushed from the pond and washed themselves in a stream, but the colours were fixed and would not be washed off. ▶

Anonymous / *Zanzibar (Tanzania)*

SONG OF THE POOR MAN

Give me a chair
and let me sit in your midst
and praise poverty
and want.

5 The face of a poor man
stays all crumpled up
by reason of the hunger and thirst
which are in his stomach.

A poor man knows not
10 how to eat with a rich man.
When he starts eating fish
he eats its head.

Go and invite him
who has no bread
15 to come and eat crumbs
and thorns in the platters.

"Song of the Poor Man" from AN AFRICAN TREASURY by Langston Hughes. Copyright © 1960 by Langston Hughes. Used by permission of Crown Publishers, Inc.

A poor man is nobody
because he has nothing.
Though nobly born
20 he is granted no favor.

A poor man is a snake—
his brothers avoid him
because of the misery
of the poverty-stricken.

25 But when a poor man is ill,
it leads his people
to show him kindness;
when a rich man is ill,
to light a lamp
30 he must wait for a slave.

Anonymous / *Nigeria*

THE TALKING SKULL

A HUNTER goes into the bush. He finds an old human skull. The hunter says: "What brought you here?" The skull answers: "Talking brought me here." The hunter runs off. He runs to the king. He tells the king: "I found a dry human skull in the bush. It asks you how its father and mother are."

The king says: "Never since my mother bore me have I heard that a dead skull can speak." The king summons the Alkali, the Saba, and the Degi and asks them if they have ever heard the like. None of the wise men has heard the like and they decide to send a guard out with the hunter into the bush to find out if his story is true and, if so, to learn the reason for it. The guard accompany the hunter into the bush with the order to kill him on the spot should he have lied. The guard and the hunter come to the skull. The hunter addresses the skull: "Skull, speak." The skull is silent. The hunter asks as before: "What brought you here?" The skull does not answer. The whole day long the hunter begs the skull to speak, but it does not answer. In the evening the guard tell the hunter to make the skull speak, and when he cannot they kill him in accordance with the king's command. When the guard are gone the skull opens its jaws and asks the dead hunter's head: "What brought you here?" The dead hunter's head replies: "Talking brought me here!" ▶

"The Talking Skull" from AFRICAN GENESIS by Leo Frobenius and Douglas G. Fox. Reprinted by permission of Stackpole Books.

Anonymous

Four Tales From Togoland

THE EYE OF THE GIANT

LONG, LONG AGO there was a great famine in the world, and a certain young man whilst wandering in search of food strayed into a part of the bush where he had never been before. Presently he perceived a strange mass lying on the ground. He approached and saw that it was the body of a giant whose hair resembled that of white men in that it was silky rather than woolly. It was of an incredible length and stretched as far as from Krachi to Salaga.[1] The young man was properly awed at the spectacle, and wished to withdraw, but the giant noticing him asked what he wanted.

The young man explained and begged the giant to give him some food. The latter agreed on condition that the youth would serve him for a while. This matter having been arranged, the giant said his name was Owuo or Death, and then gave the boy some meat.

Never before had the latter tasted such fine food, and he was well pleased with his bargain. He served his master for a long time and received plenty of meat, but one day he grew homesick,

---

"Four Tales From Togoland" by A. W. Cardinall from TALES TOLD IN TOGOLAND. Published by Oxford University Press. Reprinted by permission of International African Institute.
1. *from Krachi to Salaga,* about sixty miles. Krachi and Salaga are two towns in what is now Ghana.

and begged his master to give him a short holiday. The latter agreed if the youth would promise to bring another boy in his place. So the youth returned to his village and there persuaded his brother to go with him into the bush and gave him to Owuo.

In course of time the youth got hungry again and longed for the meat which Owuo had taught him to like so much. So one day he made up his mind to return to his master, and leaving the village made his way back to the giant's abode. The latter asked him what he wanted, and when the youth told him that he wanted to taste once more of the good meat, the giant told him to enter the hut and take as much as he liked, but he would have to work for him again.

The youth agreed and entered the hut. He ate as much as he could, and set to at the task his master set him. The work continued for a long time and the boy ate his fill every day. But to his surprise he never saw anything of his brother, and whenever he asked about him the giant told him that the lad was away on his business.

Once more the youth grew homesick and asked for leave to return to his village. The giant agreed on condition that he would bring a girl for him, Owuo, to wed. So the youth went home and there persuaded his sister to go into the bush and marry the giant. The girl agreed, and took with her a slave companion, and they all repaired to the giant's abode. There the youth left the two girls and went back to the village.

It was not very long after that he again grew hungry and longed for the taste of the meat. So he made his way once more into the bush and found the giant. The giant did not seem overpleased to see the boy and grumbled at being bothered a fourth time. However, he told the boy to go into the inner chamber of his hut and take what he wanted. The youth did so and took up a bone which he began to devour. To his horror he recognized it at once as being the bone of his sister. He looked around at all the rest of the meat and saw that it was that of his sister and her slave girl.

Thoroughly frightened he escaped from the house and ran back into the village. There he told the elders what he had done and the awful thing he had seen. At once the alarm was sounded and all the people went out into the bush to see for themselves the dread thing they had heard about. When they drew near to the giant, they grew afraid at the sight of so evil a monster. They went back to the village and consulted among themselves what best they should do. At last it was agreed to go to Salaga where the giant's hair finished and set light to it. This was done, and when the hair was burning well, they returned to the bush and watched the giant.

Presently the latter began to toss about and sweat. It was quite evident that he was beginning to feel the heat. The nearer the flames advanced the more he tossed and grumbled. At last the fire reached his head, and for the moment the giant was dead.

The villagers approached him cautiously, and the young man noticed "medicine" which had been concealed in the roots of the giant's hair. He took it and called the others to come and see what he had found. No one could say what power this medicine might have, but an old man suggested that no harm would be done if they took some and sprinkled it on the bones and meat in the hut. This idea was carried out, and to the surprise of every one, the girls and the boy returned to life at once.

The youth who had still some of the medicine left proposed to put it on the giant. But at this there was a great uproar, as the people feared Owuo might come to life again. The boy therefore by way of compromise sprinkled it into the eye of the dead giant. At once the eye opened and the people all fled away in terror. But it is from that eye that death comes; for every time that Owuo shuts that eye a man dies, and unfortunately for us he is for ever blinking and winking. ▶

THE SINGING CLOAK

ANANSI [1] AND THE Chameleon used to live in the same town. Anansi was a rich man and had plenty of children to help him with his farming, but the Chameleon was only a poor man and alone had to till his farm. Now it chanced that one year the rain fell only on the Chameleon's farm, and on Anansi's there was a complete drought. Thus the spider's farm did not come up at all, and the Chameleon's was already well up and a good harvest promised.

This annoyed Anansi, and one day he called on the Chameleon and asked him if he would sell him his farm, but the Chameleon said he would not, because if he did he would not be able to get any food during the dry season. Then Anansi was even angrier than before, and swore he would have revenge on the Chameleon.

Now it happens that chameleons do not make any roads as others do. They like to walk over the grass and bushes. Thus there was no path leading from the Chameleon's house to his farm. So that night, Anansi called all his children together and told them to clean and make a good path from his compound to the Chameleon's farm. At first, they begged their father not to do this, but as he insisted they obeyed him, and in the morning there was finished a clean road and a well-used one leading from Anansi's house to the farm.

Anansi at once went to the farm and began to pull up some cassava. Presently the Chameleon came along and saw Anansi taking his cassava and called out: "Hi! Anansi, what are you

---

"Four Tales From Togoland" by A. W. Cardinall from TALES TOLD IN TOGOLAND. Published by Oxford University Press. Reprinted by permission of International African Institute.
1. *Anansi*, the Spider, the hero of countless West African folk tales. See headnote on page 55.

doing in my farm?" Anansi at once replied: "Go away and do not vex me. Can you not see that I am busy working in my farm?"

"Your farm," cried the Chameleon, "why, it is my farm, and every one knows that." "Do not be silly; go away," answered the Spider, "or I shall get angry and kill you."

So the Chameleon went away and laid a complaint before the chief. Anansi was sent for, and when both had told him how the farm was theirs, the chief asked for proofs. Then Anansi said: "That is easy. I have a path from my house straight to the farm, which the Chameleon is falsely claiming. He has no path."

The chief saw that if Anansi was speaking true then verily the farm must be his. So he sent his messenger to see and the man came back and said that it was so. Then the Chameleon was asked what he had to say, and he said that he did not know anything about the path, that he always used to go there over the bushes and grass. This made the chief laugh, and he at once gave the farm to Anansi, who took all his children with him and gathered the crops.

The Chameleon did not know what to do. He was very poor and had but little food left to keep him alive. So he went to his house and shut the door and refused to see any one.

For many days he remained thus thinking over his wrongs and wondering how to get revenge. Then he began to dig a hole. He dug and dug and dug and made an immense well. It went far down. No man had ever seen such a well. When the Chameleon thought he had made it large enough he made some mud and began to roof the well so that soon only a very small hole was left.

Then the Chameleon went out to see Anansi. He came to the latter's house and greeted him: "Master, I am only a poor man. May I go to your farm and glean what you have left there?" And Anansi was pleased at the Chameleon's humility and told him he could. But there was little in the farm to gather. Then the Chameleon, who had deceived the spider into thinking that he was properly humbled, again sat alone in his house. This time he amused himself in catching hundreds and hundreds of that great fly which makes so big a buzzing noise. These he tied to some dried yam vines which he had brought back from the farm.

One day, the chief sent messengers to all the land to call his people together, and from every place people came into town. Then the Chameleon arose and covered himself with the dried yam vines and walked slowly like a proud and rich man to the chief's compound, and as he went he kept swinging his strange costume and the flies, being shaken, buzzed. This was wonderful, and as he drew near the chief, swinging his dress, which buzzed more and more, every one admired it and the chief himself asked to buy it. But the Chameleon refused and went home. Now Anansi was late for the meeting, and when he did arrive every one was talking about this wonderful costume. The chief told Anansi that the Chameleon had refused to sell it, and Anansi said that was nothing, and that he would buy it and would bring it to the chief.

He went and called on the Chameleon. "Friend," he said, "I hear you have a most wonderful cloak, which wherever you walk sings to you. Is this so?" The Chameleon answered that it was so, and then Anansi asked him if he would sell it.

The Chameleon at first refused, but after a time did agree to sell it if Anansi would give him some food. Anansi asked how much food he would want, and the Chameleon said that he did not require a great deal, merely enough to fill the hole which Anansi himself could see. Then Anansi laughed and said that he would willingly do that, and to show that he bore him no grudge, would give him twice as much.

Then Anansi went to his own house and called his children and told them to come with him and each to carry a little food. They all went to the Chameleon's house and began to fill the hole with food they had brought. But that hole could not be filled. All the family of Anansi worked, and for many days they carried the corn and other food to fill that hole and always the Chameleon reminded Anansi that he had promised twice the amount.

Anansi did not know what to do. He had finished all the food that there had been stored in his own bins and granaries and he had sent out in all directions to buy food. But still the hole was not filled. He sold his sheep and his cows and everything that he had, for he knew that when he did get the cloak the chief would repay him. But he could not fill the hole.

Then when the Chameleon saw that Anansi was no longer a rich man and that he had no food left for himself, he called him and said: "Friend, you have not paid me the agreed price. But I am not a hard man and I will now forgive you the rest of the debt. Here is the cloak."

Saying this he took out the cloak from its box and put it over the shoulders of Anansi.

But the cloak had been a long time in the box and the strings which held the flies were all rotted. This Anansi did not know, and when he went outside and began to swing the robe the flies all buzzed, but suddenly there came a strong blast of wind and shook the cloak too much. All the flies were released and flew away and left Anansi dressed only in the dried vine stalks of the yams.

Then all the town laughed, and Anansi grew so ashamed that he began to hide himself from that day away from the sight of man, and does not walk in the streets. ▶

THE GOURD FULL OF WISDOM

THE SPIDER [1] NOTICED one day how other people than himself were beginning to use wisdom. This did not suit him at all, as he wanted to keep all the wisdom for himself. So he collected it all and put it into a large gourd that he had hollowed out for the purpose. He then hung the gourd up on the wall of his house. But his fears were not allayed and he decided to hide it right away in the bush where no man could find it. Therefore on the following morning he took down the gourd from the wall, and accompanied by his son went forth into the bush. Presently they came to a tall palm tree, and it seemed to the spider that if he put the gourd at the top among the foliage it would be quite safe. So he began to climb the palm tree. But the gourd was a large one and the spider had slung it in front of him. So he could not make any progress. Always the gourd got in his way. Now the son of the spider had been watching his father's efforts and at last cried out: "Father, why not sling the gourd over your back?"

And Anansi the spider answered: "My son, you are right: but your words show to me that it is better for many people to have wisdom rather than one. For alone I should not have thought of that." So speaking, he opened the gourd and scattered the wisdom all over the ground so that he who may want it can gather what he will. ▶

"Four Tales From Togoland" by A. W. Cardinall from TALES TOLD IN TOGOLAND. Published by Oxford University Press. Reprinted by permission of International African Institute.

1. *The Spider.* Anansi the Spider is the hero of countless West African folk tales. See headnote on page 55.

THE HUNTER WHO HUNTS NO MORE

As you know, I have killed many animals. Do you not see the heads of all I have killed at my door? But I do not go into the bush now to hunt, for I have seen a fearsome thing. All men who hunt learn strange things, but this is more fearful than any other I have seen or heard.

I had killed a large roan. When I shot it, it ran away and I followed the blood trail. This led me to a great baobab tree and there the trail finished and I could see no more marks. I looked and looked everywhere, but I could see nothing. I grew tired and I sat down by a tree to rest, and as I was sitting there I saw an old man coming along.

He was carrying on his head a part of a white ants' nest for his fowls. When he came up he asked me what I was doing, and I told him how I had shot the large roan and how the trail had finished at the large baobab. He told me that was what one might have expected, and that if I followed him he would show me things.

He told me to leave my gun behind against the tree and then took me into the tree through a long dark hole. We came out into a wonderful village which I knew at once to be the village of the Kulparga.[1] It was a very rich place and the houses were much larger than ours and cleaner, and the people had rich clothes. But as we drew near, we heard the noise of much weeping, and we learned that the eldest son of the chief was dying.

"Four Tales From Togoland" by A. W. Cardinall from TALES TOLD IN TOGOLAND. Published by Oxford University Press. Reprinted by permission of International African Institute.
1. *the Kulparga,* a race of dwarfs who appear in Togoland folk tales.

We went to the house of the chief and there saw the young man. He was a very fine man to look at, but he had been wounded in the chest and his life was certainly near its end. I asked how the accident had occurred and I was told that there was a certain hunter in my own village who was always killing the young men of this fairy township and that they were very much afraid of him. They told me that they did not understand why he was always doing this as they had never done him any ill thing. I knew then that they spoke of me.

At last the young man died and my friend the old man told me to come away. We went back the road we had come and passed through the baobab tree. Then the old man left me. And as I came out, there at the foot of the tree lay my roan shot through the chest.

From that day to this I have never hunted. And you will hear that many other hunters have seen the same thing which I have just told you. ▶

R. E. G. Armattoe / *Ghana*
(1913–1953)

THE LONELY SOUL

I met an old woman
Talking by herself
Down a lonely road.
Talking to herself,
5 Laughing all the time,
Talking to herself
Down a country road.
Child, you cannot know
Why folks talk alone.
10 If the road be long
And travellers none,
A man talks to himself.
If showers of sorrows
Fall down like arrows
15 The lone wayfarer
May talk by himself.
So an old woman
On lone country roads,
Laughing all the time,
20 May babble to herself
To keep the tears away.
Woman, you are sad!
'Tis the same with me.

"The Lonely Soul" by R. E. G. Armattoe from DEEP DOWN THE BLACKMAN'S MIND, appeared in AFRICAN VOICES, AN ANTHOLOGY OF NATIVE AFRICAN WRITING, edited by Peggy Rutherfoord. Reprinted by permission of Drum Publications (PTY.) Ltd.

J. Benibengor Blay / *Ghana*
(1925–   )

FUNERAL OF A WHALE

THERE IS GREAT EXCITEMENT in the ancient town of Missibi in Ghana.

The previous night had been wet and stormy and one which the fishermen were not likely to forget. Caught in the storm, their canoes had been dashed to pieces on the rocks and their nets swept away on the swift current. Only the fact that they were all strong swimmers had saved the men from drowning.

The sun is not yet up when they collect again on the shore to watch for their nets. The moon is still shining and little waves dance merrily on the strand, while the sea crabs scuttle among the scattered shells. But these things do not interest the fishermen, and even the search for nets is forgotten as they catch sight of a huge object, surrounded by a shoal of fish, tossing on the rolling sea. Their slow, questing advance is halted as a nauseating stench greets them. Fingers to their noses, they crane and peer. It is a whale—and judging by the smell, it has been dead for some days.

Now, such a sight is no mere spectacle to the people of Missibi. As descendants of a strong and virile race which long ago came by sea in great barge-like ships to settle in these parts, they hold to the tradition that the sea is their home and they worship it to this day. In any crisis—whatever its nature, whether drought or famine or war—they call upon the sea for

---

help. The whale is the king of their sea. And it has been the custom, throughout their long history, to accord a ceremonial funeral to any whale that comes rolling ashore dead.

So, bound by tradition, the fishermen must bear the unhappy tidings to the ruler of the town. Their waists girdled with palm leaves and fingers to lips as signs that their news is urgent, and as yet secret, they go on their errand.

The chief's advisers are called together by the court messenger for a palaver. Now the fishermen are permitted to tell their news. Only after the chief's bodyguards have visited the beach to confirm this statement may the townsfolk be told. It is now past eight o'clock in the morning. The state drums boom out the warning of great calamity. The people from the busy market place, the farmers, coconut breakers and rice growers who have risen at cockcrow and gone to the farms, all come trooping to the palace yard, agog with excitement.

The chief comes to the courtyard with his advisers and sits on the landing of the dais. His face betokens sadness. His attendants bow and leave the palace. The drums are still booming. Outside are packed lorries and cars from up country bringing loads of hawkers and buyers to the market while the occupants move in with the still surging crowd.

The court messenger comes into the yard, bows to the chief and courtiers, commands silence and after giving a brief survey of the history of Missibi and her connection with the sea, makes his announcement to the assembled throng.

"The State is in mourning. A whale is dead and has been washed ashore. The funeral will be held at two o'clock at Aposika where the king of the sea now lies."

There is no whisper nor laughter nor cough as the great crowd moves from distant parts, out of the palace. The market day is postponed. The school bell's tolling stopped. All is sad silence. Yet it is a great day for the hawkers from distant parts, for now they will see something of which so far they have only heard. To the aged of the town it is history repeating itself, and the announcement seems to bring back pictures of half-forgotten times.

By order of a committee appointed by the chief's advisers, funeral preparations are put in hand at once. Cases of gin, beer, kola and palm wine are brought from the stores and cellars. A body of young men is engaged in the erection of bamboo huts, and the bush around the area is cleared, while musicians polish their instruments in readiness. Word is passed to neighboring places and more people arrive to swell the numbers.

At two o'clock the procession leaves for the scene of the funeral, guns booming, state guns rumbling, ivory horn blaring. The chief and his counselors are dressed in red. The womenfolk, besmeared with red clay and wearing pieces of red calico tied around their hair, are in front with the children. The men bring up the rear.

The tail of the column is as yet only at the outskirts of the town when its head reaches the place where, a little off the beach, lies the great shapeless mass of the whale. Gallons of disinfectant have already been sprinkled around to kill the smell.

Now the chief's messenger calls for silence and orders the crowd to be seated. The chief steps forward followed by his advisers. Dropping the red cloth from his shoulder and gathering the folds in his left arm, with a glass of rum held in his right hand, he first raises his eyes to heaven then looks to the ground as he pours out a libation with these words: "Tradition binds us to the sea and the whale is king of the elements there. My people and I pay you homage and lament your death. How it happened we do not know. Whether it was in combat with your fellow kings, or whether it was inflicted by those who delight in making sport of you, or whether it was a natural death, we are afflicted all the same with a great sense of personal loss. We reaffirm our traditional ties with your descendants, will look to them in anxious days for help, and beg of you, who now belong to the ages, to release this land from starvation and sickness; leave in their place health and plenty. Rest in peace."

The funeral ceremony being declared open, the women like minstrels tell the story of the whale in parables; its connection with the state is recounted and the dead one praised. The chief and his advisers are head mourners and make themselves responsible for the fair distribution of drinks, providing food for those who have come from afar and recording donations received.

The young men keep order and play native instruments, while the old correct any departure from the traditional funeral procedure. Boys and girls play "Hunt the Slipper" and "Ampay." Hunters fire off guns and firecrackers at intervals in honor of the majesty of the dead. Fishermen fish in the waves and cast their nets on the beach; farmers sow their seeds on the strand, fetish priests play tom-toms and perform their feats of walking barefoot on broken bottles and gashing their stomachs with sharp knives. Everybody, in fact, is doing something. And all the men are partly or completely drunk.

As the celebration continues, weeping becomes the order of the day; there is competition among the womenfolk in pitch, tone and rendering of phrases, and prizes are offered to those who maintain the high standard of wailing set by their ancestors.

Further away from the crowds a great number of seagulls gather. Some are twittering, others are flying around the whale. The tide begins to rise and the waves are swelling high. Deep clouds overshadow the clear blue sky, and for a while the heavens are pouring rain. It seems that nature, too, is paying tribute to the king of the sea.

At six o'clock, as the sun is setting behind the clouds, the celebrations reach their climax—the solemn spreading of a long white sheet over the whale. Now each mourner takes a pebble, a shell, a stick, a coin or anything handy and, whispering a few words, whirls it around his head and throws it in the direction of the whale. Then without a further glance, all return to town.

The funeral of the king of the sea is over. ▶

J. P. Clark / *Nigeria*
(1935–   )

NIGHT RAIN

What time of night it is
I do not know
Except that like some fish
Doped out of the deep [1]
5   I have bobbed up bellywise
From stream of sleep
And no cocks crow.

It is drumming hard here
And I suppose everywhere
10 Droning with insistent ardour upon
Our roof-thatch and shed
And through sheaves slit open
To lightning and rafters
I cannot quite make out overhead
15 Great water drops are dribbling
Falling like orange or mango
Fruits showered forth in the wind
Or perhaps I should say so
Much like beads I could in prayer tell
20 Them on string as they break

---

1. *Doped out of the deep.* Fishermen in central Africa often drop drugs into the water and then gather the fish which float paralyzed to the surface.

In wooden bowls and earthenware
Mother is busy now deploying
About our roomlet and floor.
Although it is so dark
25 I know her practised step as
She moves her bins, bags, and vats
Out of the run of water
That like ants filing out of the wood
Will scatter and gain possession
30 Of the floor. Do not tremble then,
But turn, brothers, turn upon your side
Of the loosening mats
To where the others lie.
We have drunk tonight of a spell
35 Deeper than the owl's or bat's
That wet of wings may not fly.
Bedraggled upon the *iroko*,[2] they stand
Emptied of hearts, and
Therefore will not stir, no, not
40 Even at dawn for then
They must scurry in to hide.
So let us roll over on our back
And again roll to the beat
Of drumming all over the land
45 And under its ample soothing hand
Joined to that of the sea
We will settle to sleep of the innocent and free.

2. *iroko,* a very tall, central African tree.

GIRL BATHING

Her basket of cassava set away from reach
Of a log basking smooth on the beach,
She wades gingerly up to her high
Girdled hips, her underskirt lapping her thigh
5 Like calyces a corn. And as she ducks
Under, with deft fingers plucks
Loose her hair, the sweat and dirt long dried in every pore
Fall off her back, and in their place once more
The unguent flow of limbs, the fresh
10 Warm smell of her flesh.
O girl of erect and rearing breast,
So ripe with joy for the blest,
Splash, your teeth flashing pearls, in the whirlpool
You have made, its lively cool
15 Waters lambent through your veins,
A tonic at the core of your bones.
And striding back to land, neat
On sands golden at your feet,
How iridescent breaks all
20 Your porcelain skin to tattoo beads of coral!

Bernard Dadié[1] / *Ivory Coast*
(1916–   )

MEN OF ALL CONTINENTS

I emerge from blood-spattered nights.

Look at my flanks
Plowed by hunger and fire
I was an arable land
See my callused hand,
5   black
from ever working the world.
My eyes burned by the fire of Love.

I was there when the angel drove out the ancestor
I was there when the waters consumed the mountains
10 Also there, when Jesus reconciled heaven and earth
Still there, when his smile above the ravines
Bound us together in the same destiny.

Men of all continents
Bullets still behead the roses
15 in the mornings of dreams.

"Men of All Continents" by Bernard Dadié from POESIE VIVANTE.
Reprinted by permission of *Poesie Vivante*.
1. *Dadié* (dä′dē ä).

Having left the night of artificial hopes
I would sing to you
You who hold heaven within reach
  We
who seek ourselves in the false dawn of the streetlamps.

20 I too know
Of cold in the bones, of hunger in the belly,
Of waking up startled by the clatter of carbines
But a star has always given a wink
On evenings of fires, in the hours drunk with gunpowder.

25 Men of all continents
Holding heaven within reach
You who like to hear a woman laugh,
You who like to watch a child play,
You who like to offer your hand
30 To form a chain

Bullets still behead the roses
in the mornings of dreams.

Adebisi Fabunmi
Russian City
(Oshogbo),
1966. Lino-cut.

Birago Diop[1] / *Senegal*

(1906–   )

TRUTH AND FALSEHOOD

Translated from the French by
Dorothy S. Blair

FENE-FALSEHOOD had grown big and had learnt many things.
But there were many things that he still did not know, notably
that man—and woman even less—bears no resemblance to the
good Lord. And so he took umbrage and considered himself
hard done by every time he heard any one say: "The good Lord
loves Truth!" and he heard it very often. Some certainly said that
nothing looks more like the truth than a falsehood, but the
majority stated that Truth and Falsehood were like night and
day. That is why, when one day he set out on a journey with
Deug-Truth, Fene-Falsehood said to his travelling companion:

"You are the one whom the Lord loves, you are the one whom
people no doubt prefer, so it is you who must do the talking
everywhere we go. For if I were recognized we should be very
badly received."

They set out early in the morning and walked for a long time.
At midday they entered the first house of the village which they
reached. After they had exchanged greetings they had to ask
before being given anything to drink. The mistress of the house
gave them, in a calabash of doubtful cleanliness, some lukewarm

From TALES OF AMADOU-KOUMBA, by Birago Diop, translated by
Dorothy S. Blair, and published by The Oxford University Press. Originally published as "Vérité et Mensonge" by Birago Diop, from *Les Contes*
D'Amadou-Koumba, published by Éditions Bernard Grasset.
1. *Diop* (dē op′).

water which would have made an ostrich vomit. There was no question of giving them anything to eat, although a pot full of rice was boiling at the entrance to the hut. The travellers lay down in the shade of a baobab in the middle of the courtyard and awaited the good Lord, that is to say, luck and the return of the master of the house. The latter came back at twilight and asked for food for himself and the strangers.

"I haven't got anything ready yet," said the woman, who could not have swallowed by herself the whole contents of the pot.

The husband flew into a great rage, not only on his own account, although he was famished after having spent the whole day working in the fields in the blazing sun, but because of his unknown guests, whom he was unable to honour (as every master of the house worthy of the name should do) and who had been left with empty bellies. He asked: "Is that the action of a good wife? Is that the action of a generous woman? Is that a good housewife?"

Fene-Falsehood, as agreed, prudently said nothing, but Deug-Truth could not keep silent. She answered sincerely that a woman worthy of the name of mistress of the house might have been more hospitable to strangers, and ought always to have something prepared for her husband's return.

Then the woman flew into a mad rage and, threatening to arouse the whole village, ordered her husband to throw out these impertinent strangers, who interfered in the way she ran her house and took it upon themselves to give her advice, otherwise she would return home to her parents on the spot. So the poor husband, who could not see himself managing without a wife (even a bad housekeeper) and without any cooking because of two strangers, two passers-by whom he had never seen and whom he would probably never see again in his life, was forced to tell the travellers to be on their way. Did they not remember, these ill-bred travellers, that life was not all *couscous,*[2] but that it

---

2. *couscous* (küs′küs), a highly seasoned dish made from coarsely ground meal mixed with salt water, to which vegetables, meat, or fish are added. It is eaten in different forms throughout West Africa.

did need some softening, however? Did they have to say things so crudely?

So Deug and Fene continued their journey which had begun so ill. They walked on for a long time and reached a village in the entrance to which they found some children busy sharing out a fat bull which they had just slaughtered. On entering the house of the village chief, they saw some children who were saying to him: "Here is your share," and they gave him the head and the feet of the animal.

Now, since time immemorial, since n'Diadiane n'Diaye,[3] in every village inhabited by man, it is the chief who gives every one his share, and who chooses his own—the best.

"Who do you think commands here in this village?" the chief asked the travellers.

Prudently Fene-Falsehood kept silent and did not open his mouth: Deug-Truth was obliged, as agreed, to give her opinion: "To all appearances," she said, "it is these children."

"You are insolent folk!" cried the old man in a rage. "Leave this village, go, go immediately, or else you will never leave it again! Begone, begone!"

And the unfortunate travellers continued on their way.

As they went, Fene said to Deug: "The results have not been very brilliant so far, and I am not sure if they will be any better if I go on any longer leaving you in charge of our affairs. So from now on I am going to look after both of us. I am beginning to think that even if the good Lord loves you, man doesn't appreciate you over much."

Not knowing how they would be received in the village they were approaching, and from whence came cries and lamentations, Deug and Fene stopped at the well before entering any dwelling, and were quenching their thirst, when a woman came along all in tears.

"What is the meaning of these cries and tears?" asked Deug-Truth.

---

3. *n'Diadiane n'Diaye,* a traditional hero. His name is introduced to suggest the beginning of history.

"Alas!" said the woman (she was a slave) "our favourite queen, the youngest of the king's wives, died yesterday, and the king is so heart-sore that he wishes to kill himself, so that he may rejoin the woman who was the fairest and most gracious of his wives."

"And is that the sole cause of so much lamenting?" asked Fene-Falsehood. "Go tell the king that there is at the well a stranger who can bring back to life people who have even been dead for long."

The slave went off and returned a minute later accompanied by an old man who led the travellers into a fine hut, where they found a whole sheep roasted and two calabashes of *couscous*.

"My master brings you here," said the old man, "and bids you rest after your long journey. He bids you wait and he will send for you ere long."

The next day an even more copious repast was brought to the strangers, and the day after the same thing happened. But Fene pretended to be angry and impatient; he said to the messenger: "Go tell your king that I have no time to waste here, and that I shall continue on my way if he has no need of me."

The old man returned, telling him: "The king is asking for you." And Fene followed him, leaving Deug-Truth in the hut.

"First, what do you desire as a reward for what you are about to do?" asked the king, when he came before him.

"What can you offer me?" replied Fene-Falsehood.

"I will give you one hundred things from all that I possess in this land."

"That will not satisfy me," calculated Fene.

"Say then yourself what you desire," suggested the king.

"I desire the half of all that you possess."

"That is agreed," the king accepted.

Fene had a hut built above the grave of the favourite, and went in alone, armed with a hoe. He could be heard puffing and panting; then, after a very long time, he began to talk, softly at first, then in a very loud voice as if he were arguing with several persons; at length he came out of the hut and stood with his back firmly pressed against the door.

"Things are getting very complicated," he said to the king. "I have dug up the grave, I have woken your wife, but scarcely had she returned to life and was about to emerge from beneath the ground than your father woke up too and seized her by the feet, saying to me: 'Leave this woman alone. What can she give to you? Whereas if I return to earth, I will give you all the fortune of my son.' He had barely finished making me this proposition than his father emerged in his turn and offered me all his goods and half the property of his son. Your grandfather was elbowed out of the way by the grandfather of your father, who offered me your property, your father's property, his son's property and the half of his own fortune. Scarcely had he finished speaking than his father arrived, so that your ancestors and the forbears of their ancestors are all at the exit of your wife's grave."

The King Bour looked at his advisers, and the notables looked at the king. The stranger was quite right to say that things were in a mess. Bour gazed at Fene-Falsehood, and the old men gazed at him. What was to be done?

"To help you out of your dilemma, and to avoid too difficult a choice," said Fene-Falsehood, "just give me an idea which I should bring back, your wife or your father?"

"My wife!" said the king, who loved the favourite more than ever and who had always been afraid of the late king, whose death he had precipitated, with the assistance of the notables.

"Naturally, naturally!" replied Fene-Falsehood. "Only, you see, your father did offer me double what you promised me just now."

Bour turned towards his advisers, and the advisers gazed at him and gazed at the stranger. The price was high, and what good would it do the king to see his most beloved wife again, if he were deprived of all his goods? Would he still be king? Fene guessed the thoughts of the king and of his notables: "Unless," he said, "unless you give me, for leaving your wife where she is at present, what you promised me to bring her back."

"That is certainly the best and the most reasonable thing to do!" replied in chorus the old notables who had contributed to the disappearance of the old king.

"What do you say, Bour?" asked Fene-Falsehood.

"Oh, well, let my father, the father of my father and the fathers of their fathers remain where they are, and my wife likewise," said the king.

And so it was that Fene-Falsehood, for bringing no one back from the other world, received half the property of the king, who, moreover, soon forgot his favourite and took another wife.

▶

THE WAGES OF GOOD

Translated from the French by
Robert Baldick

DIASSIGUE-THE-ALLIGATOR, scraping the sand with his flaccid belly, was returning to the channel after sleeping all day long in the hot sun, when he heard the women coming back from drawing water, scouring calabashes and washing linen. These women, who had undoubtedly done more work with their tongues than with their hands, were still talking and talking. They were saying sorrowfully that the king's daughter had fallen into the water and been drowned, and that it was very likely—indeed it was certain, according to a woman slave—that at dawn the next day Bour-the-King would have the channel drained in order to find his beloved daughter's body. Diassigue, whose hole in the channel bank was close to the village, turned back the way he had come and went far into the interior in the dark night. The next day, sure enough, the channel was drained and, what is more, all the alligators that lived in it were killed; in the hole of the oldest of them all, they found the body of the king's daughter.

"The Wages of Good" by Birago Diop, translated by Robert Baldick from AFRICAN WRITING TODAY. Reprinted by permission of Penguin Books Ltd.

In the middle of the day, a child who was gathering dead wood found Diassigue-the-Alligator in the scrub.

"What are you doing there, Diassigue?" asked the child.

"I have lost my way," answered the alligator. "Will you carry me home, Goné?"

"There isn't a channel any more," the child told him.

"Then carry me to the river," said Diassigue-the-Alligator.

Goné-the-Child went to fetch a mat and some creepers. He rolled Diassigue up in the mat, which he fastened with the creepers. Then he put it on his head and walked until the evening, when he reached the river. Arriving at the water's edge, he put down his bundle, cut the creepers, and unrolled the mat. Then Diassigue said to him: "Goné, my legs are all stiff from that long journey. Will you put me into the water, please?"

Goné-the-Child walked into the water until it came up to his knees, and he was about to put Diassigue down when the latter said to him: "Go on until the water comes up to your waist, for I would find it hard to swim here."

Goné did as he asked and walked on until the water encircled his waist.

"Go on until it comes up to your chest," the alligator begged him.

The child went on until the water reached his chest.

"You might as well go on now until it comes up to your shoulders."

Goné walked on until his shoulders were covered, and then Diassigue said to him: "Now put me down."

Goné obeyed. He was about to return to the river bank when the alligator gripped him by the arm.

"Wouye yayô! Oh, Mother," cried the child. "What are you doing? Let go of me!"

"I shan't let go of you, because I'm very hungry, Goné."

"Let go of me!"

"I shan't let go of you. I haven't had anything to eat for two days and I'm too hungry."

"Tell me, Diassigue, do you repay a kindness with another kindness or with a bad turn?"

"A good deed is repaid with a bad turn and not with another good deed."

"Now it's I who am in your power, but what you say isn't true, and you must be the only person in the whole world to say it."

"Oh! You really think so?"

"Well, let's ask a few people and we'll see what they say."

"All right," said Diassigue; "but if we find three people who share my opinion, then you'll end up in my stomach, I promise you."

He had scarcely finished uttering this threat when an old, old cow arrived to drink out of the river. When she had quenched her thirst, the alligator called her and asked her: "Nagy, you who are so old and possess all wisdom, can you tell us whether a good deed is repaid with a kindness or with a bad turn?"

"A good deed," declared Nagy-the-Cow, "is repaid with a bad turn, and believe me, I know what I'm talking about. In the days when I was young, strong, and vigorous, when I came back from the pasture I was given bran, millet and a lump of salt, I was washed and rubbed down, and if Poulo, the little shepherd, happened to raise his stick against me, he was sure to receive a beating in his turn from his master. At that time I gave a lot of milk, and all my master's cows and bulls are offspring of mine. Now I am old and no longer give any milk or calves, so nobody takes care of me any more or takes me out to graze. At dawn every day, a blow from a stick drives me out of the park, and I go off on my own to look for my food. That is why I say that a good deed is repaid with a bad turn."

"Goné, did you hear that?" asked Diassigue-the-Alligator.

"Yes," said the child, "I heard it all right."

With her thin, bony buttocks swaying like a couple of sword-blades, Nagy-the-Cow went off, swinging her old tick-bitten tail, towards the sparse grass of the scrubland.

Then gaunt old Fass-the-Horse arrived on the scene. He was about to brush the water with his lips before drinking when the alligator called out to him: "Fass, you who are so old and wise, can you tell us, this child and me, whether a good deed is repaid with a kindness or with a bad turn?"

"I certainly can," declared the old horse. "A kindness is always repaid by an evil deed, and I know something about it. Listen to me, the two of you. In the days when I was young, strong and high-spirited, I had three grooms all to myself; I had my trough filled with millet morning and night, and bran mash often mixed with honey at all hours of the day. I was taken for a bath and a rub-down every morning. I had a bridle and a saddle made by a Moorish saddler and adorned by a Moorish jeweller. I used to go on the battlefields, and the five hundred prisoners my master took in the wars were brought back on my crupper. For nine years I carried my master and his booty. Now that I have grown old, all that they do for me is hobble me at dawn, and then, with a blow from a stick, they send me into the scrubland to look for my food."

Having spoken, Fass-the-Horse brushed the scum from the surface of the water, took a long drink, and then went off, hampered by his hobble, with his jerky, limping walk.

"Goné," said the alligator, "did you hear that? Now I'm too hungry to wait any longer: I'm going to eat you."

"No, Uncle Diassigue," said the child. "You said yourself that you would ask three people. If the next person who comes along says the same as those two, then you can eat me, but not before."

"Very well," agreed the alligator, "but I warn you that we shan't go any further afield."

Then Leuk-the-Hare came running up, his hindquarters twitching. Diassigue called him:

"Uncle Leuk, you who are the oldest among us, can you tell us which of us two is right? I say that a good deed is repaid with a bad turn, and this child declares that the price of a good deed is a kindness."

Leuk rubbed his chin, scratched his ear, and then asked in his turn: "Diassigue, my friend, do you ask a blind man to tell you whether cotton is white or whether a crow is really black?"

"Of course not," admitted the alligator.

"Can you tell me where a child whose family you don't know is going?"

"Certainly not."

"Then explain to me what has happened and I may be able to answer your question without much risk of making a mistake."

"Well, Uncle Leuk, this is the position: this child found me in the interior, rolled me up in a mat and carried me here. Now I'm feeling hungry, and seeing that I have to eat, because I don't want to die, it would be stupid of me to let him go, to run after a dubious prey."

"Indubitably," said Leuk, "but when words are sick, ears have to be healthy, and my ears, to the best of my knowledge, are perfectly well, thank God, for there are some of your words, Brother Diassigue, which don't strike me as being in very good health."

"Which words are those?" asked the alligator.

"It's when you say that this little boy carried you in a mat and brought you all the way here. I can't believe that."

"All the same, it's true," declared Goné-the-Child.

"You're a liar like the rest of your race," said the hare.

"He is telling the truth," confirmed Diassigue.

"I can't believe that unless I see it," said Leuk increduously. "Get out of the water, both of you."

The child and the alligator came out of the water.

"You claim to have carried this big alligator in that mat? How did you do it?"

"I rolled him up in it and then tied it up."

"Well, I want to see how."

Diassigue lay down on the mat, and the child rolled it up.

"And you say that you tied it up?"

"Yes."

"Tie it up to show me."

The child tied the mat up securely.

"And you carried him on your head?"

"Yes, I carried him on my head."

"Well, carry him on your head so that I can see."

When the child had lifted up mat and alligator and placed them on his head, Leuk-the-Hare asked him: "Goné, are your family blacksmiths?"

"No."

"So Diassigue isn't a relative of yours? He isn't your totem?" [1]

"No, certainly not."

"Then take your bundle home. Your father and your mother and all your relatives and their friends will thank you, since you can eat alligator at home. That is how to repay those who forget a good deed." ▶

FOREFATHERS

Listen more often to things rather than beings.
Hear the fire's voice,
Hear the voice of water.
In the wind hear the sobbing of the trees,
5 It is our forefathers breathing.

The dead are not gone forever.
They are in the paling shadows
And in the darkening shadows.
The dead are not beneath the ground,

"Forefathers" by Birago Diop from AN AFRICAN TREASURY by Langston Hughes. Copyright © 1960 by Langston Hughes. Used by permission of Crown Publishers, Inc.

THE WAGES OF GOOD: 1. *your totem.* The totem of a family or clan was the species of animal or plant regarded by the group as having a blood relationship with it, and as being its guardian spirit, therefore never to be used as food.

10 They are in the rustling tree,
In the murmuring wood,
In the still water,
In the flowing water,
In the lonely place, in the crowd;
15 The dead are not dead.

Listen more often to things rather than beings.
Hear the fire's voice.
Hear the voice of water.
In the wind hear the sobbing of the trees.
20 It is the breathing of our forefathers
Who are not gone, not beneath the ground,
Not dead.

The dead are not gone forever.
They are in a woman's breast,
25 A child's crying, a glowing ember.
The dead are not beneath the earth,
They are in the flickering fire,
In the weeping plant, the groaning rock,
The wooded place, the home.
30 The dead are not dead.

Listen more often to things rather than beings.
Hear the fire's voice,
Hear the voice of water.
In the wind hear the sobbing of the trees.
35 It is the breath of our forefathers.

David Diop / *Senegal*
(1927–1960)

AFRICA

Translated from the French by
Anne Atik

Africa my Africa
Africa of proud warriors in ancestral savannas [1]
Africa of my grandmother's singing
Along the banks of her far-off river
5 I have never known you
But my gaze is charged with your blood
Your beautiful black blood spread abroad over the fields
The blood of your sweat
The sweat of your labor
The labor of your slavery
10 Slavery of your children.
Africa tell me Africa
Is it you, then, this back that bends
And sinks under the weight of humility
This trembling red-striped back
15 That says yes to the whip on the noonday roads?

Then gravely a voice answered me:
Impetuous son, that young and robust tree
That tree over there
20 Splendidly alone midst white faded flowers
It is Africa your Africa that springs up again
Springs up patiently obstinately
And whose fruits ripen with
The bitter flavor of freedom.

"Africa" first appeared in COUPS DE PILON (*Présence Africaine*, Paris, 1956).
1. *savannas*, tropical or subtropical grasslands, with scattered trees.

LISTEN COMRADES

Translated from the French

Listen comrades of the struggling centuries
To the keen clamour of the Negro from Africa to the Americas
They have killed Mamba
As they killed the seven of Martinsville
5 Or the Madagascan down there in the pale light on the prisons
He held in his look comrades
The warm faith of a heart without anguish
And his smile despite agony
Despite the wounds of his broken body
10 Kept the bright colours of a bouquet of hope
It is true that they have killed Mamba with his white hairs
Who ten times poured forth for us milk and light
I feel his mouth on my dreams
And the peaceful tremor of his breast
15 And I am lost again
Like a plant torn from the maternal bosom
But no
For there rings out higher than my sorrows
Purer than the morning where the wild beast wakes
20 The cry of a hundred people smashing their cells
And my blood long held in exile
The blood they hoped to snare in a circle of words
Rediscovers the fervour that scatters the mists
Listen comrades of the struggling centuries
25 To the keen clamour of the Negro from Africa to the Americas
It is the sign of the dawn
The sign of brotherhood which comes to nourish the dreams of
      men.

"ÉCOUTEZ CAMARADES" ("Listen Comrades") by David Diop appeared in the anthology COUPS DE PILON, published by *Présence Africaine* (Paris) 1956.

HE WHO HAS LOST ALL

Translated from the French by
Dorothy Blair

The sun shone brightly in my hut
And my women were fair and pliant
As the palm in the evening breeze.
My children glided through the great river's waters
5 With its deadly depths
And my canoes struggled with the crocodiles.
The maternal moon accompanied our dances
The frenzied heavy rhythm of the tom-tom,
Tom-tom of joy days, careless of the morrow
   In the midst of the fires of liberty.

10 Then one day, silence . . .
The rays of the sun seemed to die
In my hut now empty of meaning.
My women crushed their painted mouths
On the thin hard lips of the steel-eyed conquerors
15 And my children quit their peaceful nakedness
Donning the uniform of iron and bloodshed.
Your voice too had died
The chains of slavery have rent my heart
Tom-toms of night, tom-toms of my fathers.

"He Who Has Lost All" by David Diop, translated by Dorothy Blair, from AFRICAN VOICES, AN ANTHOLOGY OF NATIVE AFRICAN WRITING, edited by Peggy Rutherfoord. Reprinted by permission of Drum Publications (PTY.) Ltd.

YOUR PRESENCE

Translated from the French

In your presence I rediscovered my name
My name that was hidden under the pain of separation
I rediscovered the eyes no longer veiled with fever
And your laughter like a flame piercing the shadows
5 Has revealed Africa to me beyond the snows of yesterday
Ten years my love
With days of illusions and shattered ideas
And sleep made restless with alcohol
The suffering that burdens today with the taste of tomorrow
10 And that turns love into a boundless river
In your presence I have rediscovered the memory of my blood
And necklaces of laughter hung around our days
Days sparkling with ever new joys.

"AUPRÈS DE TOI" ("Your Presence") by David Diop appeared in the anthology COUPS DE PILON, published by *Présence Africaine* (Paris) 1956.

DEFIANCE AGAINST FORCE

Jacob Afolabi
The People of Odidare
(Oshogbo),
1964. Lino-cut.

You who bow you who mourn
You who die one day like that without knowing why
You who struggle, who sit up and watch so the Other[1] can rest
You who no longer look with laughter in your eyes
You my brother with the face of fear and anguish
5   Rise up and shout: NO!

"Defiance Against Force" ("Defi a la Force") by David Diop from THE
AFRICAN ASSERTION edited by Austin J. Shelton. (Originally published
in ANTHOLOGIE DE LA NOUVELLE POESIE NEGRE ET MAL-
GACHE). Reprinted by permission of the publishers, The Odyssey Press
and Presses Universitaires de France.
1. *the Other,* the white man.

R. Sarif Easmon / *Sierra Leone*
(1913-   )

THE FEUD

I

DREAMING OF HER LOVER, Nenneh Touray smiled in her sleep. Even her slumbers were pervaded by a kind of awareness that hers was no mean case of happiness: those days were the heyday of the West Indian Sugar Plantations; of the dreaded *Middle Passage* [1] whose Nineteenth Century infamy was worldwide, and had even penetrated into native gossip so deep in the West African hinterland; of intertribal wars to supply the slaves that made the sinews of an industry wringing bitterness out of Africa to supply Europe with sweetmeats. In spite of all this, Nenneh was not only on the free, African side of the great Ocean, but had that very night been betrothed, in a style befitting an African princess, to the one man in the world she would have chosen for husband.

The luckiest girl in the tribe! Yes, she realised, she was that, so soon to be the wife of her cousin, her hero, Luseni Touray. Even in her dream Luseni stood out so royally, a head taller than any man in any tribal assembly, a warrior by necessity of the times, a leader born. Soon Nenneh's smile changed to one of coyness as, in the disconnected way of dreams, the scene shifted to her

---

1. *the dreaded Middle Passage,* the part of the Atlantic Ocean between West Africa and the West Indies. Many Africans, being transported to the slave markets of the New World, died during this part of the journey from disease and maltreatment.

bridal night; to the morning after, when, with processional song and dance, with the rejoicing of the entire tribe, her maidenhood would be published to the world. That was the red letter day of a Susu [2] woman's life, cause worthy of festivity. Hence it was not at all strange in her dream that all Nenneh Touray's friends and relatives were out in the town's square dancing, while the tribal musicians—the *Yalies* [3]—played their *balanyis* [4] so gloriously that even the houses came forward from their foundations to gambol with the crowd.

Nenneh clung hard and, as things turned out, would gladly have clung forever to her dream. But she felt a sensation of discomfort that was soon sharply defined into the pain of someone smacking her very hard across the face.

"Poreh, you accursed girl!" she cried in outrage, rubbing her cheek and sitting up in the bed. "How dare you!"

"Hurry, N'ga [5] Nenneh!" the slave-girl shrieked through the gloom. *"Hurry!* The house is on fire."

Nenneh rubbed her eyes and coughed. Wood smoke was billowing into the room. A tongue of flame flashed and licked up the side of the muslin net around the bed. Swiftly the bed was ringed in fire.

With a scream Nenneh leapt down on the mat on which her servant had been sleeping on the floor beside her bed.

High above their heads the conical grass roof was ablaze. One rafter after another came crashing down in a constellation of sparks. The front door of the house stood open. The other women had already fled. There was no time to lose.

The two girls grasped each other's hand. For the moment they were not mistress and slave but fellow-humans, friends in a tight situation—a friendship welded by fire and agony.

Nenneh Touray had been sleeping with one white *lappa* tied

---

2. Susu, a West African people, dwelling mostly in Guinea and Sierra Leone. **3.** *Yalies,* a minor tribe within Guinean society, by tradition the musicians of the country. **4.** *balanyis,* antecedents of the xylophone. **5.** *N'ga* (nə gä′), Mother, a term of affection. With the diminutive it becomes *N'gadee,* Little Mother, Darling.

round her waist and reaching down to her calves. She would have tarried to find a garment to throw over her chest. But the slave-girl gripped her by the wrist, rushed her incontinently across the room, through the door and balcony to the great square of the town.

Not ten yards from the blazing house strong arms leapt out of the night, grabbed them both, pinning their arms to their sides.

"Let me go—you brute!" Nenneh yelped with pain.

For answer a stranger slapped her disrespectfully across the face.

Jolted as never before in her life, Nenneh Touray gaped and stared. Only then was she aware of the transformation around her. This was the festive square of her dream: only now every house around it was on fire.

"Allah!" she wailed, "I must be dreaming still!"

But the vise-like hold on her arm was not dreamlike. Side by side with Poreh she was propelled without dignity towards the coconut palm which, tall and lonely, stood at the square's centre.

Halfway there she stumbled across a corpse. A spear impaled the man's chest on to the ground. There was little blood from the wound. Still dazed from sleep, Nenneh recoiled at the object at her feet.

"Don't look, *N'gadee!*" Poreh shouted in horror.

Too late. Nenneh Touray had looked down—and recognised the murdered man as her father.

Stunned beyond feeling, she ceased to struggle or to wonder. She resigned herself to be coralled with the other women—and that with less gentleness than if they had been cattle—round the palm tree in the square. There she stood by Poreh, seeing horror enacted around her, but unable to comprehend anything. Most of the women were wailing and gibbering and calling on her father's name—and calling *her* name too, in an agony full of timelessness but empty of meaning. . . .

Nenneh saw, too, but without the sight registering emotionally, that scores of men dead or dying lay about the square; that the whole town was aflame, turning the night into a hot, ghastly, crimson day; that through the smoke overhead white egrets, black kites and swallows dashed ceaselessly: just as ceaselessly as the invading soldiery in the square—the dreaded "Warboys," naked but for loin cloths, with their swords and spears flashing in the firelight, completely uninhibited in murder, crazy with shedding human blood. If anything, the war-whoops of the soldiers added the final meaninglessness to everything around the girl. . . .

The rapine and slaughter did not reach to Nenneh's consciousness. But something more personal did. Between the house from which she and Poreh had fled, and her father's great *kounkoumah* house, there was a gap of some yards fenced by low, wooden palings. In the backyard behind this gap was a mango tree. She could remember it back to the earliest of her sixteen years. She had played under its shade, eaten each year of its fruit. Above everything in the town, that tree for her signified *home*. Now, with a fatal fascination, she watched it brilliantly lit up by the blaze from all the houses around it; watched its leaves shrivel, curl up, blacken and crackle. Then in an instant the whole tree roared like a round of musketry and burst into flames. From time to time as the wind blew volleys of sparks flew from it. And as time dragged on without meaning, it stood there like a skeleton glowing slowly and fitfully into ashes.

Poreh, seeing her "little mother" so stricken, squeezed her hand and whispered in her ear:

"Take heart, *N'gadee!* . . . Allah's still in heaven . . ."

Nenneh Touray turned towards her.

When Poreh looked more closely into the young face, she knew her mistress's mind had gone blank: she hadn't understood a word Poreh had said to her.

Only then the slave-girl began to cry to herself.

II

OF THE GHASTLY MARCH into slavery—a night followed by a day and another night on the road—Nenneh Touray recalled nothing. Not a hair of her head was injured in the sacking of her father's town. Nevertheless, for a week after, Poreh had had to tend and feed her as though she were an infant.

On the eighth morning, Nenneh turned suddenly to the short, muscular girl beside her.

"Poreh," she cried in dismay, "these are not my clothes!"

Poreh's face was black and oval, and would have been pretty if the brow were not so low. Its normal cast of a silent sorrow deepened, and tears settled in her long, half-closed eyes.

Nenneh looked with apprehension at the native-woven *taimlay* over her chest, at the indigoe-dyed *lappa* around her waist, at the slippers on her feet. Her eyes flew from her garments to the objects and outhouses in the back yard. She clutched desperately at Poreh's arm.

"P—P—Poreh . . . this—isn't *home!*"

Very distressed, Nenneh surveyed the mudhouses, the kitchen behind them; the mortars and pestles for pounding rice; above all, the small bushes crowded with ripe Chile peppers to one side of the kitchen. Everything here was ugly compared with those at home. Last of all, her gaze, now very troubled, rested on the calabash tree with its shining, gourd-fruits each twelve inches across.

Only then she recalled how the mango tree in the backyard at home had exploded and burned. She threw her arms round Poreh's neck and began to sob, brokenheartedly.

Poreh held on to her, and began to cry with relief: "I thank Allah, N'ga Nenneh, you recognise me again."

As suddenly as Nenneh had begun to weep she stopped and braced herself for the worst.

"Recognise you, Poreh?" Now and then a sob escaped her. The fingers she raised to her forehead were long and slender. She pushed the headkerchief back on her head—a gesture full of tiredness, to reveal a high, cleanly chiseled brow. Below her plaited hair the face was oval, nut-brown; and, though tear-stained, exquisitely, refinedly beautiful. Her lips, very dark pink, were very boldly, even passionately cut—the hallmark of the high-born Susu woman. "Poreh," she sighed, "I begin to remember things that'll kill me if they are true."

The slave-girl led her towards the calabash tree and made her sit down on a log in its shade.

"And I feel," Nenneh ended brokenly, "as if I've been crying for years."

"You've cried three times since we came here, *N'gadee.*"

Nenneh contracted her brows, but could remember nothing.

"You must remember, little mistress," Poreh urged, squeezing her hands between hers. "Three times this Daimba has sent for you—you know, Daimba Seisay. This is his principal town."

"You must be mistaken, girl," Nenneh corrected her—corrected her habit, not because she recalled what had happened to her. "Why, he succeeded his father not six months ago, if my memory does not confuse me . . . And, and . . . the old man and Father were friends: even good friends, as kings go."

"Well," Poreh insisted with diffidence and pathos—as though it was a pain to her to contradict her mistress—"both old men are dead now. And the young king intends to marry you. . . ."

Nenneh Touray leapt off the log. Her eyes blazed with anger as she looked down on Poreh. Without pausing to think, she leaned forward and slapped the girl across the face.

"You're lying!" she cried hotly. "Not—not after he's murdered my father!"

For a moment Poreh looked as if she was going to cry. But, used all her life to this kind of treatment from the proprietors of her life and liberty, she did not complain. "It's true, *N'gadee*" she said, biting her lip. "Three times he's called you to his house to tell you so. Each time, unable to speak but understanding what people say to you, why—each time you've covered your face with your hands and burst into tears . . ."

Nenneh's pride collapsed at the information. Trembling, she sat down on the log, leaned over and buried her face in the slave-girl's lap.

"What shall I do, Poreh—what shall I do?"

Downtrodden from her birth, the slave-girl had no answer to her own problems—let alone to her mistress's. She shook her head—even though Nenneh couldn't see the gesture—and remained silent!

When after some minutes Nenneh sat up again, she had stopped crying. But, in spite of the sunshine, she felt horribly chilly and lost. Poreh guessed she was troubled; that a problem was weighing down on her mind; and that whatever the answer to that problem—or even if there were no answer at all—it was going to plague young Nenneh even more than the fact of her father's death. "P—P—Poreh," the question came at last in this guise, "what happened to our people?"

At this point a cockerel trumpeted a challenge at one end of the yard and, head down, sped towards a hen pecking the ground near the pepper bushes. A more powerful bird—the lord of the roost—rushed from the opposite end of the yard, beat his eager wings against Nenneh's legs, and summarily skirmished and routed the usurper of his rights.

"A few of the men kept as slaves"—Poreh spoke in a whisper. "Most of the women shared out among the warriors. The rest sent down to the Coast to be sold to the white men . . ."

Laconic and brutal as the information was, it was no worse than Nenneh had expected. It was the logic of the times. Her father had done the same thing to other tribes. Only she had never, never realised it had been so bad for the others as it was turning out for her . . . She cleared her throat several times before she was able to continue. Even then her voice shook to ask: "Luseni Touray: was he—among—the captives?"

"I can't say, *N'gadee*," Poreh told her as gently as she could. "But," with tenderness as the girl wilted, "no one saw him fall that dreadful night."

While Nenneh shivered at this reprieve, several young slave-girls came from behind the yard balancing on their heads bundles of faggots, gourds of drinking water, baskets of vegetables.

At the same time a young woman came from the back door of the house opposite the calabash tree, and made straight towards the girls on the log.

"Poreh," the newcomer asked with the greatest self-assurance, "is that half-witted mistress of yours still crying?"

Poreh jumped off the log, curtsied hastily to her, and retired behind the calabash tree.

Nenneh Touray surveyed the newcomer. Then, her anger rising slowly like a ferment, she rose from the log. From her own much greater height she looked down on the woman.

"Where I come from," she said to the other's great astonishment, "women of the *Yalie* tribe are only allowed to wag their tongues while we free-born dance."

"I may be a *Yalie*—but I'm proud of it," the small woman's voice cracked like a whiplash across the air. "But," she continued, incensed by the reference to the parasitic place of her tribe in Susu society, "I—this *I!*—am mistress here. Understand this once and for all: *here* it is *you* who are a slave—an insignificant one among many taken in war."

For seconds together they glared at one another without exchanging a word.

"And now, saucy one," the stranger continued, sure she had put the wench in her place, "I'm glad you've found your tongue at last. Your bubblings were becoming rather a bore. But unless you want to have your tongue cut out of your head, be careful how you wag it in front of my husband, Daimba. He's asked me to take you along. Poreh, you stay here. Now, then, *come along!*"

It was an order—and both knew it.

But the freeborn Susu girl was not bred to take orders—and most certainly *not* from a Yalie woman. She bristled up and, under the brown, her face went red with anger and chagrin. Yalie Woanday smiled with delight at her annoyance. *She,* too, was very beautiful—though in a very distinct way from Nenneh. She was small, and in her elegant native costume, as smart as a firefinch. Each ear was pierced in fifteen different places along the edge, and each hole sported a small gold earring. Her face was small and black, her nose long, slightly upturned and excessively impudent. Nenneh had disliked her at sight. At home, now, she would have had her shipped to the Coast to be sold into slavery—but now to have to take orders from *her!*

Nenneh bit her lip—and, a testimony to the weirdness of the new life in which she now found herself, turned for guidance to the slave-girl lurking behind the calabash tree.

Poreh understood. She shook her head sadly, held her finger to her lips to enjoin caution—and waved her towards the house from which the Yalie woman had come.

Nenneh Touray followed Yalie Woanday through the house, through the great square in front. Except that the *barri* or tribal meeting place stood in the middle of the place, the square looked much like the one Nenneh used to know at home. And the great *kounkoumah*—a large, oblong native-built house—may also have been her Father's house. Her heart began to beat fast as she approached it. She stooped slightly to pass under the eaves and enter the front balcony.

"And how is N'ga Nenneh today?" asked the man in the balcony.

He was sitting astride a raffia hammock strung from the rafters. His feet rested on a sheep-skin rug atop one of the eighteen-inch-high mounds—which served as seats—to each side of the passage leading to the door in the inner wall: a very typical Susu husband, served hand and foot at breakfast by all his wives, backed by a reserve of women slaves. . . .

While the Yalie woman climbed the single step up the mound, Nenneh Touray stood in the passage looking up with misgiving at the man who now held her destiny in his hands. She knew him as Daimba Seisay. And he, as he looked down at her, thought the whole campaign worthwhile that could have brought him such a prize. He was smiling at her. Yet though strong, beautiful white teeth showed behind the lips, the smile could not hide the sardonic, down-drooping at the corners of the mouth. The face was long and strong, a dark brown. It was not unhandsome. Nevertheless, neither the smile nor his good looks altered the impact the man made on the girl: Daimba Seisay's face revealed only too clearly a personality driven by boundless arrogance and ruthlessness, never doubting in the glory and rightness of its cause.

"He's smiling," Nenneh thought, in the bitterness of both bereavement and slavery, "though it was he who murdered my father." Confronted with murder and pleasantry so blandly united in the man's nature, the girl not inexcusably began to feel weak at the knees. Weak, and very helpless.

"Lost your tongue again, saucy one?" Woanday asked with a soft laugh of malice. She had moved to the far side of the balcony, and was leaning against the rope supporting that end of the hammock, looking sardonically over her husband's head at her enemy.

"Woanday," Daimba Seisay remonstrated in a deep and rather pleasant, playful voice, "you mustn't antagonise one who'll soon be sharing household duties with you."

"Daimba Seisay," Nenneh forced herself to speak, "my father . . ."

". . . died fairly and bravely in war—" the king finished her sentence for her. He had wiped the smile off his face, knowing it was not fitting in the circumstances. Talking of death, he could not but sound serious. All the same, the tone of his voice left the girl in no doubt that her father's death was a matter of indifference to him—though he was quite prepared to use it as a political lever. "No man could have died more bravely . . ."

"Fair war!" Nenneh burst out in anger. "Father was at war with no one. He was murdered without provocation."

The man in the hammock frowned. There was a Jovian grandeur about his face when he frowned and like Jove his displeasure promised thunder.

"Young woman," he said gravely, "murder is not a gracious word to level at a king. You must not forget your father's dead; and that I, yes *I* am all you have in the world for father or friend."

"Or master!" Woanday interpolated sweetly.

"Quiet, Woanday," Daimba ordered. He strove against it, but the smile leapt out of his eyes to play like ghostly cynicism around the corners of his lips, but without invading his features.

"Only Allah I know as Master!" Nenneh Touray cried with the desperation of freedom staring slavery in the face—at the same time darting Woanday a look intended to keep that loathsome Yalie in her place.

But Woanday only laughed at her.

"She keeps forgetting, my husband," she said, "that *she* is one of many slaves brought here with ropes round their necks."

"A rope round Daimba Seisay's neck wouldn't make a slave of him," Nenneh turned hotly on her tormentor. "If you were not such a baseborn, beggarly Yalie you'd see I'm at least as well-born as he . . ."

"For a slave," Woanday retorted, even more hotly, for she was offended at the taunts about her tribe. "For a slave you are. . . ."

"She's right, my dear Woanday," the man interrupted her. "I mean," turning from one to the other and trying to embrace both in a smile of affability, "in her claim to be as good as you or me. And that, N'ga Nenneh," turning again to the girl he had orphaned, "is why I propose to marry rather than to sell you."

"I'm already promised to . . ." Nenneh began, but stopped when Yalie Woanday tittered, and then proceeded to laugh sarcastically at her. Even Daimba, in his more sophisticated and cruel way, was amused at her. For a while Nenneh struggled to control her anger. She perceived that a man who had killed her father to gain physical possession of her would pay scant respect to a previous engagement. "Only if you think me a slave, Daimba Seisay," she blurted out—and the statement sounded weak and absurd to herself—"would you want to compel me to marry you."

"Indeed!" ejaculated Woanday, astounded at the woman's madness and conceit. "Ain't we cocky! Slavery to marry Daimba Seisay!"

That young man's face had gathered into an angry, threatening mask. For some moments he was so angry his lips seemed to swell and the veins in his throat throbbed with a violence that threatened to burst them. "Slavery, indeed!" He looked so truculent as he leaned forward in the hammock that the girl in the passage backed away from him. He shook his fist and shouted at her: he had absolute power of life and death over everyone in his pocket-handkerchief plot of Africa. Young though he was, both as man and as king, absolute power had corrupted him beyond redemption. "Young woman," he blazed at her, "we are all free-born till a sword stronger than ours strikes ours from our hands. You are my slave by conquest. And I honour you by wanting to marry you. . . . *Slavery!* Ha-ha-ha!"

He leaned back in the hammock and began to laugh in a way so darkly sardonic it frightened the girl more than his anger had.

"The trouble with freeborn Susu women," he wagged his finger at her, even the harsh merriment dying out of his features, "is that you're all pampered and spoilt. This very day, Nenneh Touray, I'll take you to see what slavery *is*. Then you can make your choice between it and *me*."

III

A LARGE RETINUE followed the King.

The honey-coloured grass-thatches of Daimba Seisay's town soon thinned out as the road meandered out into the fields of manioc. Within a mile they were winding their way along a narrow track, while the sharp, pale-brown leaves of elephant grasses swished and whispered against their clothes, and the West African sun blazed down on them out of a shimmering sky. They passed huts solitary in the bush, a great baobab tree in fruit, several oil palms drooping their leaves in the heat. The ubiquitous and hardy "Monkey Apple" trees and large termite nests in the landscape made the view so much like the countryside around her home, they brought a lump into Nenneh Touray's throat.

They walked in single file. Sandwiched between Daimba Seisay in front and Woanday behind, Nenneh was the only stranger in the outing.

"This," said Yalie Woanday, over and over again, laughing at her new enemy, "this should put my saucy one in her place." She was the one discordantly cheerful member of the party.

In another mile, sweating with the heat and the exertion, they came to the brow of a hill overlooking the biggest river in those parts.

Below them the river wound in many peaceful loops, vanishing far to their right in a silver-blue mist shining in the sun. Both banks were densely covered with mangroves—so that the loops of the river looked like disconnected lakes. The mangroves possessed the earth as far as their eyes could see. As they paused there, the wind blew up from the valley a stench of decaying vegetation.

"That," Daimba Seisay told his captive, pointing towards a spot in the near bank, "that, Nenneh Touray, is slavery."

Tears settled in Nenneh's eyes as they strained to make out whether it was men or women who, with bare bending backs, were toiling in the valley of despair below them. They were cutting mangroves, clearing the swamps against the rainy season, when paddy rice would be transplanted stalk by stalk into the mud. Now the mud was not oozy. Except in the depths of the swamps, or in treacherous places where one suddenly sank up to the waist or disappeared forever, the mud had dried and cracked into millions of hard cakes, between which human feet too often slid—to be pulled out with the soles ripped to shreds. Every mortal down there ran the risk hourly of being bitten by swamp snakes—among the most venomous of their kind—or being carried away by crocodiles.

Nenneh observed with a sinking of the heart that though there were scores upon scores of slaves, and they appeared to be toiling so hard, the surface they had cleared looked hardly longer than a handkerchief spread on the landscape to dry. . . .

"Ah, N'ga Nenneh," Daimba Seisay murmured, watching the play of emotions in the girl's face, "hold back your tears till you see their misery at close quarters."

At his command the party moved off down the hill.

They had not gone half a mile when the head of the column halted.

"Why aren't you working?" The question was shouted out, raspingly, by the man at the head of the line.

"I'm having to rest a little . . . My chest is bleeding again . . ."

The rest of the answer was just a blur in Nenneh's ears. She stumbled against Daimba's heel, and fell face-down in the grass by the wayside.

Very anxiously the King bent over her to help her up.

"I hope you're not hurt?"

"No—no," Nenneh returned, trying to control her voice. "You

stopped so suddenly I—I didn't have time to pull up . . . Sorry
. . ." she mumbled and turned her back to him.

Woanday noted that she was an unconscionably long time
dusting her clothes.

"Fishing for Daimba's sympathy," she thought, cattily.

Meanwhile things were taking a course at the head of the line
that threatened disaster.

The slave to whom the question was put was sitting on a
boulder under a tamarind tree just off the path. A *machete* lay at
his feet. The strip of cloth tied round his chest was freshly
stained with blood in the left armpit. He leaned rather wearily
with his head against the tree trunk.

As the people ahead made way for the king, and Nenneh and
Woanday came up behind him, the slave leapt off the rock in
great excitement and bounded to the path.

"Nenneh Touray—*you!*" he rushed towards her, not so much
glad as crazy with joy to see her again.

Nenneh backed away from him.

"Is he crazy?" she asked Daimba Seisay, shrinking in timidity.

The slave stopped as though a spear had been jabbed into his
stomach.

"Only wounded," said Daimba with indifference, wiping the
sweat off his face. "He was taken in your father's town. So I
suppose you may know him."

"*Know him!*" Nenneh cried with a haughty pride. "Am I
supposed to know every one of my father's slaves?"

"*I* a slave! *I!! Slave*—this *I!!!*"

The young man, taller than any human she had ever seen,
looked so pained and horrified Yalie Woanday was moved with
pity for him.

"Misfortune comes to anyone in war, young man," she observed softly. "King today—slave tomorrow."

"But *I* her father's slave!" The words jerked out of the slave's
throat. He looked first towards Woanday—then at Nenneh, who
continued to regard him with a scorn that wounded him. He
shook his head—clearly he couldn't make head or tail of
anything.

Meanwhile, to have his two women drawn into conversation with a wretch of a slave had set Daimba Seisay's anger on the boil.

"Nobody cares who you were," he cut the man's talk short with a brutal arrogance. "But you must be more than a fool if you don't realise you are a slave *now*."

The slave's chest heaved at this affront. A fresh drop of blood oozed out of the bandage over his wound, and crept like a crimson tear down his side. But he must have had the discipline of a soldier, and he held his peace.

It was at this point that, with the inconsequence that men always find so disconcerting in a woman, Nenneh said:

"I'm thirsty, Daimba Seisay. I saw some *Malombo* fruits up there by the path." She pointed back along the track. "Please order the slave to go and pick some for me."

At this the young man drew himself up fiercely. His discipline did not extend to his dealings with the fair sex. Indeed, he looked so dangerous in his wrath that some of the men backed away from him, badly wounded though he was.

"I will *not* do it for Allah himself!" he shouted back—even before Daimba Seisay gave the order.

Incensed at the affront to his authority, the King's face suffused with blood.

"*Sinneh*—" he shouted, "execute him."

Sinneh was a veteran "warboy"—and so inured to bloodshed he looked upon his appointment as the king's killer-in-chief as a badge of honour. He was a short man, his naked arms and chest superbly muscled. He advanced from the group, sword in hand, upon the slave.

In a flash the wounded man leapt back under the tamarind, snatched his *machete* off the ground—and turned to face Sinneh.

Sinneh neither increased nor slackened his pace.

Just when it seemed nothing could stop the bloodshed, Nenneh Touray rushed between the two men.

"No! No!! No!!!" she screamed in agony, pushing the two men away from each other. She fell back on the boulder and began to sob: "NO! . . . Allah knows—I've seen—too much bloodshed—already——Free-born or slave, young man—if you knew my Father—and saw him die—as I did—you'd not refuse his daughter—such a small request . . ."

Daimba Seisay could only grumble at this damnable unpredictablcness of womankind. But, with good grace, he ordered Sinneh to desist.

The slave threw down his weapon. Without another word, he walked up the path to the spot Nenneh had indicated.

All breathed in peace again. Only Woanday was thinking Nenneh must be a very queer fish. She needed watching. Women who cried so easily could tie men into knots. Certainly, she was not prepared to yield such a right over Daimba to any woman yet born . . .

"I see no fruits here," the slave's voice broke in on Woanday's jealous thoughts.

Nenneh Touray ran up the track to show him.

She soon returned with half a dozen bunches of orange-red fruits the size of tangerines.

"They're lovely!" she laughed gratefully through her tears.

And so they moved down into the swamps.

IV

WHEN ALL THE WORLD was abed that moonless night, the slave sat alone on the boulder under the tree. The barking of a dog in the slaves' hamlet lower down the valley sounded faintly through the night—so faintly that when the wind soughed through the leaves overhead the barking was inaudible. In the sky the Milky Way shone like a girdle of silver round the waist of the Universe. And, to the slave, the stars shone so brightly they appeared to be glow-worms just beyond the level of the tree-tops.

After midnight a gentle patting on the ground made the young man start. It was the sound of footsteps lightly running. He jumped off the rock and ran into the path.

"Nenneh Touray!" he gasped.

"Ah—my Luseni!"

She ran into his arms gasping and sobbing together. Their first moments of bliss were too rapturous and choking for words. Deep in their hearts, each had believed the other dead or, worse still, sold into slavery. But now—

"Are you alone, *N'gadee?*" Yes, he called her his "little mother," his Darling that Death had given him back again. He asked the question all solicitude, incredulous at the feat.

"Yes, my dear," her sighs blended with the whispering of the leaves overhead. "Tonight, I couldn't risk coming even with Poreh . . . Allah has been merciful to us, Luseni."

He understood. When he had picked the *Malombo* fruits for her that afternoon, she had made this tryst with him in a whisper upon which Death might have eavesdropped. His heart had beat so violently at his good fortune born of her constancy that it had set the blood flowing from his wound.

"But for you," he murmured, while a shiver ran through him and while he felt more grateful than he'd ever dreamed he could be to a woman, "they'd have murdered me in cold blood today."

He led her deep into the grasses on the far side of the tamarind tree, pulled her down among the foliage beside him.

"Yes," she sighed again, very simply. "Allah is merciful. He made me hear your voice before I saw you. Otherwise, I'd foolishly have rushed into your arms. And if Daimba Seisay were even to suspect you are my husband-to-be . . . Ugghh!" she trembled in his arms.

In their perilous position, only two considerations counted with them: to escape; and, because they might fail in this, to crowd into those starry, dangerous moments together what happiness might have sufficed in normal times for a lifetime. Even in her dreams the girl had not been so happy in her innocence as she was now yielding herself to this man. Her maidenly shyness vanished with the fear that rude hands might pluck her from what was in fact her bridal bed and plunge a dagger straight into her heart. Thus she yielded herself almost with violence to his desires. At the same time she told herself that, at the worst, she had stolen a march on the enemy who would mock her by marrying her; that at the best she had assured Luseni of a rare affection by defying a tyrant to yield to his slave.

"Where shall we go from here?" asked Nenneh, now become a woman.

"To my twin-brother's: Lansannah's town is the nearest. It's very well fortified, too."

"How soon, my dear—how *soon?*"

"As soon as my side heals."

"Yes, yes," she stroked his face agitatedly. In that light she was only a shadow between him and the stars. "But how soon will that be, darling? Don't forget I have to cope with Daimba Seisay and that jealous, firefinch Yalie Woanday—I wish she didn't hate me so! . . ."

"A month at the latest," he promised.

During that month she came sometimes once, sometimes twice a week, to meet him, risking her neck every time she did so. She was never sure she'd reach him when she set out—or return to the town alive having kept her tryst. And yet it never entered her head she should not go.

The last night of all Poreh came with her.

Yes, Poreh came, carrying a bundle on her head—not a large bundle: but it was all they possessed between them—a few miserable wearing apparel. . . . But how little that counted now —now that they were to make their bid for freedom!

How high their hearts beat out there, under the stars! Nenneh Touray was trembling so with excitement she feared she'd let Luseni down by fainting. Here was freedom at last—freedom within reach! To live and breathe freely, without that uncanny feeling that she was being watched by eyes she could not see; that her body was at the absolute disposal of someone for whom her only emotion was fear; to live without the constant foreboding that some danger would befall Luseni in the valley of slaves. How strange this thing called freedom was! Born free, she had never dreamt what it meant till she woke up that night to find her home in flames—Allah! was it only five weeks ago? . . .

And then she heard Luseni's whisper, barely above the sound of the wind rushing through the leaves all around them.

"Yes, we're ready and here, dear Luseni!" Nenneh whispered back, scarcely daring to breathe.

At her answer he emerged out of the night's shadows to greet them.

And at once he led them down the track, destination—Liberty.

In the starlight they were only shadows. Three shadows moving in a line, moving with high purpose down into the valley. There, in a tiny creek of the river, Luseni had concealed a small dugout, just large enough to take them across the river.

Luseni in front, *machete* in hand; Poreh in the rear, bundle on head—softly, surely the three moved through the night.

They had taken not more than a hundred steps to liberty when a voice thundered through the night:

"HALT!"

Luseni's *machete* flew up in his strong right hand. A heavy club smashed down from some point in the night, caught Luseni on the wrist—the *machete* flew from his grasp to swish and clatter in the grasses.

In a twinkling the man and two women found themselves ringed in a circle of spears whose points pricked their throats and the backs of their necks.

"Sinneh, light the torches."

It was Daimba Seisay's voice. The captives recognised its doom in the night—knew their fates were sealed.

Nenneh Touray's heart contracted into a hard, painful knot in her chest. Death indeed had come to claim them. But how—how? *She* had been so careful; and Poreh, she was certain, could not have breathed a word of their plan to anyone: their lives and liberties conjointly depended on silence. O Allah—what had she brought upon Luseni? . . .

Meanwhile, while Eternity stood still, they heard the whirr of wood being rubbed on wood. And soon, too soon, six palm-oil flambeaux were kindled and incarnadined the scene.

They made a ghastly light indeed—the light in miniature that rose from Nenneh Touray's home, and shone on her father's body in the square that dreadful night. And twenty of the very men who had sacked her father's town were now here around her, to complete the circle of treachery and murder. *Murder!* Were she and Luseni to die after all their sufferings? Allah could not be so cruel! Why, their lives had hardly begun! Surely, Allah owed them something beside pain and violence and lost hopes and purpose. . . . Why—

"Bring them here," Daimba Seisay ordered.

Violent hands descended on the captives and hustled them to the shade of the tamarind—Nenneh's tree of reunion with her lover, her arbour of love, and now, she was sure, her place of death.

Alimamy Daimba stood to one side of the boulder, his back to the trunk of the tree. His face showed ghastly in the light: it looked not so much angered as insane—insane with jealousy, wounded pride, and hurt, despotic majesty. Looking into that face, Luseni would sooner have expected mercy from a hungry, wounded leopard.

"Woanday," said Daimba Seisay bitterly, "you were right."

The small woman stepped lightly out of the shadows. She was smiling in this her hour of triumph. Her comment was almost superfluous: "You see, Nenneh Touray, a Yalie woman can do something else besides sing and dance."

Nenneh started violently. Only then she understood. The Yalie woman was so embittered with jealousy and a sense of inferiority that she had spied on her and betrayed her to her enemy. Oh, the madness of humans! Betray her, she thought, betray her when she should have done her best to help her escape so as to leave Daimba to her Yalie wiles and charms! Oh, the utter pointless madness of it all!

"Ah, Yalie Woanday!" the words, overcharged with despair, burst out of Nenneh Touray's breaking heart. "Ah, Woanday! I did not want your husband. You could have let me go in peace with mine. . . ."

"*Your* husband!" Woanday's scream struck out eerily through the night. She recoiled and staggered so that one of the warboys had to hold her up. "*Your—*" she gasped and stared at Nenneh, the horror of what she had done breaking on her.

"Yes, Woanday . . . I was betrothed to Luseni the very night

your husband sacked my father's town . . . and have indeed
. . . been his wife . . . this last month . . . Ah Woanday! Ah
Woanday! . . ."

Her words rang like a deathknell in the night.

No less stricken than the woman she had betrayed, Woanday
came forward and took Nenneh's hand. She turned instinctively
with a prayer on her lips to Daimba. But the prayer died within
her, unuttered.

"You told us," said Daimba Seisay, struggling to sound calm,
while his eyes blazed with madness and hatred at Nenneh, "you
told us he was your father's slave. But you *knew* he is my slave
—and that it was my intention to marry you. I cannot, therefore,
forgive the disgrace you have brought upon my name. I shall
punish *you* with life. As to *him,* the question is not whether he is
to die—but how? . . ." He remained silent for a while, while the
chimera of power drove him headlong into fiendishness. And
then he smiled in a way that killed the young girl before him
over and over again. "Sinneh," turning to his specialist in murder, "cut me a stout stake, and sharpen it very fine at one end.
And you, Hamid, fetch the heaviest stone you can carry."

The women trembled at these strange orders.

"Bah Daimba," Woanday began timidly. Even in that light her
face looked pinched, and she shivered involuntarily every now
and then.

"Quiet, woman!"

He did not have to repeat the order.

Minutes of agony slipped by.

The sharp sound of steel on raw wood struck repeatedly
through the night. The flambeaux burned. Doubled over a stone,
Hamid came from the shadows and set his burden down at the
king's feet.

Soon, too soon, Sinneh brought forth *his* offering: a stick a
yard long, thick as a man's wrist. He knelt down on the ground
at his master's feet, set one end of the stick on the stone. Then,
with deft blows of his *machete,* he sharpened the stick to a point.
How curiously sweet and fragrant the raw wood smelled in the
night!

"Bring the man here." Daimba ordered at last.

Luseni struggled fearfully with the men who fell on him.

Nenneh and Poreh pushed aside, Luseni was dragged forward, thrown flat on his back—spread-eagled at the king's feet.

The six men with their flambeaux drew in. The night was warm, so still that the six flames burned straight up, the smoke rising thick and straight up like a tube over each torch, joining it to the blackness of the night.

Through the sombre light Daimba Seisay looked across the group struggling at his feet to where Nenneh stood, dumb with terror, too dazed even to cry. Not knowing that he did so, Daimba laughed—laughed like a madman—before he ordered:

"Hamid, Sinneh—drive the stake through his heart."

At this terrible command Nenneh wrenched her arms free of the men who held her, ran across to fall at the tyrant's feet, weeping.

"Daimba—Daimba—a woman bore you . . . Have pity on me . . . My Father—O, I'm too young to suffer so! . . . For Allah's sake—let him go! . . . I promise I'll—I'll never see him again . . . Or—Or—kill me first! . . ." Screaming and wailing at the top of her voice, in truth she had no idea what she was saying.

"Allah be kind to you, Nenneh . . ." cried the man on the ground. "Daimba Seisay, we kill and we are killed, and mercy is only in heaven. I do not ask for mercy . . . But I do ask this of you as a Moslem: let your men kill me swiftly—with a sword."

At this, even the warboys looked as though they expected their king to change from brutality to the sword. But they looked to him in vain.

"Sinneh!" Daimba Seisay roared in a tone of finality and rising anger, ashamed that his soldiers should be so soft-spirited.

And then Hamid set the point of the stake over Luseni's heart, steadied the shaft with both hands.

With apparently little effort Sinneh's mighty hands closed over the stone on the ground and raised it up.

"Ah—AAAAHHHH!!!!!! . . ."

At the first blow of the stone on the stake, Luseni's yell of agony burst out and echoed through and through the night. He writhed so violently that he pulled the dozen men holding him down as though they were puppets. At the second blow he wrenched his right foot free. A savage, chance kick with the heel caught one of the men flush on chin and throat: immediately there was a sharp crunch of bone, and the soldier fell dead and twitching with a broken neck.

But the others grabbed the freed limb, and held their victim down.

Five times more Sinneh crashed the stone on the stake, while Luseni yelled and writhed in agony.

At the seventh blow the point of the stick ripped and tore through Luseni's chest. His cry ended in a gurgle. Blood gushed and foamed through his mouth. His limbs quivered violently— and soon were still.

At the last blow Sinneh struck so viciously that the stake ran clean through their victim's chest and was firmly driven into the ground.

Nenneh Touray had fainted at the ghastly sight. She lay limp at Daimba's feet. Woanday was leaning over her, lying on the ground by her, her whole body shaking as she sobbed hysterically.

Poreh was made of sterner stuff than the princesses and parasites of Susu society. Born and bred in domestic slavery, she knew that, as a slave, she was just as doomed as Luseni for her part in the night's misadventure. Therefore, taking advantage of the general confusion, she sidled into the shadows and vanished into the night.

v

A GAUNT WOMAN came through the dusk and along the track to the brow of the hill overlooking the swamps. An indigoed *lappa* tied under her armpits and reaching down to her calves was her sole garment. Her arms and face were nut-brown, but the forearms up to the elbow were stained with native indigo or *garra* dye. Beneath her closely tied head her plaited locks peeped out, more grey than black. Her oval face was lined and would have been lovely still but for her eyes which, sunk deep in their sockets, were hard with an unfeminine lustre.

She left the track and passed under the branches of a tree towering thirty feet above her. She trod the grass down around her and soon came upon an old tree stump, partly eaten by termites.

She sat down on the stump, very, very still, looking casually down into the valley. The river had spread into a lake—it was the rainy season—and the mangroves made a forest at sea. On the nearer bank there was a break in the wilderness of water and swamps, paddy rice standing prosperous and green in many a crowded acre. Except for the ants crawling ceaselessly up and down the tree above her, there was not one other living creature in sight.

The woman looked up into the branches of the tree. As she did so, her eyes glowed with terrible, inward fire. But no sound escaped her. She had clearly learned to control her feelings over the years, though her eyes now and again might betray her.

Rain-clouds were gathering. There was no real sunset. The grey light drained out of the sky. The storm broke, the rain came rushing down.

But still the woman, drenched and roared over by the elements, sat immobile on the tree stump, waiting, waiting. She sat there for hours while the night grew wilder and wilder. Neither lightning, nor thunder, nor the penetrating wetness had power to disturb her patience.

At last, through the continuous rush of rain, she heard voices:

"She could not possibly have come in this weather," said a man querulously in the dark.

"Bah Lansannah," retorted a woman's voice, "you don't know N'ga Nenneh."

"You're right, Poreh," called the woman at the tree stump. "I'm here."

"My friends," continued Nenneh Touray, going forward to meet them, "welcome! Lansannah," shaking hands with dead

Luseni's twin-brother, "this tree above us is witness that I have kept faith with your brother. It has grown from the stake our enemy drove through Luseni's heart. Look well on it!" As if in answer to her command the heavens fulminated again. "And you, the son I've seen but twenty times in twenty years, yet never by Allah's daylight, what think you of it?"

"My father's heart was stronger than my mother's womb," said a deep, rich voice. "It has bred in twenty years a son five times as tall as I am!"

She embraced him to her chest, tenderly, briefly.

"Had it been your mother's heart," cried his uncle, "the stake could never have gone through it—*never,* not even if it was sheathed with iron! Woman, twenty years is a long time—can't you forgive?"

"Lansannah," the woman answered, "Poreh will tell you I was a soft and kindly girl that lost her senses to see her father dead. If they'd killed my Luseni with a sword or a spear—as he begged in his last hour—Allah! It wasn't much to beg for!—I'd have forgiven. But—and Allah have mercy upon my withered soul—I cannot forget his agony. I heard him—even last night—I heard —I hear him, daily, yelling. Day and night these twenty years his tortured voice has rung in my ears. . . . And all the love I had for him my enemy took away and left nothing but hate and mockery. Forgive, Lansannah? *Forgive!*" her voice quavered and cracked with emotion. *"Never!"*

"You have suffered much, my mother," the youth told her gently. "I've come to avenge the living more than the dead."

"Avenge me?" his mother cried in astonishment. "I never saw it in that light before, Son. Are you strong enough for this work, boy? Or shall we wait another year? . . . Time means nothing— Justice is everything. . . . Stand in the lightning; let me look at you . . ."

It was raining so heavily now that she had to shout to make herself heard. They stood silent for a minute. Then the lightning forked and hissed and swished down, lighting up the rain-filled heavens like a vast bowl of milk. The earth trembled to the thunder-clap that followed. In the glare Nenneh Touray saw the gleam of a spear-point above the head of a giant standing six foot six inches.

"Tall as his father was!" she murmured with pride and satisfaction. "Kind Poreh," she went on in louder tones, with a subtle and deeply affectionate expression in her voice, "my boy's foster-mother, my sister rather than slave! Tonight your work is done. I have treasured you more than my own blood over the years. And now I give you what I've found is more precious than life itself: your freedom. . . . Allah bless you, dear friend, for the way you stood by me in my troubles . . . Lansannah Touray, bless you, too . . ."

"Let me come with you, my sister," the man pleaded.

"No, Lansannah," her voice turned suddenly harsh, reflecting the hardness life had shown her for twenty years. "If young Luseni and I fail, let their vengeance fall on no more than our two heads. You could then avenge your brother's death and ours . . ."

"Yes, Uncle," the young man agreed. "We are quite willing to die. And now, Mother, I'm ready."

"Lansannah," Nenneh Touray could not help her voice trembling—no one can face death completely unmoved, "if we don't return by dawn, you'll know we have failed. You and Poreh must then return home."

"We shall not fail, Mother!" the youth cried with confidence.

When the lightning flashed again, only two figures remained under Luseni's tree.

VI

A HUNDRED YARDS up the track a woman walked sure-footed through the storm. She held the neck of a spear whose butt rested in the hand of a tall man behind her. The man could not see where he was going, but he followed resolutely wherever the spear led.

An hour later, the lightning flashes revealed the man and the woman passing by the *barri* in Daimba Seisay's town.

"He sleeps there," said the woman, pointing to the king's house down the square, "every night. Tonight Woanday sleeps with him."

The young man drew the spear into the front balcony after him. Out of the storm the air smelt both close and of wood-smoke. High above their heads the rafters were dimly visible in a pink glow from the top of the inner wall; they all converged towards the point of a cone truncated by the wall.

"The strongest rafters are here, my son," Nenneh Touray whispered. She felt for his hand in the dark and raised it to the roof.

Heavy though his sword was, young Luseni gripped it without effort between his teeth. The rafters groaned as he clung to them with his powerful hands and heaved himself up. Hand over hand, toes clawing and holding on to the purlings lower down, the man climbed to the space between the top of the inner wall and the roof.

After what seemed an age to the woman waiting outside, the front door softly opened. "Come in, Mother."

In dead silence Nenneh Touray drew the spear into the house after her. Very, very softly she closed the door.

A wood fire was burning in the middle of the round house. To the far side of this large, central room stood a four-poster bed.

The intruders tiptoed towards the bed. The woman with the spear peered through the fire-glow.

"Yes," she whispered, "it's they."

Near the bedhead was a low, wooden stool. A crude metal lamp stood on top of it.

"Light the lamp, Mother," the young man whispered.

The woman obeyed. The rain water dripping from her hair hissed in the fire as she bent over it.

The sleepers stirred uneasily as the oil-lamp spread a sudden, ochre brightness over the room.

Gripping the hilt of his sword in his left hand, the young giant bent over the bed. With his right hand he grabbed the man by his trousers-waist, lifted him right out of the bed—and threw him flat on his back on the mud floor.

Daimba Seisay opened his mouth to shout. The sword point pricked his throat, and a foot heavily stamped the breath out of his chest.

"Silence!" hissed the man with the sword.

"Luseni!" Daimba Seisay croaked, his eyes almost jumping out of his head. The name stuck in his murderer's throat, and his expression was so craven and fearful he must have been sure he was seeing ghosts.

"Luseni is my name," said Nenneh's son, coldly.

Woanday jumped up from the bed. She stared wildly about her. She was too terrified to scream. Time had not much changed her and her husband: they had prospered and grown fat, that was all.

"Sit on that stool, woman," Luseni ordered, pointing with his sword.

"Twenty years ago," Woanday gibbered, not moving from the bed, "I saw you die under the tree."

She trembled violently at the look Luseni directed at her—got up, and staggered to the stool.

"Do I kill them here, Mother?"

The prostrate man and his wife looked towards Nenneh. A terrible figure she made leaning on the spear. Never had Justice taken a more unrelenting form—nor ever did her proceedings promise to be so summary.

"The woman shall not die," said Nenneh Touray calmly. "She repented after Luseni's death, and has always been secretly kind to me since."

"Good!" said young Luseni, raising his sword above Daimba's head. "It goes against the grain of my manhood to kill a woman —even in a feud."

"This, surely, is a ghastly dream," muttered the man on the floor. Sweat was pouring out of his face, and all over his naked chest.

The storm was raging outside with increased fury. A thunderclap louder than any yet that night cracked like doom overhead.

Nenneh's eyes glowed like a coal fire.

"His spear pierced my father's heart." She looked and spoke

like a sybil. "Before my eyes he drove a stake into my Luseni's heart. It is just that a spear should end his wicked life."

Luseni reached for the spear.

"No. Not here!" his mother uttered a weird, sepulchral whisper. Her eyes appeared to expand in their sockets and looked so terrible that even her own son was afraid to look into them. "This is Allah's own vengeance weather. Do you think we can take them to your father's tree?"

Luseni started at the suggestion. "Very just!" was his comment. "A spear to match Grandfather's, and the stake that killed your husband to witness his execution. Allah counsels you well, Mother! . . . But the woman. Should we leave her here she'll raise the alarm against us."

"We'll take her to your Uncle's town, Luseni. She may return here later if she likes."

Thereupon Luseni handed his sword to his mother. In a few instants he had torn the bedcloth into the strips from which it was made. He gagged their prisoners, tied their hands behind their backs.

Which done, he raised Daimba Seisay from the floor, passed the spear shaft between his arm and chest, bound the arm securely to the spear. He did the same with Woanday.

Nenneh Touray took the spear head, followed by Woanday and Daimba. Young Luseni carried the butt of the spear, walking in the rear of the cortège, sword in hand at the ready.

All four grimly silent or silenced, they walked out of the house.

VII

AN HOUR before dawn they found Lansannah Touray and Poreh still patiently awaiting them under the tree.

Luseni ungagged their victims, unbound Daimba Seisay from the spear—and threw him on the sodden ground: near enough to the spot where his father had lain twenty years before.

It was still raining, raining.

Poreh held up the fainting Woanday.

"Daimba Seisay," said Lansannah in a voice that sounded gravely through the dark, "when kings do wrong, only Allah can punish them. He has designed that this weak, humble woman should bring you to justice and your just downfall. Are you prepared to die?"

Young Luseni felt his hair stand on end. Nor, indeed, was the occasion without solemnity. Three of those who had stood there twenty years before could bear testimony to the heinousness of the man's crime. That crime had blasted at least one young life. Yes, Justice was there all sombre and sacred, and they all felt awed, knowing that what they were doing was not so much right as the rightest thing in the world.

"Tell me, my good man," said the man on the ground, "what is *justice?*"

"As a king," Lansannah grumbled, *"you* at least ought to know."

"But I do not know," said Daimba Seisay, calmly. "As a king, I've tried to be just. But I believe justice is such a godly concept that we men are presumptuous to think ourselves capable of understanding it, let alone administering it, inviolate."

"We did not come here to argue," said young Luseni coldly, not yet old enough to understand the wisdom of a king's whole lifetime. "The question is: are you ready to die?"

"It is so written." Daimba's voice rose from the ground imbued with the fatalistic calm of his Moslem religion. "A thousand times these twenty years I had it in my mind to put the woman to death. I just hadn't the will . . . Her first husband's death weighed much on my conscience . . . Still, I cannot bear to enter Eternity with this mystery unsolved in my mind. Who, *now*, is this Luseni? Nenneh had but one child, and I saw that child dead the day it was born . . . People always said Nenneh Touray was a witch."

"There's no mystery, no witchcraft," said the woman, her voice colder than the rain. In the hour of a triumph for which she had waited twenty years, she sounded curiously unelated. "Two weeks after she ran away from this spot that dreadful night, Poreh came back to me secretly in the night. She's here now. . . ."

"*Allah Akhbarr!*"[6] Daimba burst out in astonishment.

". . . yes, she's *here* now as she was here twenty years ago. When Poreh came, I already knew I was pregnant. I prayed for a son to avenge my Luseni's death. Only Allah knew how hard I prayed. And he was kind to me . . .

"In my hour of travail, I stole to the marshes. Poreh attended me.

"Well, Daimba Seisay, my belly wasn't big for nothing. I brought forth twins. Boys . . ."

"Allah Akhbarr!" Daimba exclaimed again, beginning to understand.

"Yes, twins. Luseni was big. Lansannah very small. He died the same day—and you, Daimba, were pleased to see the end of my husband's line—as you imagined! But I had made Poreh take Luseni back to his uncle. This Luseni is he you see here now—and his Uncle Lansannah too is here. And," she ended grimly, "you and I are here. There's no mystery, Daimba—only justice!"

"But woman, woman!" Daimba burst out. "For five years you were my wife . . ."

"Yes." The woman's voice chilled him like an icicle. There was a change in her. She suddenly sounded weary, infinitely old. "You'd have sold me into slavery if I had refused to be your wife. Only Allah knows how it hurt my woman's pride to yield my body to you. But I learned to steel myself to it, for dead Luseni's sake."

"Truly, you're Vengeance and not a woman!" the man cried in astonishment that had something of admiration in it. "I woke up one night when you slept with me. Through the dimness of the fire, I saw you looking at me when you thought I was asleep. Allah knows I'm no coward. But I knew then you hadn't a woman's spirit, that you had it in you to bring death. And since that night I'd not had you in my bed . . . And yet," disjointedly, "and yet I did not kill you!"

---

6. *Allah Akhbarr,* God is great. [*Arabic*]

"Daimba Seisay," Luseni asked with that disdain mingled with cruelty possible only in youth, "are you by any chance begging us for mercy?"

"Beg a woman and child for mercy!" Daimba Seisay laughed sardonically. "I have killed—and now I'm killed. There's an end to all. Nenneh Touray, be merciful to my Woanday as you say she was merciful to you. And now, boy, have done with talk. Pooh, boy! Daimba Seisay can face death with spirit."

"Yes, Luseni," Nenneh Touray shouted hysterically, "avenge your father's death!"

The young man took the spear from her.

For a minute the sound of falling rain filled the countryside. Then, from under their feet, a deep sigh seemed to issue out of the very bowels of the Earth.

"He is dead!" said Luseni.

"It cannot be!" Yalie Woanday wailed. "Daimba! Daimba! Daimba! . . . Ah!" She rushed forward, stumbled over the corpse, threw herself over the rapidly cooling form. "Ah— Daimba!" she wailed harrowingly through the night.

The two men pulled Woanday up, Poreh held her sobbing against her faithful heart.

Feeling lost—not unnaturally, now that the prop of her life was knocked away by her enemy's death—Nenneh Touray came forward shakily and felt in the darkness for the shaft of the spear. As she followed it down to the spot over Daimba's chest, the lightning flashed.

In the glare she saw all too briefly the spear sticking out of her enemy's heart. But she saw most clearly that Daimba Seisay's face was smiling peacefully in death.

"It was not so Luseni died," she cried bitterly, rising from the ground. "Is he dead? Really dead? . . . Lansannah, Luseni—*he* made no noise . . ."

True, he had made no noise. He had been too proud even to cry out in the agony of death. And who could tell if, knowing that he was expiating a murder twenty years old, he had not gone with relief tantamount to ecstasy, to meet his Maker with the slate wiped clean?

"He was at least a man!" Luseni exclaimed in a tone of admiration. "Pity he had to be our enemy. And now, my Mother, come home with me—and complete the journey you started twenty years ago."

But his words had only added wormwood to his mother's bitterness.

Now that vengeance was achieved, Nenneh Touray was overcome by an overwhelming sense of failure. Even a sense of doubt. . . .

"Yes, Nenneh," cried her brother-in-law, who was by now heartily sick of the weather, "come home and relax after two whole decades."

Thus Nenneh and Poreh resumed their journey interrupted so long ago. True, a Luseni was with them again—but how different from that first journey of hope!

Such were Nenneh's thoughts as she went with her kith and kin. She took the first twenty, thirty, hundred paces home, to the very Lansannah's town the other Luseni would have had them journey. And then, very abruptly, she stopped and refused to budge a foot further.

"*He* made no noise, Luseni . . ." She spoke but faintly, so that they just only heard her in the rain.

"Don't distress yourself, dear Mother. Daimba Seisay is quite dead."

"N'ga Nenneh," urged Lansannah, damning the woman in his heart, "come, let's away. Even Allah can't kill a man twice!"

"*Wait!*" Nenneh Touray cried with a note of urgency. "My friends, my child, be patient with me. Twenty years is a long time to wait for this . . . I'll run back and make quite, *quite* sure . . ."

Before they could restrain her she had bolted away up the track and disappeared into the night.

And then, as the two men and women stood helpless and miserable in the wet waiting for her, the thunderstorm gathered its forces for a Parthian shot.[7] After *that* the rain did perceptibly

---

7. *a Parthian shot,* a parting shot.

abate—but then they had ceased to care. A white ball of fire tore through the dome of the night, exploded into the branches of a colossal tree of fire—whose stem instantly leapt towards the earth. A tearing sound and a peculiar sulphurous smell seemed to hit the hillside around them. The thunderclap that followed reverberated with such violence the airwave tossed the four people into the grasses by the track as if they were all made of chaff.

Luseni got up first, considerably shaken.

"Uncle! N'ga Poreh!" he called, almost scared, "are you two all right?"

"Yes, my boy," Lansannah answered from several yards away, where the thunderblast had hurled him. "But I fear for your mother."

The men left Poreh to help the half-concussed Woanday, and ran up the valley to Nenneh Touray's help.

They found her under Luseni's tree.

The spear shaft sticking out of Daimba's chest guided them to the spot where she lay.

The lightning had cleft Luseni's tree from top to bottom. One of its branches lay over Nenneh Touray as it lay, impartially, over Daimba Seisay. For they found her at the bottom of the foliage, gripping tight to the spear in Daimba's heart, lying dead across his chest.

"Allah," Lansannah cried in awe, feeling the hairs rise at the back of his neck, "Allah has at last made peace between them."

►

C. O. D. Ekwensi / *Nigeria*
(1921–   )

RITUAL MURDER

THE TWO BLACK MEN were afraid. Kofi could read it in their eyes. They did not wish to leave him. They stood on the steps of the palace, stubbornly loyal.

"We will wait for you here," they said. "We are your bodyguard. Your wife said we must not lose sight of you."

"There's no need, brothers. I'm quite safe."

They came nearer, their arms gesturing wildly. "You make light of the danger, Kofi."

"Nothing can happen to me." Kofi slung the velvet robe over one shoulder. "Do not fear. A new paramount chief is in office, true. . . ."

"And he will wash the golden stool [1] with human blood. Maybe yours. . . ."

Kofi laughed.

They were uneasy. "But, Kofi . . . Look! . . . Can't you understand?"

It was useless. Kofi had mounted the steps, and the door of the palace had opened and shut.

"He's mad," said one, shrugging. The other one scowled at him for a while. "Yes . . . really mad."

In the distance the West African sunshine blazed downwards. Two girls hawking biscuits strolled past the palace, their cotton

---

"Ritual Murder" by C. O. D. Ekwensi from AFRICAN VOICES, AN ANTHOLOGY OF NATIVE AFRICAN WRITING, edited by Peggy Rutherfoord. Reprinted by permission of Drum Publications (PTY.) Ltd.
1. *the golden stool,* the most sacred object in Ashanti, a region in the north of Ghana. The *Omanhene,* the paramount chief, is the custodian of the golden stool.

dresses a feast of colour. They made eyes at the two men on the steps. Cars, lorries, hand-trucks, horse-drawn carts, were moving along the street. A policeman was directing the traffic, and he paused to show a white man the right road. It was impossible to contemplate ancient evil beneath this façade of Western law and order. Surely no harm could come to Kofi.

Kofi followed the guide through a dark corridor.

"They're expecting you," the guide said. "You'll find them in the black room."

"The black room?"

"Yes. . . ."

The room where, away from the eyes of the law, gruesome rites were performed; wherein stood the golden stool waiting, always waiting for a new *Omanhene* to die, so that a new one might wash it with blood. In the dark days, a slave's blood was easy to come by. But not now. The white men frowned on the use of human blood. For years the blood of a dove, a sheep, had provided a legal substitute.

The guide said: "Knock on the door. I leave you."

Kofi looked at the massive door. He looked behind him at the dark corridor. He was alone. There was no turning back. He flung his shoulders back and breathed deeply. His knees were trembling. He knocked. No one answered; but the door gave when he pushed and he went in.

At a table in the centre of the room, six men were playing cards. The air smelled strongly of spirits. They turned and looked at Kofi grimly, their hard bare torsos etched out by the smoky hurricane lamp.

"Shut the door and sit down, Kofi." They indicated an empty seat at the table. A whole bottle of raw gin was pushed across to him. "Drink some! . . . It isn't poisoned!"

He was uncomfortable. He held his breath in the stuffy atmosphere. The mystery, the suspense, the secrecy irritated him. He did not wish to be a party to anything furtive.

"I am here now," he said. "What did you want me for?"

Apiedu, the eldest of the half-brothers, waved aside Kofi's fears. "Have patience, my boy," he soothed. "You'll soon know."

"I haven't got all day . . . there's work to do. The old *Omanhene,* your father, is dead. His affairs are in disorder. It is my duty . . ."

"We know you were his secretary. And that is why we sent for you. With your intimate knowledge of his private affairs, you are going to be very useful. You will be well paid, of course, if you co-operate."

They passed the raw gin round, and each of them sucked from the bottle and handed it to the next man. Kofi glanced about him uneasily. In a corner of the room, he could barely see the golden stool. It was not so golden now, with the dark stains on it. On top of the stool was a wickedly sharp knife . . . the *saw-paw* of the ritual murders. It was the same knife that had buried itself in the hearts of many a slave some half a century ago.

"Kofi," said Apiedu. "We want to ask you a little favour."

"Go ahead."

"It's about that money," Apiedu said. "Come, Kofi! You know about it!"

Kofi swallowed. "I . . . I. . . ."

"Ten thousand pounds. . . . My father took it out of the treasury and founded Kofo and Co. Everybody in the smallest village in West Africa knows about it. Of course the business is doing very well. But the new *Omanhene* may not like it; just as he may not like to take over our father's wives. He'll make changes. He'll tell the Government what happened. Where will we be then?"

Kofi said nothing. Apiedu glanced round the table. His brothers were dealing out cards with half an ear on the discussion.

"Ten thousand pounds is a lot of money for the auditors to overlook. And now, Kofi, what are *you* going to do about it?"

"Me? I . . . I don't understand . . ."

"It's easy! You are the only man in Africa who has access to the fatal papers. You alone can dig up the evidence the new *Omanhene* might want if he decides to make trouble. Got that? Well, we're asking a very simple favour. We want you to go back and destroy every scrap of evidence pointing to the theft of that ten thousand."

"I . . . I can't. It isn't my business to audit accounts. I have nothing to do with the money of the state."

"That's right! . . . You have nothing to do with it, but you know where to find the rope that will hang us. Go and burn that rope." The brothers had stopped playing their game. "If you talk too much, Kofo and Co. will be given to the state. We will go to jail. There'll be hard work to do. . . ." He glanced at his soft hands. "We have never worked in our lives, and it is too late to start now. Why do you look so worried? This is but a little favour we have asked of you. And your reward is . . . two thousand pounds!"

Kofi looked at them helplessly. It was true he knew about that deal: every single man involved in it. And he knew many more things besides. He could make life completely intolerable for the late chief's sons. He looked up. The light threw dark shadows on their faces. Their eyes were hard, unforgiving. He saw them through the smoky haze of the lamp, and somehow tried to fight against the mad idea that this was unreal, a mere dream.

"Give me time," he begged. "I have not yet come to that business. When I come to it, I'll know how to fix things."

The brothers exchanged glances. No one spoke.

"I . . . I don't think there is anything more," Kofi said, rising. "I must go now. Don't worry! Everything will be all right." Did they believe him? The room was so still that he wanted to shout at them. Slowly he backed towards the door.

"Where are you going, Kofi?" They were all standing now.

"Don't you trust me? I've told you . . . there's nothing to worry about. Let me go home to my wife and children."

Apiedu laughed. "He's going home. Ha! ha! . . . And we'll be here . . . waiting!"

Panic seized Kofi. He had sensed something sinister beneath it all. In a sudden burst of recklessness he sprang for the door. But he was too late. They were between him and the massive structure. And he knew then that they meant to murder him.

"What did you want to do?" Apiedu said softly. "To go out and betray us?"

"Go and sit down," said Lampey.

Kofi stood his ground. "You cannot frighten me," he bluffed. "I came to the palace gate with two men. Your own guide brought me to this door. My wife knows where I am. If you do anything to me, everybody will know. Go back to your drink and don't touch me. You'll only regret it. I've given you my word: everything will be all right."

"Nonsense!" said Apiedu.

Kofi did a very foolish thing. Perhaps he thought he was being brave. He pushed Lampey aside and seized the door handle. Almost at once, something hard struck him on the back of the head, and he fell against the door and slid downwards.

"Bring him over to this corner," said Apiedu.

"But he's not dead."

"That's just it . . . his blood will be still warm . . . for the stool."

"We'll all hang!" said Kwame, the youngest brother. "God knows I am innocent."

"You can't prove it," Apiedu said. "We've done this thing to help you. Nobody will ever suspect us. Why would we want to kill any one? We have no motive. But the new *Omanhene*, he has . . . he wants to wash the stool . . . an age-old ritual. And he kills Kofi. He cannot tell the white men, because no one will believe him. His hands are tied. And remember this: he has been boasting that he will not use pigeon's blood, or sheep's blood . . . so we're all right!"

"He's dead," said Lampey, who had been holding him.

Silence fell in the room.

"Two of you go for a cart," Apiedu said. "Hide it somewhere. As soon as it is dark we'll take the body away."

Kwame paced up and down the little room.

"You're frightened, Kwame."

"I've never seen a man killed before!"

Apiedu smiled. "Yes! But there's a reason, Kwame! Either we put this new *Omanhene* into trouble, or he puts us. There's no other way. We must live!"

"I don't want to live in that way. Let me work till my hands peel rather than kill a man and . . . and use his blood."

"Shut up, Kwame!"

Kwame pulled up, sweating and trembling. The others did not move.

Under the palm trees, in the market places, men and women talked about the missing official. With lips scarcely open, they hissed out the terrible word: *murder.*

"The *Omanhene* has killed Kofi, now he wants us to help him look for the man he has killed and buried."

And away on the rolling grassland where the nomads grazed their cattle, Apiedu was amusing his brothers.

"The police are so stupid! Look what a fuss they made about those drops of blood in the black room: giving it to the Government pathologist to analyse and to prove it was human blood. What else could it be?" He laughed. "But there's no blood without a body! Where is Kofi?"

"They will catch us," Kwame said. "We are wasting time by hiding here." Fear and hunger had worn him down.

"We are safe here," Apiedu said.

"Yes," put in the others.

Kwame spat. "They will catch us. If not to-day, to-morrow. But they will surely hang all of us. . . ." He broke off suddenly.

"Look! . . ." he panted. "See him!"

The brothers looked, but there was nothing to see. Kwame was gazing at the door of the hut, his face working.

"He is going mad," Apiedu said uneasily. "Sometimes he hears the voice of our father . . . sometimes he sees the spirit of Kofi."

"Who knows?" said Lampey. "Perhaps he may be seeing something."

Apiedu looked startled. "You too? Are you getting the fever?"

That night, after they had retired to their grass beds, Lampey suddenly cried out. "He's lying on my bed. . . . He's here! . . ."

A light was fetched. "Where is he?" said Apiedu.

"He was here in the bed beside me. I swear! I wouldn't deceive you, would I, Apiedu?"

Apiedu looked at him scornfully. "You are even worse than the boy, Lampey! Who's next?"

"He . . . he was here," said Lampey. "He lay beside me on this bed!"

"Yes," Apiedu said, "but where is he now?"

Lampey looked foolish. He had scared the whole party and now they crowded together around the lantern, and kept vigil the whole night through.

Long before dawn, Apiedu went out into the grassland. It was chilly. A mist hung in the air. In this lonely part of the veld no one was about. Their only contact was the next village where Lampey sometimes went to buy food. It seemed that the hard life, the fear of the police, the contemplation of the future which held nothing for them, was troubling his brothers. Something had to be done, and soon too.

He paused and looked about him. Somewhere ahead of him, leaning against a tree, was a dark figure. It was a man. Who could it be, at this early hour and in so lonely a place? Apiedu walked on, and the figure detached itself from the tree and moved quickly towards him, forcing him to step out of the narrow footpath.

The black man in the dark cloth passed him like a flash and disappeared behind the bend. The mist hung thick. The air seemed to become more chilly. It could have been a dream, if he had not noted that bare bald head, those bulging eyes. Back in the little hut, he asked Lampey whether they had a visitor.

"No," said Lampey.

Apiedu described the encounter as lightly as he could and dismissed it. But Lampey returned to the subject.

"Apiedu, you may be a very brave man; but let us go to Koforidua . . . to the fetishman. We can consult him about this evil spirit."

"Yes," said Kwame. "I was about to say the same, but I was afraid you would laugh at me."

"It is the best thing," agreed the others.

The three brothers entered the hut of the fetishman stealthily.

"You wish to make a confession?" said the priest. "Sit down!"

"We are haunted," Apiedu said.

"We cannot sleep," Lampey added. "At night, the man we

killed comes. Sometimes he sleeps beside one of us." He shivered.

"And you want something to drive off this evil spirit?"

"Yes."

"I shall give you a powder to burn. But the preparation of this powder requires one very special ingredient. It may be too late to get it. Then I can do nothing. Something from the dead man's body."

Apiedu looked uneasily round. "We buried him. . . ."

"Yes, I know. Long ago?"

"Three weeks. What do you want? Tell me, I'll get it for you . . ."

The old man smiled. "That would destroy everything. I have to get it myself. You will come with me, and you will bring with you digging implements. It will have to be at night. No one will see us."

Apiedu said: "I . . . I must consult my brothers first. I. . . ."

"If you are afraid, let things lie. In my business privacy comes first. You can be sure I shall not discuss your affairs with anyone."

When they had gone, the fetishman looked up his manuscripts. It was a long time since he had handled a case of haunting.

The door darkened. New clients? But these two, the white man in plain clothes and the black man in a black robe, were not clients.

"I am a police officer," said the white man. "May I come in?"

"This is the new *Omanhene*. We have reason to believe that the sons of the late *Omanhene* visited you not long ago."

"Yes," said the *Omanhene*. "What did they tell you?"

"Long may you reign, chief! They were having stomach trouble." The fetishman smiled.

The white man smiled. "Those six boys are murderers. They have framed your chief here. We have no evidence against them. If you do not say what you know I will take it that you are a party to the crime. And in that case, I must ask you to come with me to the station. The car is outside."

"What do you want to know?"

"Just what you know."

"It is against my practice . . . but those boys are haunted."

The white man tapped the *Omanhene* on the shoulder. "And this is the ghost who did all the haunting. For three weeks he has been watching the brothers."

The fetishman's mouth widened. Then he grinned. "I see. So he is the ghost? Now, these boys want my help, and I want something—from the body. If they agree, they will take me to the spot to-night. If not . . ."

"I'm sure they'll come," the white man said. "And we'll be there, too! They won't know, of course."

"I knew they couldn't stand it," the *Omanhene* said. "Kwame was the first to break; the last was Apiedu."

"The reward for their capture is three hundred pounds," the police officer said.

"I do not want your money."

In the night the brothers slipped into the hut. They were wearing long dark caps pulled low over their eyes. "It is chilly outside," said Apiedu. "We are here, now. Let us go quickly!"

The fetishman put on a cape woven from elephant grass. "You'll have to carry me," he said. "I'm lame."

The brothers took him into the valley where a stream trickled over the sands. Kwame was shivering.

"The body is there," Apiedu said, "under the stream. We stemmed the water, then dug a hole and buried him. After that, we let the water flow over him."

"You can do the same now," said the old man. "You've got your tools?"

"Yes, we have our tools."

"You will have to excuse me while you work."

The fetishman turned away. He limped up the valley. The white man was in police uniform now. And so was every man in the party behind him. He did not speak to them.

From a bag under his arm he drew out a little packet and poured a powder down his throat.

"Eighty years," he muttered, "and I have never betrayed anyone." He sank on his knees, waiting for the poison to act. ▶

LAW OF THE GRAZING FIELDS

THIS IS THE LAW of the wandering cattlemen of the savanna: that a man may elope with the woman of his choice, maiden or matron, wife or spinster. But woe betide him if he is caught on the run. Yet all is well if he can but get his beloved home without being caught.

On the evening of our story a brother and sister were quarreling. Modio, the brother, had just pushed Amina, the sister, violently.

"Kai!" Amina shouted, springing deftly backward, "Take your hands off me." Her lips were parted, but not in a smile, and her full breasts heaved so that the necklaces of silver and fruit seemed to come to life. Amina just managed to retain her balance by clutching at the wall of the grass hut. "Don't you dare touch me again!"

"By Allah," Modio raged, "I'll teach you some sense."

She glared at him. He was crouching before her, his hands curved like the claws of a hawk about to strike, his muscles tense. "You'll go nowhere!"

"You lie!" she cried. "This night I will be with Yalla. He's the husband I've chosen."

"What of Jama, the husband our father chose for you? What of the cattle Jama's been paying?"

"That is your affair," she said. "Did you—Oh, let me go, you devil. Are you mad?"

She felt the stroke of his rough hand across her mouth. His arm tightened about her waist and she was struggling as he carried her out to his own hut. With his bare foot he kicked open the door; dust rose in a cloud. He thrust her in. She fell forward on her face in the dust and lay there, her body heaving with sobs.

"Law of the Grazing Fields" by Cyprian Ekwensi from AN AFRICAN TREASURY, selected by Langston Hughes. Reprinted by permission of Harold Ober Associates Incorporated and David Higham Associates, Ltd. Copyright © 1960 by Langston Hughes.

Amina was young and in the fullness of her bloom. Her long hair, unplaited, fell over her back and lay buried in the dust. Tears mingled with the red cream she had painted on her cheeks.

"You wretch," she heard her brother say from the other side of the door. He was fastening the door and presently she heard him stamp away, cursing her.

She let the tears flow freely as if tears alone could heal the ache in her heart, the desire for the man she had chosen. But there must be hope, she thought. No one, nothing could shut her away from Yalla forever. She must go to him, she must.

Hatred burned within her breast. Was it her fault that she did not like Jama? Her father had accepted the cattle first and told her about him later. He turned out to be a weak-kneed, effeminate man. A man who could not weave mats or take the cattle out to graze. A coward who had wept and begged as they flogged him at the *sharro*.[1] He had taken his flogging, it was true, but he had not taken it like a man and it would be humiliating to marry him. Her father might give her away to Jama, but he would not be present when the other maidens would taunt her with having married a coward: "And how's your husband? The one who stays in bed till sunrise, who must not be soaked by the rain? Ha, ha! A husband, indeed!"

The mistake had been Yalla's, for he had not honored the arrangement in full. It had been a simple arrangement. She and Yalla were to escape from the camp before Jama brought the bulls that were the final installment of the bride-price. Yalla was to have come to the hut at the hour when the hyenas began to howl over the grazing fields. He was to screech in the manner peculiar to the gray hawk that steals chickens and she would then know that he was waiting for her under the dorowa tree.

She had waited for Yalla's screech. In the early hours of the evening before the hyenas slunk out of the rocks, she had thought about her man—tall, wide-shouldered, with a copper ring in his plaited hair, a man who could break a stubborn bull or calm the wildest pony in her father's stables. Yet when he

---

1. *the sharro,* an initiation ceremony.

smiled or held her hand, his face was so gentle and so sweet. She liked to place her head against his deep wide chest and look up into the darkness of his brown eyes. He was fond of playing with her ears, and sometimes he irritated her and she would threaten to go to Jama. What a contrast Yalla was to Jama. Jama, the coward. Could Jama protect a home from the gales that swept the grazing fields? Could he outwit the wild dogs, and the hyenas, the leopard and the lion, when they came to raid the herd?

A husband indeed. She had been his "wife" ever since she could remember. Five hundred head of cattle was a good price, but she was no article for sale.

Early this evening Yalla had come up to her father's settlement. He had stood outside near the dorowa tree and had whistled to her. She had been very excited. To think she was leaving her home for good. There could be no good-bys, no tears. She was running away with a man they would gladly kill. There was dead silence over the veld. Amina had peeped out cautiously. There was the veld before her. It was all hers and Yalla's if only they would dare. The stunted trees, bowing in the cold wind, the rushing streams, the rocks, the thorn forests. They were all calling out to her and to Yalla to go forth and conquer them; to begin their own camp with a group of bulls and cows—their own. Yalla had screeched again, impatiently, and this time he did sound like the gray hawk. She had not hesitated.

She ran. She took nothing with her, not even one of the wooden ladles that her mother had given her for stirring the milk. And that was when her brother had intercepted her. She did not know that he had been hiding all the while in a nearby tree. He had a pack of wild cattle-dogs with him, and these he at once unleashed on Yalla. He had seized Amina and had laughed at her threats and clawings and curses. For Yalla and Amina the law of the grazing fields was broken.

Now she was a prisoner in the hut, but Amina found it impossible to imagine that Yalla never would be hers. There must still be a chance. If only he could somehow manage to free her from this prison and take her to his hut before Jama paid the full price of five hundred cattle, she could still be Yalla's by right of his might. No one could deny this law of the grazing fields. All cattlemen knew it and respected it. But how was Yalla to know where she was, or when Jama would be coming. Everything was over, Amina decided with a fresh burst of tears.

"Oh, Yalla, my Yalla! Come and save me, Yalla. I am yours and you are my man!"

She pushed and screamed and threatened until her brother warned her to be quiet. But how could she be quiet when her body itched from the dust and the thorns? Oh, death! It were better to die than to live as Jama's wife.

Already she could hear an argument about the saddling of the horses. Her other brothers had returned from the fields. One of them said she must wear a black veil, and the other said a white one was the custom. Such trifles! The eldest brother said he would ride behind the bride; he couldn't trust her for a moment after what she had been through with Modio. And all this because of five hundred head of cattle.

Quite suddenly she became conscious of silence. The chattering ceased and the coarse jokes. A fearful pause lay over the veld. She began to cough. The air in the little room hung heavy and thick. And then her brother's voice cut in hoarsely.

"Fire!" he shouted. "Fire! . . . Yes . . . whoo . . . fetch water . . . Fire!"

Amina started. Heavy fumes began to fill her little prison. She was coughing and gasping fearfully. Desperation gave her the strength of ten. She flung herself at the door. The fumes were now pouring in through every crack in the hut. The boys outside shouted and yelled, keeping the cows from panicking. Their shouts beat dimly against her ears. She was choking. Did they not even remember her? Could they be so cruel? Were their cows more valuable to them than her life?

A rough hand thrust open her door, and a man's gruff voice urged her, "Follow me. It's Yalla."

Her heart gladdened, but no words came to her choking lips. The man's arm circled her waist and swept her off her feet. The thatch caught her hair, and the man's hands detached the burrs tenderly. She must be dreaming. She felt the air rush into her throat. She saw the yellow sheets of flame shoot skyward in dazzling columns. And, as she raised her hand to shield her eyes from the glare, Amina saw her brothers dashing here, there and yonder, collecting sleeping mats, money purses, milk bowls. It was a dream no longer. That voice—it was real. "There she is! . . . Brothers, there's our sister. Catch her! . . ."

"Yalla," Amina sobbed, "what shall we do? They are coming."

"Let them try. My hut is five miles from here. It will be a good race." She felt herself carried across the encampment and saddled on to a horse.

"Away, now!" Yalla shouted. "Away. . . ."

Every forward leap of the horse jarred her bones. Her hair streamed in the wind. Behind them came her brothers. Relentless, cunning riders, angered beyond repair. Amina could clearly hear the clatter of the pursuing horses. By Allah! What could she do?

Twang.

That was an arrow. Best to give up now.

"Oh, Yalla, let us get down and go back home. It's useless running in this manner."

The man's laugh, big and thunderous, made her feel silly. Was he laughing at the poisoned arrow that might have stiffened his back and sent him coughing and clutching to his death? What a nerve! Their horse had begun to pant under the combined weight. They were now in a part of the scrub with few trees and many rocks and hills. This was where clever horsemanship would tell. This was where this thief would lose her or gain her forever. She held her breath. Her body prickled with a thousand pains but she knew the prize that lay ahead and it gave her courage.

The horse labored. Even Yalla, man that he was, ground his teeth in pain and weariness, urging his steed ahead with a slashing whip.

"Yee-whoo!" he shouted, the sweat running down his face and falling into Amina's eyes. "Yee-whoo! . . ."

She was the first to see the light in the distance.

"My hut," Yalla said. "My lonely hut!"

"Our hut, you mean."

He laughed again.

Twang! And Yalla moaned. "They've shot me! My back . . . Allah save me, I'm dying. . . ."

Before the words were out of his mouth, Yalla was sliding down the saddle, for an arrow's poison acts fast. Yet more arrows twanged past even as the distance between them and their pursuers narrowed.

"If I die, you go ahead. They can't touch you once you're in my hut. It is the—the . . ."

Terror, panic. Amina looked over her shoulder and saw her elder brother's figure looming out of the darkness. Yalla had barely enough strength to crawl. Amina dragged him on. She was a girl of the veld, fresh, strong and brave. His strength waned fast. Ahead of them, the cows in the gloom bolted out of their paths. Rams bleated anxiously. A cock cackled, waking all the rest which now set up a deafening crow. They were actually in Yalla's settlement, but not in the hut.

"You thief!"

A few yards behind the paddocks, just beyond the poultry yard, Amina bent down. With all her might, she seized Yalla and pushed him into the hut, falling in after him.

He breathed a sigh of relief.

"My wife!" he moaned. "Mine at last! . . . But first, this arrow. You can still save me. . . . The antidote . . ."

Amina's brothers drew up before Yalla's hut.

"You thief!" they raved. "Give us our sister."

"Thief?" he sneered. "You are the thieves. Have you not stolen the bridal horse?"

"Our father, Jama, will know no rest till you've compensated him his cattle."

"Leave that to me," Yalla said. To Amina he murmured, "Oh, my back. The antidote . . ."

The brothers wheeled their horses and cantered slowly back to their own camp. One of them said: "That lad, Yalla, he is a man. Setting fire to our camp, stealing our sister, and then calling us thieves for taking back our own horse which we saddled for another bridegroom! The law of the grazing fields. He's won." ▶

D. O. Fagunwa / *Nigeria*
(1900–1963)

THE FOREST OF THE LORD

Translated from the Yoruba by
E. C. Rowlands

AKARA-OGUN began his narrative saying, "My friend, when it was now the twenty-fifth year since my father had come into the world he made himself ready one morning and betook himself to hunt in a certain strange forest which lies near our town. Our townsfolk call this forest the 'Forest of the Lord,' because it is a place which is full of fear. The hunters indeed fear this 'Forest of the Lord' more than the 'Forest of Spirits' and it is a fixed law in our town that no hunter must go there to hunt until he has become an elephant-killer, because that place is a place of wonders. The birds there speak with human voices and the animals buy and sell with each other. Many of the trees there have no roots, yet their wood is fresh and their leaves are glossy and green. A mouse in the Forest of the Lord is bigger than an ordinary bush-rat and a snail is bigger than a tortoise. Powerful sprites and grim hobgoblins are in league there and all sorts of bold snakes cast fear on hunters, for it is there that the chief snake of all the world lives, whose name is 'Angry Python'."

Before my father set out from his house he showed himself to

"The Forest of the Lord" by D. O. Fagunwa (from IGBO OLODUMARE by D. O. Fagunwa), translated by E. C. Rowlands, from A SELECTION OF AFRICAN PROSE, compiled by W. H. Whiteley. Copyright 1945 by Thomas Nelson & Sons, Ltd. Reprinted by permission of the Clarendon Press, Oxford.

be a hunter indeed, for many were the charms which he tied round his waist, while his fingers were covered with such rings as elders wear. No fewer than six oxen were killed as an offering in our house. My father summoned the medicine-men of our town together and provided them all with food. Ancestral medicines were stored in our house in profusion. Six whole months had he spent scurrying to and fro in preparation for this visit to the Forest of the Lord, because those who used to go there did not return—they used to fall into the hands of one sprite after another. My father was indeed a man of energy. Some men excel others in manly qualities and Olowo-aiyé [1] had these qualities to the full.

It was a never-to-be-forgotten day in our house when my father had finished his preparations to go hunting in this forest and it was now time to bid farewell to all his relatives. The medicine-men were gathered together indoors and the elephant-killer hunters were gathered together on the veranda, while the children had taken refuge on the roof. All sorts of people were met together in the courtyard, the goats scattered hither and thither, women were weeping, men were weeping, men of worth could find no words to speak, men of honour sat with glum faces. But my father got himself ready like a European soldier, he tied medicines to his body like a diviner, he walked as one going to a wrestling bout and he stood firm as policemen stand before their commander.

When it was now time to start, he called all the household together and spoke to them saying, "The time has now come that I must go to the place where mighty men go, to the dwelling-place of strange creatures, to the place which is dark before me. I shall leave well-being behind me and go to meet trouble. But trials are the father of fortune-making and a good name is better than a new wife. If I endure today's difficulties I shall find fortune in the future. If I return with joy from the Forest of the Lord my name will long be heard of in the world. You my people, never think meanly of yourselves. Always aim at something which is impor-

---

1. *Olowo-aiyé* (ō lō′wō ī′yā).

tant. A man who aims at achieving something important, even if he fails to achieve his aim will achieve something nearly as important. But the man who only aims to achieve something unimportant has no standing in the assembly of the mighty. He who prays for ten fine gowns, even if he fails to get ten he will get eight, and he who prays for six pairs of trousers, even if he fails to get six he will get five. But he who prays to God for one pair of trousers, if he gets two pairs he must indeed give thanks to Almighty God.

"I see you all here with glum faces, it is true, but my own heart is strong and firm like a shiny stone in the river. Progress is far from the man of two minds, and I am not in two minds as I go on my way. By the power of Almighty God who created me I shall surely return home. The man of two minds imagines in the morning that death is coming upon him and by midday he is dead, yet he might well have lived several days more in this world. A man's heart is his priest. Let me be going. Greet all the people of my house and see to my affairs in my absence. So now a man goes on his way. Tell all the people from me that a man of might has gone as a man of might to where men of might go, a man of note has gone as a man of note to where men of note resort. Let neither children nor elders, if they are gentlefolk, say that travellers in the Forest of the Lord do not return, and let all honourable people the world over be awaiting the return of a great man."

So spake Olowo-aiyé and then set off on his way to the Forest of the Lord. His eyes had changed their colour, they were blood red. In his haste he almost forgot one important medicine contained in a small medicine-calabash, and this medicine was such that if he did not take it with him finding his way to the forest would itself be difficult. The mouth of this calabash was plugged with cuckoo, *aluko* and vulture feathers and with red parrot-plumes, and its sides were stained with many sorts of blood. My own father's father had first owned it and he had obtained it from the belly of a python. For before we were born many of our family had been hunters and our grandfather whom I have just mentioned was the first man from our town to go hunting in the Forest of Spirits. It was then that he killed this python and found this wonderful medicine-calabash inside it. If a person pronounces a charm over this calabash and mentions the name of the place where he is going, the wind will blow on these feathers and they will point in the direction of the place. Indeed, my friend, if I had not forgotten the charm I would teach you it, because it is not more than five and twenty words in length, and after teaching you the charm I would search out the calabash and give it you.

The Forest of the Lord is very far, indeed it is two whole days' journey from our town. There are some big wildernesses on the way and also large rivers, which flow swiftly and sound mightily as they fall over rocks. There are many plants on the way, both those which are good and those which are harmful. Countless thousands of thorn trees bar the way as one walks along and filthy litter of every sort conspires with troublesome creepers twined about the trees to fall down on people's heads as they pass by. Furthermore, the wild animals do not let one rest. Brown monkeys and baboons and other monkeys with long tails jump from tree to tree. Their faces are like those of human beings and so too are the nails on their fingers. Truly monkeys resemble human beings closely; it seems as if the Creator made them relatives of each other.

Many different things are found in the wilderness. There are countless great trees and tall palms with the mistletoes which cling to them, and animals which live on the tops of the big palms. There are sharp-beaked birds whose attention is fixed on the base of the palm leaves so as to lose no chance of finding nuts to eat. There are squirrels which frequent the creepers, slender snakes looking round for dark recesses in which to hide, vipers lurking under the grass, pythons which inhabit the banks of rivers, and numerous poisonous snakes which hide in holes. There are snails which love damp places and tortoises which crawl under dried leaves. There is the coucal which flies at a middle height and the dove which frequents the high places. This bird plays the part of the cockerel in the wilderness, reminding the hunters of the time.

There are trees which have long since fallen to the ground and which have no more strength and which are covered with mushrooms. There are the paths of various animals, which differ from each other. The path of the mouse is narrow and smooth, but the path of the wild-boar is broad and flat. My friend, hearsay is not equal to experience and you yourself should experience the trials which beset one in the wilderness. All these difficulties my father had to endure as he made his way to the Forest of the Lord. But yet—and it is I who say it—all these things which I have described amounted to nothing compared with his experiences when he reached this forest.

On the first night after my father left home he slept on the way and by the time the sun was high in the sky on the next day he had almost reached his destination. At three o'clock in the afternoon he came to a forest which bordered on the Forest of the Lord itself. The name of this forest was the "Wilderness of Silence," because of all places under the sky that place is the most silent. A solitary sprite lives in this forest and he is fiercer than a clap of thunder. This sprite will not allow anyone to pass through to the Forest of the Lord. He gives the hunters much trouble and yet he is no more than two feet tall. He lives inside an ant-hill and he is indeed an imp of Satan who always bears with him a scourge.

When my father reached this forest everywhere was as silent as the grave. All the leaves on the trees were drooping and not one struck against another, as if there was not the slightest breeze. All the branches of the trees stood stock-still as when soldiers stand before their commander. The creepers were doubled up like sick men and the animals had rejected the place as a haunt. The birds had flown away each to his own place and every living thing was as dejected as a debtor who sits pondering on his debt. The whole forest was as still as when some great bereavement has befallen a man and his friends and acquaintances sit quiet.

Indeed, my friend, since in all this evil forest there was only my father with this little imp who lived inside an ant-heap, my father's passage through this place was fraught with difficulties.

After my father had wandered about for some time in this great wilderness he and this small imp came in sight of each other. That was indeed a notable day when those two sighted each other, when injury met trouble, when hobgoblin met sprite, when two lions came face to face. The name of this imp was the "Little Devil of the Ways." He wore no coat and he wore no trousers; he had no hat on his head and tied no cloth round his loins, for it was with leaves that the wretch covered his nakedness. He had only one eye and that was wide and round like a great moon. He had no nose at all because his eye was so much bigger than the ordinary bounds of an eye. His mouth was as wide as a man's palm and his teeth were like those of a lion, and these teeth were red as when a lion has just finished eating a meal of raw meat. The sprite's body was covered with hair like a garment and resembled that of a European dog. A long tuft of hair grew on the top of his head. From his shoulder there hung a scourge and from his neck a great bag which filled one with fear. This bag was smeared all over with blood and on this blood was stuck the down of birds, while various medicines were attached to its sides —medicine-calabashes, fish-bones and parrot-plumes, cuckoo and *aluko* feathers, cowrie money used in olden days,[2] the horns of various animals large and small, including a horn of the antelope which devours okra on the farms, and also feathers of the bush-fowl which roams about in the wilderness. All these things were attached to the great bag carried by the little imp of the ant-hill, whose name is the Little Devil of the Ways.

As he approached his legs made a thin rattling noise because of a mass of snail shells which had been cut into small pieces shaped round like shillings and which had been strung together like beads and arranged on his legs by the imp from his ankles to his knees. His fingers were all covered with iron rings which were dark like the fingers of a woman who dyes with indigo. Ah! I tell you the truth, this was a very evil sprite.

When my father appeared on this side and the sprite appeared

---

2. *cowrie money . . . days.* The brightly colored shells of a small mollusk were formerly used as money throughout West Africa.

yonder the two of them stopped and looked at each other, because when elephant meets elephant needs must that trees crash down on each other. The sprite was advancing and my father was going on to meet him. When they had almost come up to each other they again stopped and looked at each other— things were about to happen. Little Devil was the first to speak. He opened his great mouth and said—

"Who are you? What are you? What do you amount to? What do you rank as? What are you looking for? What do you want? What are you looking at? What do you see? What are you considering? What affects you? Where are you coming from? Where are you going? Where do you live? Where do you roam? Answer me! Human being, answer me in a word! One thing is certain—you have got into trouble today, you have climbed a tree beyond its topmost leaves, you have fallen from a height into a well, you have eaten an unexpected poison, you have found a farm-plot full of weeds and planted ground-nuts in it. You man without understanding, you do not know that the lion and the antelope do not meet, that the leopard and the ox do not make friends together, and that on the day a cat spies a mouse the life of that mouse comes to an end. You saw me and I saw you, you were approaching and I was approaching, and yet you did not take to your heels. You walked in my presence as if you had no care. Are you not afraid? Does not your heart thump with alarm? Have you never heard of me? Has no one told you about me? The skulls of greater men than you are in my cooking-pot and their backbones are in the corner of my room, while my seat is made from the breast-bones of those who are thoughtless.

"I am the little imp of the ant-hill, whose name is the Little Devil of the Ways. Because a dispute arose between me and another in heaven they said I had acted dishonestly towards the Almighty and so those heavenly beings determined that I must leave my abode there. So I left heaven and went beneath the earth and I lived for a hundred years with the dead who are beneath the earth and I learned much wisdom among them. It was then that I learnt that of the many deaths which the people of the world die very few are pre-ordained from heaven. The people of the world bring death on each other by their own hands. A fool may kill one man unintentionally, another can be killed by overwork unintentionally, another can be killed by laziness unintentionally, another can be killed by gluttony unintentionally, while another can be killed by greed unintentionally. Sometimes a cunning man seeks a way to kill his neighbour but instead of that neighbour he himself goes off to the other world. Sometimes a false friend seeks a way to kill another and himself goes to the other world. Sometimes a rich man seeks a way to kill a poor man and himself goes off to the other world. Sometimes again a man of low degree seeks a way to kill a man of high degree and himself goes off to the other world. The loose talker plays with death, the prodigal plays with death, the gadder-about plays with death, the haughty man plays with death and so too does the trickster. Why is this? It is because the Creator gazes at the creature along with the work of his hands and his manner of life among other creatures, and the Creator will surely give the creature the reward of the work of his hands whatever changes there may be in circumstances, either in this world or in the next.

"I am the little imp of the ant-hill, whose name is the Little Devil of the Ways. When I left the dwelling-place of the dead I came to this Wilderness of Silence and made an ant-hill my dwelling-place. In this wilderness I found animals, here too I found birds, and here too I found spirits, but all these I have driven away, so that I no longer have anyone to live with. I alone am here and I eat the leaves of the forest. But today, now that I have unexpectedly found you, I give thanks, because my luck has brought me something. It is many a long day since I have had human flesh to eat. When I have killed you I shall enjoy your flesh for three days. With your skull I shall make okra-stew, with your breast-bone I shall make vegetable-stew, and your buttocks will make thick fat in pepper-stew. What is left of you I shall put aside in my house, in the ant-hill. Ah! I give thanks to the Lord today, I give thanks to all the deities today. I give thanks to all the spirits of the world, I give thanks to the lucky medicines inside my bag, and further I give thanks to that important sprite,

Prince of the Forest, the imp who rules the ant-hill, who is my kinsman."

This was how the sprite spoke to my father, and my father answered as it is fitting that one strong man should answer another. He looked the Little Devil of the Ways up and down as when an impudent woman with a contemptuous glance looks at her husband and said, "He who tries to lift up rain in a sieve deceives himself. He who stands in the way of a railway train will find himself in Kingdom come. An elder who sees a snake and does not run is in a hurry to die. The animal which looks disdainfully at a hunter will sleep by the hearth-stones. The person who puts his trust in war involves himself in trouble.

"Any sprite who disregards me will find himself travelling from place to place in the other world. It is I who say so. Today I tell you sprites of the Forest of the Lord that when the Creator created all things which are in the world he made man to be their head. I want you to know today that pride is the beginning of destruction. Pride it is which precedes a fall. It is contrary to the laws of men and is opposed to the ordinances of God. Instead of me becoming your prey I can give your flesh to the beasts of the forest and turn you into food for the birds which fly among the trees. It is true that you have been meeting with men and turning them into inhabitants of your cooking-pot. But, Little Devil of the Ways, do not forget that some cocks are bigger than other cocks, some goats are bigger than other goats, some sheep are bigger than other sheep, some birds are bigger than other birds, some people are bigger than other people, some hunters are bigger than other hunters. It is I who tell you, I am stronger than those you have met before; I am not of their rank, I am of the rank of their fathers. You are puffed up with pride. You little sprite of the ant-hill, you Little Devil of the Ways. I am above the rank of your great-grandmother. To hell with you! What do you amount to? To hell with you seven times! You are in trouble today. Get ready, let us grapple with each other."

My friend, my father had barely finished speaking these words when the two of them began grappling with each other. This was a hard fight when a man met a spirit, and the whole forest resounded. The Little Devil of the Ways was tough and so too was Olowo-aiyé, my father, that hero who lived in this world and entered into combat with a being from the other world. When the fight first began Little Devil was trying to find an opportunity to cling to my father's hips and press his back against a thorny tree, and also to lift his leg on to his shoulder and push him on to the bushes and so injure his opponent. But this proved very difficult, because just as he had these ideas, so my father had other ideas. He was trying to find a way to lift Little Devil on to his shoulder, to get the dwarf sprite clear from the ground, to lift the wretch right above his head, to throw the rascal half a league away, so that Little Devil should travel from one place in the other world to another. But these attempts failed, because just as he was exerting himself like a lion, so Little Devil was exerting himself like an elephant and a great cloud of dust rose up in the face of the sky. The earth began to shake and the sound of their trampling feet was more than that of ten men. They glared at each other and grasped each other tightly as when a creeper clings to a tree on the farm, and both were panting like a hunter's dog. This was a hard day for the little sprite of the ant-hill, whose name is Little Devil of the Ways.

Presently, this wicked hobgoblin jumped at my father and clung to his middle, and when my father was struggling to grasp him by the leg he jumped on to his shoulder and grasping my father by the neck he began to beat him about the ears with great violence. This angered my father and he pushed the sprite along until he came to a thorny tree-trunk and then violently pushed him against the thorns. This caused the wicked sprite to give a loud yell and to jump down from my father's shoulder. So then my father gripped him by both ankles and he lifted Little Devil above his head and threw him forward in fury, hoping to smash the wretch's skull. But this plan failed. When my father looked in front of him, this creature was again standing firm and laughing and looking at my father as if the fight had only just begun.

My father now became weary of this struggle and he thrust his hand into his bag and was searching for a charm inside it when his eye suddenly lighted on an ancestral flute which we used to keep at our home. So he took this flute and began to blow it and the sound of this flute filled the whole place. He spoke of how God is the ordainer of victory and how He is the owner of all things which exist both in this world and in the next—the wealth of the sons of men and the treasures beneath the earth and everything which is on the face of the sea and in the sky. He spoke also of how there is no hindrance in the way of the Almighty. Everything which the Creator wishes to do He can do and no one can hinder the Almighty from exalting whom He wishes. My father described with his flute how the deceitful rises in the morning dark green like a plantain by the water-side, but when the sun is high he dries up like wood and by the evening he has withered completely away. The man of intrigue tells his friends that he has got himself a suit of clothes, but when the just man appears he points his finger at the other saying he is stark naked.

Such were the words of the songs which my father sang full of compassion on the day that he and the little sprite of the ant-hill met each other, and the songs were echoed throughout the forest. Now this flute was sweeter than a king's flute and as the song of the flute was a lament it could not fail to enter the recesses of the sprite's brain. The true man humbled the false, the Little Devil dropped his head like a banana-leaf, the sprite of the ant-hill began to look down on the ground pensively and the little creature opened his mouth and spoke, saying:

"The sons of men have changed and wise men have appeared among them. Much time has passed since I came here to make my dwelling-place and no one hitherto has tried to change my heart. But since the time that God created me I have noticed that the patient man never ends up with regret, but only he who foolishly lets patience be ruined. From today onwards I will not behave roughly towards people of the world, I will not be irritable with the sons of men, I will not be peevish with animals, I will not be rough with the leaves of the forest. For your words have changed my heart and I will not behave as a boor any more. But do not ever think that it is merely a spirit of laziness which leads me to utter these words. If you think so, then we must agree that you do not understand my words. You will be like one who calls a sheep an ox or a lorry a bicycle or this world the next world. The patient man sees a quarrel and draws back and the fool thinks he is a coward, but when the patient man enters a quarrel, all the fools topple over like trees. I thank you for the lament which you sang, a song full of wisdom which reminded me of my Creator. If it were not for this song which you sang I would have fought for three whole days, because I have fought so before. I have fought a battle for three months, I have fought one for six months, I have fought one for a whole year, I, the little sprite of the ant-hill, whose name is the Little Devil of the Ways."

So the sprite spoke and my father put his anger aside and they greeted and shook hands with each other, and each went off in his own direction. But according to the law of nature a fight does not pass without the fighter suffering some injury, whether the fighter turn out the winner or the loser. My father had scraped his back against a tree, had torn his hunter's wallet, had lost an important charm, and had smashed his pipe. So too Little Devil had suffered hurt, two of his teeth had been dislodged, one of his rings was lost, and his leg was sprained, so that he walked like one suffering from guinea-worm.[3] That is why wise people rank quarrels with poison and avoid them every day, because quarrels are not proper for human beings, they are like fish-bones in the throat. But foolish people are in the habit of lighting a European torch and looking for quarrels all over the town.

So Olowo-aiyé went on his way and travelled on, he and God, and when he had nearly passed through the Forest of Silence he came to a little flowing stream which was bright and cool. There my father stopped and poured water on his body, and after that he ate some ripe bananas and took a cola-nut from his wallet and slipped it into his mouth. His mind was now at rest like the mind of a man who has contracted a debt of two pounds but the Lord

---

3. *guinea-worm*, a parasitic worm, common in tropical regions, which grows to a length of several feet. It infests domestic animals as well as man.

has preserved his secret and he unexpectedly finds an opportunity of making ten pounds.

Less than ten minutes after leaving this stream my father had left the Forest of Silence behind him and had come out to a wide, open place. The verdure there was fresh and green like the front of a European's house, bushes were more numerous there than tall trees and each tree and bush in all that neighbourhood was very beautiful, standing as they did with rounded shapes. Some were white and some were dark and some were like a rainbow, which has both bright and dark colours. A broad roadway went on straight ahead, that is, the path which my father was following had now become bigger. Great stones were arranged on the right and left sides of this road. Behind these stones bushes had been planted along the road and these were in flower and were very beautiful. My friend, as the proverb says: "When one's peer in age dies it is a warning to one's self." When Olowo-aiyé saw these things he knew that the Forest of the Lord was near, so my father girded himself like a man.

The wise man and the fool appear the same in a time of enjoyment but in a time of trouble the wise man stands out clearly. My father behaved like a wise man at this moment. He carefully placed his belongings on the ground and went beneath one of those trees and prostrated himself before God, saying:

"O God who created me. O Lord who created the Forest of the Lord, O marvellous One who created every marvel, O Creator who created every hunter that lives in the world, the time has now come that I want you to be my support. Some men come into the world and when they leave the world their name passes away with them. These men pass through the world like a snake over a rock and we see no trace of them. Others come into the world and when they leave the world their evil name remains behind them, as when a black spot comes on to a white cloth and the washerman washes the cloth until it almost tears and the spot merely stands out more clearly. Please, my Creator, do not make me like one of these people. I humbly beg today that you make me like one of those people who come into the world and are like a moon which shines benignly for generation after generation. Their name remains after they are gone and those coming after them compete as in a race to be like them. As I go on my way today, grant that I may return like a man, so that when my time comes to die people will not be asking each other after I am gone, 'Was this man ever born?' "

This was how Olowo-aiyé spoke, and the Lord heard in the other world, because there is no man who is equal to an angel and there is no supporter equal to God. So my father went on his way singing and whistling and striding along like a soldier.

He had not long started on his way when he looked in front and saw two women coming along the road talking and laughing and slapping their hands as is the habit of countless women. These two women behaved as if they had made their home in that neighbourhood and were enjoying their life in that forest. Indeed they were dressed in fine clothes as if they were in the middle of a town. One of them was light in colour and was tall and stout, with the appearance of a married woman, but the second was somewhat slender and not very tall. She was dark in colour and her teeth were white like fresh maize. Both of them were good-looking, their manner of speaking was that of gentlefolk, and their manner of walking was that of people who live at ease.

When they met my father he greeted them and they answered him in the restrained way which it is proper to use in answering someone with whom one is not acquainted. My father then went on his way and they went on theirs. But anyone would wonder how two gentlefolk such as these came to be in this wilderness, and this thought led my father to glance back to look at them. But at that very moment the younger of the two women also looked back and when their glances met they smiled at each other and then again set off on their way. The second time that my father looked back, his eyes again met those of this woman. Now at this time my father had as yet no wife, but was unmarried. Nevertheless he braced himself and again went on his way. But when it was now the third time that he looked back and this woman also looked back and he smiled and she smiled and the teeth of this beautiful woman were white like a wall which has been whitewashed, then Olowo-aiyé turned round, the hero turned his back on the Forest of the Lord and followed after this woman. May the Lord save the sons of men from women who cause trouble, who wear their head-ties forward on the head.

When my father began to approach her, this woman stood still but her companion walked on a little and stood away at some distance because when a man and a woman want to have a private conversation a third person is bound to be a hindrance to them. See, my friend, be careful in your behaviour. If you accompany a companion to the house of his betrothed wife, think deeply before you attempt to take part in any conversation which they are having together, otherwise you will be like a dirty spot on a white cloth, and though they may have a smile on their faces in talking to you they are bound to be saying in the secret places of their hearts, "This rascal will not let us enjoy our private talk."

When my father came up to this woman he greeted her, "I hope your household is prosperous, I hope you are well, I hope no trouble affects you." The other gave him favourable replies. After answering his greetings the woman asked with a smile, "Have I not been acquainted with you before somewhere?" My father answered, "Yes, I have that feeling too. Is it your compound which is at the end of our yard?" And in fact a blacksmith's compound lay at the back of us, and a girl who was a witch had been living there before Olowo-aiyé began wandering about the forests as a hunter. It was some time since my father had seen this girl. It turned out that this girl had left their compound, she and her elder sister, and had come to live in the Forest of the Lord. It was only when my father asked about this that he came to understand the circumstances. The woman answered him as follows:

"It is true that I am that girl called Ajediran [4] who used to live in the blacksmith's compound. When a quarrel broke out one day the people of our compound told lies about us and declared that it was we who had devoured their children. Yet at the time

---

4. *Ajediran* (ä jä′dē rän).

of which I am speaking I and my sister had not yet become witches. The children of men gave us a name which we did not deserve, and by the time three months had passed all the people throughout our town had come to believe that we were witches. Can the sons of men be so foolish? As soon as two or three people have said something everyone else will give up thinking for themselves and will be repeating something which to them is mere hearsay. So the sons of men gave me and my sister a name which we did not deserve. In the end we became angry and sought witchcraft and found it, and in our rage we turned ourselves into witches and have remained so until today. So you see that there are some people in the world who are like a protruding root in the middle of a path and who are a stumbling-block to the children of the Lord. When a person is not behaving in a deceitful way they will say he is behaving so, until the person concerned makes up his mind that, since the sons of men say he acts in a way in which he does not act, he might as well act so in fact. This is one of the most important causes of stumbling for those whom the Lord has created to live on the face of the earth.

"I tell you, man of might, that when my sister and I finally became witches we caused people great affliction, because we devoured young and old. We killed important people in the assembly. In the end this affair filled the Lord God with anger, because although the sons of men had behaved foolishly before, we too had now behaved stupidly like monkeys. So one morning one who was a past master in witchcraft and fiercer even than we, cornered us in our compound and gave us battle and drove us away, so we ran here to the Forest of the Lord. I can never forget this affair as long as I live, because had it not been for this I should by now have found a man to marry me. Because of this I beg you earnestly, you handsome hunter, do not think shame of me because of the question which I shall ask. I want you to remember that the evil custom of the sons of men does not permit a woman to choose the husband whom her heart desires. It is men who have the right to speak first to ask a woman to marry them. If a woman wants to marry a man it is a difficult matter for the woman to express her wish. This custom of the children of men inflicts hardship upon one half of them, and yet, as the proverb says, if a man sees a snake and a woman kills the snake, provided the snake does not escape there is no offence committed. I want you to understand clearly that if a woman is attracted to a man and reveals to the man her wish, no offence is committed. It is ignorant people who say that a woman who herself woos a man must have base desires. Before a woman would venture to do so the fire of love in the bottom of her heart must be stronger than the fire of a furnace. Without a doubt, you mighty hunter, you are not one of those ignorant people. You attract me greatly and I want you to be my husband and myself to be your wife, so that our going-out and our coming-in may be one."

See, my friend, the surprising thing in this story is that this woman's sweet words caused my father to taste love for the first time in his life. Love boiled up and covered his eyes like palm wine inside a calabash, and so for the sake of beauty Olowo-aiyé forgot his character, for the sake of bright eyes he forgot wisdom, for the sake of white teeth he caused himself to become the husband of a witch. From that day forward my father took trouble as a burden on his back and took trouble to be his wife.

▶

Adebisi Fabunmi The Hanging Gardens of Babylon (Oshogbo), 1966. Lino-cut.

Alfred Hutchinson / *South Africa*
(1924–   )

ABOARD AN AFRICAN TRAIN

Because of his work for the African National Congress, Alfred Hutchinson was arrested by the Union of South Africa in 1956 on charges of high treason. When the prosecution temporarily withdrew the indictment, he fled the country without a passport. This excerpt, which tells of a part of his journey, is from his book Road to Ghana.

THE STATION [1] was full of migrant miners returning home. Escorts taking the men home stood herding them. These were the men of the Mzilikazi (Witwatersrand Native Labour Association [2]) who were returning home after their contracts in the mines. And the station belonged to them. They wore patchwork trousers and miner's hob-nailed boots and sombreros of all descriptions: yellow, orange, black, red. They tugged the hats down with knotty hands. They wore cheap wire spectacles or goggles, some on their noses, others on their foreheads. Their socks were tattered, did not match, and some had tops only. Some wore battered khaki shorts and were barefoot, and one of them was on crutches. Loaves of bread were tied to bundles standing on the ground. They swaggered a bit and looked at us, the surface people, with contempt, and they looked at women with a terrible longing in their eyes.

Copyright © 1960 by Alfred Hutchinson. Reprinted from ROAD TO GHANA by Alfred Hutchinson by permission of THE JOHN DAY COMPANY, INC., publisher and Victor Gollancz Ltd.
1. *The station,* at Mafeking in the Union of South Africa, about 150 miles west of Johannesburg, where Hutchinson's journey began. **2.** *Witwatersrand Native Labour Association.* Witwatersrand, the region around Johannesburg, produces much of the world's gold.

"These can kill you," said the woman beside me reading the look.

I pulled out the fish and chips and the loaf of bread from my paper bags and asked the man from Salima to eat with me. We ate slowly and washed the food down with cold drinks. Railway policemen walked up and down the platform among the miners and stopped to chat with the escorts who had the W.N.L.A. brass letters on their caps glittering in the morning sun. The woman at my side chattered with a dry ecstasy in her voice about the terrible look the miners had in their eyes.

A man came pushing a wagon with various articles on it. He was selling. The man from Salima bought soap and razor blades, and I bought soap and razor blades too. But then I made the mistake of taking the articles from the wagon.

"Don't touch!" the man shouted at me. "Don't touch!" I said I was sorry. "Don't touch! Wait till you're given!"

A railway policeman wandered up to us. I made a profusion of apologies and the man from Salima made more on my behalf. I slunk back to the bench and buried myself in a newspaper.

A howl, a whoop, tore me from the newspaper. A train, laden with migrant workers, was coming into the station headed for the mines. The windows were packed with black faces. An answering howl and whoop rose from the train as the train pulled to a stop. Then the men on the platform broke ranks and their boots crunched the ground as they swarmed to the windows of the train going to the mines. The whoop rose again and again, a terrifying jellying sound. It churned and boiled and twisted with a nameless agony—rejection, welcome, derision—bundled into one. The miners going home swaggered as they interrogated the newcomers. They cuffed them. And some of the men on the train returned blow for blow. At various points actual fights threatened and a railway policeman cuffed and clouted the returning miners where the cuffing and clouting had gone too far. The eyes were red and blank with a nameless agony. It was stupid, senseless, terrifying. What had been done to the poor people, I kept thinking in despair. And the whoop rose and fell, jellying and uncertain and crackling with the despair of fallen leaves.

They swore and cursed. They cuffed and clouted and chatted a bit. And clouted and jeered.

The Bulawayo [3] train pulled in at ten o'clock. The men from Mzilikazi lifted their bundles to their shoulders and heads and formed an Indian file. There was a fourth class on the train and the miners packed into the fourth-class carriages. We trooped into the third-class. I did not want to lose sight of the man from Salima. There were six of us in the compartment: the man from Salima, an old man wearing wire spectacles, a sickly looking chap with an expensive green hat, a boy in a shoddy green jacket and cheap grey hat, and a big, black, old woman. It was an African train except for the driver and the conductor.

The train swung westward. I wondered when we should reach Francistown and how it would go at the nearby border of the Union and Bechuanaland.[4] I sat tense as the train swung with slow looping movements, like an African woman playing with her hips. We were swinging westward towards the desert. The land grew dry and tedious and the grass and trees were withered and coated with brown dust. There was no urgency in that train: it swung and rocked and we swung and rocked with it. We looked out of the window, glancing at each other's faces as we did so. But no one spoke for a long time.

"Hai," said the sickly chap with the green hat, "the train of Nyasaland!" [5]

That began the conversation. We all began to complain about the slowness of the train. The old man in the wire spectacles said that he had been days on the train already. He was from Cape Town and uttered a word or two in Xhosa—the African language spoken in Cape Town. He was returning to Nyasaland and asked the others where they were going. Except for the old black woman who was going to Salisbury, we were all going to Nyasa-

---

3. *Bulawayo,* a city in southwestern Rhodesia. 4. *the Union . . . Bechuana-land.* The former British territory of Bechuanaland, now the Republic of Botswana, forms part of the northern border of the Union of South Africa. 5. *Nyasaland.* The former British territory of Nyasaland, now the Republic of Malawi, lies between Tanzania, Zambia, and the Portuguese territory of Mozambique.

land. Even the old woman originally came from Salima, the home of my coal-black friend.

"A person only works for train fare," said the old man taking a pinch of snuff from a Royal Baking Powder tin.

We agreed that we only worked for the train fare back home. But I thought that a single ticket from Johannesburg to Salisbury for £2 13s. 11d.[6] was very cheap, notwithstanding the class we were travelling. The sickly man pursed his singularly thin lips tightly as if fighting back pain. He had a look of world-wiseness in his eyes which the others in the compartment did not have. There was something knowing and mocking in those eyes. They did not ask me what I was going to do in Blantyre [7] and that made me feel easy. But I was thinking about the border and dreading what might happen. If the news of my escape had leaked, there I would surely be arrested and turned back. The train swung easily like an African woman slowly swinging her hips. In trepidation I waited for the border. The train swung on and on and on until surely we had crossed the border. There was no border post: no checking of passes [8] or customs. I was in Bechuanaland. One hurdle had been jumped. Anything could still happen.

In the compartment next to ours a man was taking his Union wife and two children with him to Nyasaland. The woman and the children were a pitiful sight. The children were half blind with filth and dirty sores. Flies swarmed round their eyes and the woman, exhausted with hunger and neglect, did not even wave the flies from the children. The man sat. He too was prostrated by helplessness.

It grew hot on the train and the lavatory began to stink. Dirt began to pile in the corridors and flies buzzed. At the sidings desert women and children, insubstantial and wraithlike in their trailing, shapeless, dirty white dresses, came to sell homemade cold drinks in bottles, bottled tea, scones and hunks of dubious meat. The meat was too much for the price they asked and we

6. *£2 13s. 11d.*, slightly over $7.50. 7. *Blantyre,* a city in southern Malawi. 8. *checking of passes.* Under South African law, blacks must carry an identification card, or "pass," and produce it on demand, or else be subject to arrest.

asked why among ourselves and decided not to buy it. At intervals through the morning and afternoon a man in a guard's cap came to the door and pointed the spout of a kettle at us, stood silent for a long time and then went his way. He was selling tea, they said. But he did not utter a sound.

We swung throughout the day and the shadows of the thorn trees lengthened with the dipping western sun. Past Atloss, Artesia, Gaberones, Pilane. . . . At intervals the train stopped for a long time for no apparent reason, and the white driver got out and sat African-wise on a stone chatting to other whites, or made water on the bushes at the side of the railway. It was the all-African train. And then again we swung onward carrying miners and new blue Massey-Harris tractors and water tanks with us. I stood in the corridor a long time looking at the thirsty land, at the tedious thorn trees and bare hills.

A man came to lean against the window.

"Going to Nyasa?" he said. I nodded. "Going to fetch horse medicines?" I spread my hands dubiously and shrugged to say that perhaps I was fetching "medicines" of luck for horse racing. "Ah, don't deny it. Don't tell me—I know!" The man laughed. "In two months you'll have a shop and a motor car. The medicines of Nyasaland are strong," he said with pride, "but don't let them cheat you. You must get out of the towns. Not Blantyre—right out—away from the towns."

I winked an eye and he winked back. That meant he understood. It was the life. I had found an explanation for going to Nyasaland: I was going to buy horse-racing *mutis*.[9] He would never know that I had never seen the inside of a race course and didn't gamble because I hadn't the nerve for it. The woman who had spoken about the look in the miners' eyes came to the window. She was going to Nyasaland, she told me, to her husband. She had been to visit her people in Orlando. She was itching for a flirtation and I hastily gave her trail. As the evening grew she stood in the corridor with a strong young Nyasa. She had hooked her man.

---

9. *mutis*, good luck charms. From a Zulu word for *herb*.

A chap speaking Xhosa collared me again and again for a cigarette. He was a Nyasa returning home but he wanted very much to be "Xhosa." He was full of city-talk and this frightened me off. I did not want to be identified with the city. There was a pretty young girl in the next compartment going home to Bulawayo. She was Zulu-breed, strong-thighed and solid—a descendant of Mzilikazi's, who had blazed a bloody trail north, fleeing the wrath of the Zulu monarch, Tshaka.[10] She was thickly powdered and tortured the chaps of the train with her city ways and inaccessibility. She broke into a jive, there in the corridor, to one or both of the gramophones playing simultaneously in different compartments. And the men groaned listening to the gramophone records, and said it took them "back there"—meaning Johannesburg—which they had probably never seen.

I found the man from Salima adding sums of money with a stub of a pencil and some paper. He was adding £15 10s. plus £15 10s. The first time he got it wrong. The second time it was right. There was something strange about this man in the brown jacket frayed at the sleeves and the fawn trousers which were thin at the knees. He was solid, unequivocally honest, I thought, looking at him. He had a terrific self-containedness—like a man long used to living and relying on himself.

The sickly man was huddled in a corner.

"How's it?" I said to the sick man.

"That woman has finished me, S'bali (brother-in-law). She's killed me," he said, trying to smile through the pain, while carefully brushing the expensive green hat with the palm of his hand. "I've left her—left her with house, furniture, three children and all."

"Yours?" I said, meaning the children.

"Yes, S'bali, two boys and a girl."

The trouble had started, he said, when he spoke of going to

---

10. *Mzilikazi . . . Tshaka.* The Zulu chief Tshaka conquered all of Natal province in southwestern South Africa in the 1820's. His rivals fled north and south. Mzilikazi went north and colonized Matabeleland in what is now Rhodesia.

Nyasaland for a time. The city woman would not hear of it, especially as she knew that he had two wives and children in Nyasaland. She didn't want to lose her "milch-cow." Nyasas were regarded as "milch-cows" by Johannesburg women, he explained. She had immediately procured *mutis* to stop him from going. And his illness had started. She had even confiscated his pass in order to stop his departure. He had told her to keep it if she wanted to: he was going. He thought he would get better in Nyasaland. I thought he was suffering from T.B.

"When did you leave Nyasaland, S'bali?" I said.

"Long ago, S'bali. In 1952."

"Six years ago!" I said. "That's a long time!"

The old man turned his wire spectacles to me.

"What do you say of me, S'bali," he said, calling me brother-in-law also. "Fourteen."

"Fourteen!"

"I left a baby boy, S'bali. He's a man now."

I turned to Moses Banda, the man from Salima. He had left home six years ago. Mweli, the sick man, six. Moyo, the youth, three. The old man, fourteen. These were long times to be away from home, especially from a wife and children.

"That's too long," I said.

"We can't help it, S'bali," said Mweli. "It's hard to get into the Union and the longer you stay the better."

"Blantyre?" said Granny looking at me. "That's just next door. He is from Salima—where I come from," she said, pointing at my friend. "You can take a good wife there," she added. I expressed interest. "Not Blantyre—no, no. The women are all crooks. They'll eat your money and when it's finished, leave you! Get to Salima and get a good Thonga girl. She'll look well after your things." I told Granny that my grandmother had been a Thonga like her, and she promptly married me to someone— most likely a relation of hers. She invited me to spend a few days at her home in Salisbury. From the time of the "marriage" Granny referred to me respectfully as *Mkwenyana* (son-in-law).

Granny started scolding Moyo, the youth. The big hulking, ugly woman had a heart of gold. Granny, I thought, had been too long away from home and wanted to scold someone and had picked on Moyo because he was the youngest in the compartment.

"You'll get lost, you!" she said to the boy, who was adjusting his hat to a jaunty angle. That hat was the symbol of his manhood and throughout the day I watched him fuss over it.

"I won't. I know. I'll take a bus from Lusaka to Mzimba."

"This child is lost, Mkwenyana," said Granny, turning to me. "He doesn't know where he is going. He says he is going to Mzimba but here he is going to Lusaka."

"I'm not lost," said Moyo with dignity. "I know. I left that way."

Moses Banda, the man from Salima, was again adding sums of money. They looked like the same figures he had been adding all the time. Whenever he got tired of listening to us or looking out of the window, he pulled out his pocket book and pencil and the addition started. I turned from Banda to Moyo who had put on his wisest airs.

"Are you sure you won't get lost?" I said.

"He doesn't know anything," said Granny.

Moyo had left home in 1955 in a band of fourteen other boys. They had taken a bus from Mzima to Lusaka and from Lusaka a train to Bulawayo. In order to avoid the pass blitz at Plumtree they had walked in the bush from Bulawayo to Mafeking—a journey that took a month. Then from Mafeking in the Union of South Africa, they caught a train to Johannesburg. He had never worked in Johannesburg, the city of his dreams, but had been sent to a farm in Delmas. I asked him whether he would return to the Union.

"Never. When I want work, it will be Bulawayo," he said.

Moyo bent down and pulled his suitcase from under the seat and opened it. I peeped inside. There was an old blanket, two or three battered torches, and, at the bottom of the case, a quantity of sprouting potatoes. He pulled out a Farmer's Weekly Diary of 1957 and a stub of a pencil and began making squiggles on it. He made sounds, incomprehensible sounds, as he made the meaningless squiggles. I thought I heard him say *verdomde* (damned)—

Afrikaans [11] which he had most certainly picked up on the potato fields. Granny shook her head pitying the poor boy who would get lost. He took out his ticket and looked at it, making incomprehensible sounds. Moyo couldn't even read the fare he had paid for his ticket home. Moyo had been South. Poor Moyo.

The train swung like a buxom African woman coquettishly flouncing her hips and we swung with it. Moyo adjusted his hat in case it had lost the correct angle. Mweli sat looking at nothing out of his sick eyes. And the old man sat looking at the night through the window. Moses Banda had made a new column of figures: the same figures. He had been a tailor at Iscor near Pretoria for six years. Now he was returning home with three tailor's sewing machines and other things. It was his money which he kept adding over and over again. I had thought he was a miner with hands like that.

The gramophones played in the swinging train. People who had never seen Johannesburg said that the songs reminded them of the city. The woman who had itched for a flirtation clung to her young muscled man, and the young girl of Zulu breed with her thickly powdered pretty face played hard-to-get and wrought havoc with the young men's hearts. And the train swung northward through the night. The train swung into Francistown, still in Bechuanaland, at five-thirty in the morning. We were approaching Plumtree where our passes would be checked. I grew restless and a flutter of panic drove me to ask to see my companions' passes. Granny did not have one and was defiant about it. She had travelled like that for many years. What was this new-fangled thing of passes about, she said. The passes were all different from one another and different from mine. They said mine would do; that it was more official than all.

At Plumtree Rhodesian African policemen in black fezzes and big black boots jumped on the train and asked for our passes. I steadied my hand as I handed mine. The policeman glanced at me and handed it back. I almost sighed with relief. Granny glared at the young policeman. "Granny, where's your pass?"

11. *Afrikaans,* the Dutch dialect spoken in South Africa.

"What pass? I've been travelling like this long before you were born! Child, ask your mates for a pass!"

"Get a pass next time, Granny," said the young policeman walking out of the compartment.

I had crossed the border into Southern Rhodesia. Someone whispered in Zulu: *"Zishile* (it's burnt)," which meant that someone was in trouble. I peeped into the corridor and right next door an African policeman had mounted guard over the door. A white official had been sent for. The man taking his wife and two children to Nyasaland had not taken passes for them. I was terror-stricken. Now there would probably be a recheck on the passes, and questionings. And it wouldn't take much to prove that I was no Nyasa returning home. I should be arrested and handed back to the Union. I couldn't resist peeping into the corridor, and when I next peeped a white official was there. But the man only received a warning—not even a fine.

One of the men returning to Nyasaland began a conversation with the African policeman in the corridor about conditions in the Union. "There's not a bush, not even grass to hide in," the man was saying. "Here at least you can hide behind a bush. It's like a road, and a policeman sees you miles off." The policeman looked at the bushes in silence.

"But there are Nyangas (medicine men)—where do they get the roots from then?" said the policeman.

"There are quacks galore. . . . As you say, where would they dig the roots from?" said the returning man. "There are quacks without number, that's true."

Then the man from Johannesburg told the policeman about the pass laws. A garden boy had been picked up for a pass right in the garden where he worked and his missis looked for him in vain. A servant who had been sent to the greengrocer's had been picked up for a pass with basket and vegetables and the missis found him after a search at the police station.

"I used to hear it was nice," said the policeman.

"Then go and see for yourself," said the man returning from the Union.

"No," said the Rhodesian policeman. "I'm all right here." ▶

Kalungano / *Mozambique*
(1929–   )

DREAM OF THE BLACK MOTHER

Translated from the Portuguese by
Philippa Rumsey

To my Mother

Black mother
Rocks her son
And in her black head
Covered with black hair
5 She keeps marvellous dreams.

Black mother
Rocks her son
And forgets
That the earth has dried up the maize
10 That yesterday the groundnuts were finished.

She dreams of marvellous worlds
Where her son would go to school
To school where men study.

"Dream of the Black Mother" by Kalungano, translated by Philippa Rumsey, from AFRICAN WRITING TODAY edited by Ezekiel Mphahlele. Reprinted by permission of Penguin Books Ltd.

Black mother
15 Rocks her son
And forgets
Her brothers building towns and cities
Cementing them with their blood.

She dreams of marvellous worlds
20 Where her son would run along the street
The street where men pass by.

Black mother
Rocks her son
And listening
25 To the voice from afar
Brought by the wind.
She dreams of marvellous worlds,
Marvellous worlds
Where her son will be able to live.

Jomo Kenyatta / *Kenya*

(1891–   )

THE GENTLEMEN OF THE JUNGLE

ONCE UPON A TIME an elephant made a friendship with a man. One day a heavy thunderstorm broke out, the elephant went to his friend, who had a little hut at the edge of the forest, and said to him: "My dear good man, will you please let me put my trunk inside your hut to keep it out of this torrential rain?" The man, seeing what situation his friend was in, replied: "My dear good elephant, my hut is very small, but there is room for your trunk and myself. Please put your trunk in gently." The elephant thanked his friend, saying: "You have done me a good deed and one day I shall return your kindness." But what followed? As soon as the elephant put his trunk inside the hut, slowly he pushed his head inside, and finally flung the man out in the rain, and then lay down comfortably inside his friend's hut, saying: "My dear good friend, your skin is harder than mine, and as there is not enough room for both of us, you can afford to remain in the rain while I am protecting my delicate skin from the hailstorm."

The man, seeing what his friend had done to him, started to grumble; the animals in the nearby forest heard the noise and came to see what was the matter. All stood around listening to the heated argument between the man and his friend the elephant. In this turmoil the lion came along roaring, and said in a loud voice: "Don't you all know that I am the King of the Jungle! How dare anyone disturb the peace of my kingdom?" On hearing this the elephant, who was one of the high ministers in the jungle kingdom, replied in a soothing voice, and said: "My lord, there is no disturbance of the peace in your kingdom. I have only been having a little discussion with my friend here as to the possession of this little hut which your lordship sees me occupying." The lion, who wanted to have "peace and tranquillity" in his kingdom, replied in a noble voice, saying: "I command my ministers to appoint a Commission of Enquiry to go thoroughly into this matter and report accordingly." He then turned to the man and said: "You have done well by establishing friendship with my people, especially with the elephant, who is one of my honourable ministers of state. Do not grumble any more, your hut is not lost to you. Wait until the sitting of my Imperial Commission, and there you will be given plenty of opportunity to state your case. I am sure that you will be pleased with the findings of the Commission." The man was very pleased by these sweet words from the King of the Jungle, and innocently waited for his opportunity, in the belief that naturally the hut would be returned to him.

The elephant, obeying the command of his master, got busy with other ministers to appoint the Commission of Enquiry. The following elders of the jungle were appointed to sit in the Commission: (1) Mr. Rhinoceros; (2) Mr. Buffalo; (3) Mr. Alligator; (4) The Rt. Hon. Mr. Fox to act as chairman; and (5) Mr. Leopard to act as Secretary to the Commission. On seeing the personnel, the man protested and asked if it was not necessary to include in this Commission a member from his side. But he was told that it was impossible, since no one from his side was well enough educated to understand the intricacy of jungle law. Further, that there was nothing to fear, for the members of the Commission were all men of repute for their impartiality in justice, and as they were gentlemen chosen by God to look after the interests of races less adequately endowed with teeth and claws, he might rest assured that they would investigate the matter with the greatest care and report impartially.

The Commission sat to take the evidence. The Rt. Hon. Mr. Elephant was first called. He came along with a superior air, brushing his tusks with a sapling which Mrs. Elephant had provided, and in an authoritative voice said: "Gentlemen of the Jungle, there is no need for me to waste your valuable time in relating a story which I am sure you all know. I have always regarded it as my duty to protect the interests of my friends, and this appears to have caused the misunderstanding between myself and my friend here. He invited me to save his hut from being blown away by a hurricane. As the hurricane had gained access owing to the unoccupied space in the hut, I considered it necessary, in my friend's own interests, to turn the undeveloped space to a more economic use by sitting in it myself; a duty which any of you would undoubtedly have performed with equal readiness in similar circumstances."

After hearing the Rt. Hon. Mr. Elephant's conclusive evidence, the Commission called Mr. Hyena and other elders of the jungle, who all supported what Mr. Elephant had said. They then called the man, who began to give his own account of the dispute. But the Commission cut him short, saying: "My good man, please confine yourself to relevant issues. We have already heard the circumstances from various unbiased sources; all we wish you to tell us is whether the undeveloped space in your hut was occupied by anyone else before Mr. Elephant assumed his position?" The man began to say: "No, but—" But at this point the Commission declared that they had heard sufficient evidence from both sides and retired to consider their decision. After enjoying a delicious meal at the expense of the Rt. Hon. Mr. Elephant, they reached their verdict, called the man, and declared as follows: "In our opinion this dispute has arisen through a regrettable misunderstanding due to the backwardness of your ideas. We consider that Mr. Elephant has fulfilled his sacred duty of protecting your interests. As it is clearly for your good that the space should be put to its most economic use, and as you yourself have not yet reached the stage of expansion which would enable you to fill it, we consider it necessary to arrange a compromise to suit both parties. Mr. Elephant shall continue his occupation of your hut, but we give you permission to look for a site where you can build another hut more suited to your needs, and we will see that you are well protected."

The man, having no alternative, and fearing that his refusal might expose him to the teeth and claws of members of the Commission, did as they suggested. But no sooner had he built another hut than Mr. Rhinoceros charged in with his horn lowered and ordered the man to quit. A Royal Commission was again appointed to look into the matter, and the same finding was given. This procedure was repeated until Mr. Buffalo, Mr. Leopard, Mr. Hyena and the rest were all accommodated with new huts. Then the man decided that he must adopt an effective method of protection, since Commissions of Enquiry did not seem to be of any use to him. He sat down and said: *"Ng'enda thi ndagaga motegi,"* which literally means "there is nothing that treads on the earth that cannot be trapped," or in other words, you can fool people for a time, but not for ever.

Early one morning, when the huts already occupied by the jungle lords were all beginning to decay and fall to pieces, he went out and built a bigger and better hut a little distance away. No sooner had Mr. Rhinoceros seen it than he came rushing in, only to find that Mr. Elephant was already inside, sound asleep. Mr. Leopard next came in at the window, Mr. Lion, Mr. Fox and Mr. Buffalo entered the doors, while Mr. Hyena howled for a place in the shade and Mr. Alligator basked on the roof. Presently they all began disputing about their rights of penetration, and from disputing they came to fighting, and while they were all embroiled together the man set the hut on fire and burnt it to the ground, jungle lords and all. Then he went home, saying: "Peace is costly, but it's worth the expense," and lived happily ever after. ▶

Camara Laye / *Guinea*
(1928–   )

from THE AFRICAN CHILD

Translated from the French by
James Kirkup

Camara Laye grew up in Kouroussa, a town on the Niger River in Guinea. In this West African society, the culture was of mingled Islamic and ancient African traditions. The boy found himself by heredity a member of the Guinea caste of copper-smiths, a craft aristocracy. In a culture where ritual and custom had governed life for generations, he grew up in a time of change.

I

I WAS a little boy playing round my father's hut. How old would I have been at that time? I cannot remember exactly. I still must have been very young: five, maybe six years old. My mother was in the workshop with my father, and I could just hear their familiar voices above the noise of the anvil and the conversation of the customers.

Suddenly I stopped playing, my whole attention fixed on a snake that was creeping round the hut. He really seemed to be "taking a turn" round the hut. After a moment I went over to him. I had taken in my hand a reed that was lying in the yard—there were always some lying around; they used to get broken off the fence of plaited reeds that marked the boundary of our compound—and I thrust this reed into the reptile's mouth. The snake did not try to get away: he was beginning to enjoy our little game; he was slowly swallowing the reed; he was devouring it, I thought, as if it were some delicious prey, his eyes glittering with voluptuous bliss; and inch by inch his head was drawing nearer to my hand. At last the reed was almost entirely swallowed up, and the snake's jaws were terribly close to my fingers.

I was laughing, I had not the slightest fear, and now I know that the snake would not have hesitated much longer before burying his fangs in my fingers if, at that moment, Damany, one of the apprentices, had not come out of the workshop. The apprentice shouted to my father, and almost at once I felt myself lifted off my feet: I was safe in the arms of one of my father's friends!

There was a terrific commotion going on all round me; my mother was shouting harder than anyone; and she gave me a few sharp slaps. I began to weep, more upset by the sudden uproar than by the blows I had received. A little later, when I had calmed down a little and the shouting had died down around me, my mother solemnly warned me never to play such a game again; and I promised, although I could not really see where the danger in it lay.

My father's hut was near the workshop, and I would often play there beneath the veranda that ran round the outside. It was my father's private hut. It was built like all our huts, of mud that had been pounded and moulded into bricks with water; it was round, and proudly helmeted with thatch. It was entered by a rectangular doorway. Inside, a tiny window let in a thin shaft of daylight. On the right there was the bed, made of beaten earth like the bricks, spread with a simple wicker-work mat on which was a pillow stuffed with kapok. At the rear of the hut, right under the window where the light was strongest, were the tool-boxes. On the left were the *boubous* [1] and the prayer-rugs. Finally, at the head of the bed, hanging over the pillow and

---

1. *boubous,* loose cotton garments, draping the whole figure.

watching over my father's slumber, there was a series of pots that contained extracts from plants and the bark of trees. These pots all had metal lids and they were profusely and curiously garlanded with chaplets of cowrie shells; it did not take me long to discover that they were the most important things in the hut: they contained the magic charms, those mysterious liquids that keep evil spirits at bay, and, smeared on the body, make it invulnerable to black magic, to all kinds of black magic. My father, before he went to bed, never failed to smear his body with a little of each liquid, first one, then another, for each charm had its own particular property: but exactly *what* property I do not know: I left my father's house too soon.

From the veranda under which I played I could keep an eye on the workshop opposite, and they for their part could keep an eye on me. This workshop was the main building in our compound. That is where my father was generally to be found, supervising the work, forging the most important items himself, or repairing delicate mechanisms; here it was that he received his friends and his customers, so that the place resounded with noise from morning to night. Moreover, everyone entering or leaving our compound had to pass through the workshop, so that there was a perpetual coming and going, though no one ever seemed to be in a hurry: each one would pause to have a word with my father and spend a few moments watching the work in hand. Sometimes I would draw near the door, but I rarely went in, for everyone used to frighten me there, and I would run away as soon as anyone tried to lay hands on me. It was not until very much later that I got into the habit of crouching in a corner of the workshop and watching the fire blazing in the forge.

My private domain at that time consisted of the veranda that ran round the outside of my father's hut; and the orange tree that grew in the middle of the compound.

As soon as you had crossed the workshop and gone through the door at the back, you could see the orange tree. If I compare it with the giants of our native forests, the tree was not very big, but its mass of glossy leaves used to cast a dense shadow that was a cool refuge from the blazing sun. When it was in flower, a heady perfume was wafted over the entire compound. When the fruit appeared, we were allowed only to look: we had to possess our souls in patience until they were ripe. Then my father, who, as head of the family—a family of innumerable members—governed the compound, would give the order to pick them. The men who did the picking brought their baskets one by one to my father, who shared them out among the inhabitants of the compound, his neighbours and his customers; after that we were permitted to help ourselves from the baskets, as much as we liked! My father was an open-handed and, in fact, a lavish giver; no matter who turned up, he would share our meals; and as I could never keep up with the speed at which such guests used to eat, I might have remained everlastingly hungry if my mother had not taken the precaution of putting my share on one side.

"Sit here," she would say, "and eat, for your father's crazy."

She did not look upon such guests with too kindly an eye; there were too many of them for her liking, all bent on filling their bellies at her expense. My father, for his part, ate very sparingly: he was a very abstemious man.

We lived near the railway track. The trains travelled along outside the fence of plaited reeds which marked the confines of our compound; in fact they ran so close to it that sparks from the engines would sometimes set fire to the palisade, and we all would have to rush to put it out at once, if we did not want to see the whole thing go up in flames. These alarums, rather frightening, but rather exciting too, made me watch every train that went by; and even when there was not a train in sight—for at that time the traffic on the railroad depended entirely on the river traffic, which was very irregular—I would go and spend long periods just looking at the gleaming metal rails. They always glittered cruelly under the fierce sun, for at this point there was no foliage to diminish its intensity. Baked by the sun from early morning, the ballast of red stone was burningly hot: so hot in fact that the oil which fell from the engines was immediately evaporated, leaving not the slightest trace. Was it this oven-like warmth or the oil, the inescapable smell of the oil, which attracted the snakes? I do not know. The fact is that I often came across snakes crawling over the sun-baked ballast; and inevitably the snakes used to creep into the compound.

Ever since the day I had been forbidden to play with snakes, I would run to my mother as soon as I saw one.

"There's a snake!" I would cry.

"What, another?" my mother would shout.

And she would come running out to see what sort of a snake it was. If it was just a snake like any other snake—actually, they were all quite different!—she would beat it to death at once; and, like all the women of our country, she would work herself up into a frenzy, beating the snake to a pulp, whereas the men would content themselves with a single hard blow, neatly struck.

One day, however, I noticed a little black snake with a strikingly marked body that was proceeding leisurely in the direction of the workshop. I ran to warn my mother, as usual. But as soon as my mother saw the black snake she said to me gravely: "My son, this one must not be killed: he is not as other snakes, and he will not harm you; you must never interfere with him."

Everyone in our compound knew that this snake must not be killed; excepting myself, and, I suppose, my little playmates, who were still just ignorant children.

"This snake," my mother added, "is your father's guiding spirit."

I gazed dumbfounded at the little snake. He was proceeding calmly towards the workshop; he was moving gracefully, very sure of himself, and almost as if conscious of his immunity; his body, black and brilliant, glittered in the harsh light of the sun. When he reached the workshop, I noticed for the first time, cut out level with the ground, a small hole in the wall. The snake disappeared through this hole.

"Look," said my mother, "the serpent is going to pay your father a visit."

Although I was familiar with the supernatural, this sight filled me with such astonishment that I was struck dumb. What business would a snake have with my father? And why this particular snake? No one had to kill him, because he was my father's guiding spirit! At any rate, that was the explanation my mother had given me. But what exactly *was* a "guiding spirit"? What were these guiding spirits that I encountered almost everywhere, forbidding one thing, commanding another to be done? I could not understand it at all, though their presences were around me as I grew to manhood. There were good spirits, and there were evil ones; and more evil than good ones, it seemed to me. And how was I to know that this snake was harmless? It looked the same as any other snake; it was, of course, a *black* snake, and certainly there was something unusual about it; but after all, it *was* only a snake! I was absolutely baffled, but I did not ask my mother about it: I felt I would have to ask my father himself about it, almost as if this mystery was something in which women could have no part; it was a mysterious affair that could only be discussed with men. I decided to wait until nightfall.

Immediately after the evening meal, when the palavers were over, my father bade his friends farewell and went to sit under the veranda of his hut; I went and sat near him. I began by questioning him in a roundabout manner, as all children do, and on every subject under the sun. Finally, unable to restrain myself any longer, I asked: "My father, what is that little snake that comes to visit you?"

"What snake do you mean?"

"Why, the little black snake that my mother forbids us to kill."

"Ah!" he said.

He gazed at me for a long while. He seemed to be considering whether to answer or not. Perhaps he was thinking about how old I was, perhaps he was wondering if it was not a little too soon to confide such a secret to a twelve-year-old boy. Then suddenly he made up his mind.

"That snake," he said, "is the guiding spirit of our race. Can you understand that?"

"Yes," I answered, although I did not understand very well.

"That snake," he went on, "has always been with us; he has always made himself known to one of us. In our time, it is to me that he has made himself known."

"That is true," I said.

And I said it with all my heart, for it seemed obvious to me that the snake could have made himself known to no one but my father. Was not my father the head man in our compound? Was it not my father who had authority over all the blacksmiths in our district? Was he not the most skilled? Was he not, after all, my father?

"How did he make himself known?" I asked.

"First of all, he made himself known in the semblance of a dream. He appeared to me several times in slumber, and he told me the day on which he would appear to me in reality: he gave me the precise time and place. But when I really saw him for the first time, I was filled with fear. I took him for a snake like any other snake, and I had to keep myself in control, or I would have tried to kill him. When he saw that I did not receive him kindly, he turned away and departed the way he had come. And there I stood, watching him depart, and wondering all the time if I should not simply have killed him there and then; but a power greater than myself stayed my hand and prevented me from pursuing him. I stood watching him disappear. And even then, at that very moment, I could easily have overtaken him; a few swift strides would have been enough; but I was struck motionless by a kind of paralysis. Such was my first encounter with the little black snake."

He was silent a moment, then went on: "The following night, I saw the snake again in my dream. 'I came as I foretold,' he said, 'but thou didst not receive me kindly; nay, rather I did perceive that thou didst intend to receive me unkindly: I did read it thus in thine eyes. Wherefore dost thou reject me? Lo, I am the guiding spirit of thy race, and it is even as the guiding spirit of thy race that I make myself known to thee, as to the most worthy. Therefore forbear to look with fear upon me, and beware that thou dost not reject me, for behold, I bring thee good fortune.' After that, I received the serpent kindly when he made himself known to me a second time; I received him without fear, I received him with loving kindness, and he has brought me nothing but good."

My father again was silent for a moment, then he said: "You

can see for yourself that I am not more gifted than any other man, that I have nothing which other men have not also, and even that I have less than others, since I give everything away, and would even give away the last thing I had, the shirt on my back. Nevertheless, I am better known than other men, and my name is on everyone's tongue, and it is I who have authority over all the blacksmiths in the five cantons. If these things are so, it is by virtue of this snake alone, who is the guiding spirit of our race. It is to this snake that I owe everything, and it is he likewise who gives me warning of all that is to happen. Thus I am never surprised, when I awake, to see this or that person waiting for me outside my workshop: I already know that he or she will be there. No more am I surprised when this or that motor bicycle or bicycle breaks down, or when an accident happens to a clock: because I had foreknowledge of what would come to pass. Everything is transmitted to me in the course of the night, together with an account of all the work I shall have to perform, so that from the start, without having to cast about in my mind, I know how to repair whatever is brought to me; and it is these things that have established my renown as a craftsman. But all this—let it never be forgotten—I owe to the snake, I owe it to the guiding spirit of our race."

He was silent; and then I understood why, when my father used to come back from a walk he could enter the workshop and say to the apprentices: "During my absence, this or that person has been here, he was dressed in such and such a way, he came from such and such a place and he brought with him such and such a piece of work to be done." And all marvelled at this curious knowledge. Now I understood how my father obtained his information. When I raised my eyes, I saw that my father was watching me.

"I have told you all these things, little one, because you are my son, the eldest of my sons, and because I have nothing to hide from you. There is a certain form of behaviour to observe, and certain ways of acting in order that the guiding spirit of our race may approach you also. I, your father, was observing that form of behaviour which persuades our guiding spirit to visit us. Oh, perhaps not consciously. But nevertheless it is true that if you desire the guiding spirit of our race to visit you one day, if you desire to inherit it in your turn, you will have to conduct yourself in the selfsame manner; from now on, it will be necessary for you to be more and more in my company."

He gazed at me with burning eyes, then suddenly he heaved a sigh.

"I fear, I very much fear, little one, that you are not often enough in my company. You are all day at school, and one day you shall depart from that school for a greater one. You will leave me, little one. . . ."

And again he heaved a sigh. I saw that his heart was heavy within him. The hurricane lamp hanging on the veranda cast a harsh glare on his face. He suddenly seemed to me like an old man.

"Father!" I cried.

"Son . . ." he whispered.

And I was no longer sure whether I ought to continue to attend the school or whether I ought to remain in the workshop: I felt unutterably confused.

"Go now," said my father.

I got up and went to my mother's hut. The night was full of sparkling stars; an owl was hooting nearby. Ah, what was the right path for me? Did I know yet where that path lay? My perplexity was boundless as the sky, and mine was a sky, alas, without any stars. . . . I entered my mother's hut, which at that time was mine also, and went to bed at once. But sleep evaded me, and I tossed restlessly on my bed.

"What's the matter with you?" asked my mother.

"Nothing."

No, I couldn't find anything to say.

"Why don't you go to sleep?" went on my mother.

"I don't know."

"Go to sleep!" she said.

"Yes," I said.

"Sleep . . . Nothing can resist sleep," she said sadly.

Why did she, too, appear so sad? Had she divined my distress?

Anything that concerned me she sensed very deeply. I was trying to sleep, but I shut my eyes and lay still in vain: the image of my father under the storm-lantern would not leave me. He had suddenly seemed so old, he who was so youthful, so active, more youthful and more active than any of us and who in the running of races never let himself be outstripped by anyone, whose limbs were swifter than the limbs of all our young men. . . . "Father! . . . Father! . . ." I kept repeating it. "Father, what must I do, what is the right thing to do?" And I wept quietly, and weeping I fell asleep.

After that, we never mentioned the little black snake again: my father had spoken to me about him for the first and the last time. But from that time forth, as soon as I saw the little snake, I would run and sit in the workshop. I would watch him glide through the little hole in the wall. As if informed of his presence, my father at that instant would turn his eyes to the hole and give a smile. The snake would proceed straight towards him, opening his jaws. When he was within reach, my father would stroke him with his hand, and the snake would accept the caress with a quivering of his whole body: never did I see the little snake attempt to do the slightest harm to my father. That caress, and the answering tremor—but I ought to say: that appealing caress and that answering tremor—threw me each time into an inexpressible confusion: I would imagine I know not what mysterious conversation . . . the hand inquired, and the tremor replied. . . .

Yes, it was like a conversation. Would I, too, converse like that one day? No: I was still attending the school. Yet I should have liked so much to place my hand, my own hand, on the snake, and to understand and listen to that tremor too; but I did not know how the snake would have taken my hand, and I felt now, that he would have nothing to tell me; I was afraid that he would never have anything to tell me. . . .

When my father felt that he had stroked the snake enough, he left him alone; then the snake would coil himself under the edge of one of the sheep-skins on which my father was seated, facing his anvil.

OF ALL the different kinds of work my father performed, none fascinated me so much as his skill with gold. No other occupation was so noble, no other needed such a delicate touch; and, moreover, this sort of work was always a kind of festival: it was a real festival that broke the monotony of ordinary working days.

So if a woman, accompanied by a go-between, crossed the threshold of the workshop, I would follow her in at once. I knew what she wanted: she had brought some gold and wanted to ask my father to transform it into a trinket. The woman would have collected the gold in the placers of Siguiri, where, for months on end, she would have crouched over the river, washing the mud and patiently extracting from it the grains of gold. These women never came alone: they were well aware that my father had other things to do than to make trinkets for all and sundry; and even if the making of jewellery had been his main occupation, they would have realised that they were not his first or his only customers, and that their wants could not be immediately attended to.

Generally these women required the trinket for a certain date, either for the festival of Ramadan or for the Tabaski[2]; or for some other family festivity, or for a dance ceremony.

Thereupon, to better their chance of being quickly served, and the more easily to persuade my father to interrupt the work he had in hand, they would request the services of an official praise-singer, a go-between, and would arrange with him in advance what fee they would pay for his good offices.

The praise-singer would install himself in the workshop, tune up his cora, which is our harp, and would begin to sing my father's praises. This was always a great event for me. I would hear recalled the lofty deeds of my father's ancestors, and the names of these ancestors from the earliest times; as the couplets were reeled off, it was like watching the growth of a great

---

2. *Ramadan . . . the Tabaski,* Mohammedan observances.

genealogical tree that spread its branches far and wide and flourished its boughs and twigs before my mind's eye. The harp played an accompaniment to this vast utterance of names, expanding it and punctuating it with notes that were now soft, now shrill. Where did the praise-singer get his information from? He must certainly have developed a very retentive memory stored with facts handed down to him by his predecessors, for this is the basis of all our oral traditions. Did he embellish the truth? It is very likely: flattery is the praise-singer's stock-in-trade! Nevertheless, he was not allowed to take too many liberties with tradition, for it is part of the praise-singer's task to preserve it. But in those days such considerations did not enter my head, which I would hold high and proud; for I used to feel quite drunk with so much praise, which seemed to reflect some of its effulgence upon my own small person.

I could tell that my father's vanity was being inflamed, and I already knew that after having sipped this milk-and-honey he would lend a favourable ear to the woman's request. But I was not alone in my knowledge; the woman also had seen my father's eyes gleaming with contented pride; and she would hold out her grains of gold as if the whole thing was settled: my father, taking up his scales, would weigh the gold.

"What sort of trinket do you desire?" he would ask.

"I want . . ." And often it would happen that the woman did not know really what she wanted, because she would be so torn by desire, because she would have liked to have many, many trinkets, all out of the same small quantity of gold: but she would have had to have much more than she had brought with her to satisfy such a desire, and eventually she would have to content herself with some more modest wish.

"When do you want it for?" my father would ask.

And she would always want it at once.

"Why are you in such a hurry? How do you expect me to find the time?"

"It's very urgent, I can assure you," the woman would reply.

"That's what all women say, when they want an ornament. Well, I'll see what I can do. Now are you happy?"

Then he would take the clay pot that was kept specially for the smelting of gold and pour in the grains; thereupon he would cover the gold with powdered charcoal, a charcoal which he obtained by the use of plant juices of exceptional purity; finally he would place a large lump of the same kind of charcoal over the whole thing.

Then, having seen the work duly undertaken, the woman, by now quite satisfied, would go back to her household tasks, leaving her go-between to carry on with the praise-singing which had already proved so advantageous to her.

On a sign from my father, the apprentices would start working the two pairs of sheep-skin bellows which were placed on the ground at each side of the forge and linked to it by earthen pipes. These apprentices remained seated all the time, with crossed legs, in front of the bellows; at least the younger did, for the elder would sometimes be allowed to take part in the craftsmen's work and the younger—in those days it was Sidafa—only had to work the bellows and watch the proceedings while awaiting his turn to be elevated to less rudimentary tasks. For a whole hour they would both be working the levers of the bellows till the fire in the forge leapt into flame, becoming a living thing, a lively and merciless spirit.

Then my father, using long pincers, would lift the clay pot and place it on the flames.

Immediately all work would more or less stop in the workshop: actually while the gold is being melted and while it is cooling all work with copper or aluminium is supposed to stop, for fear that some fraction of these less noble metals might fall among the gold. It is only steel that can still be worked at such times. But workmen who had some piece of steel work in hand would either hasten to finish it or would openly stop work to join the other apprentices gathered round the forge. In fact, there were often so many of them at these times pressing round my father that I, the smallest, would have to get up and push my way in among them, so as not to miss any of the operation.

It might happen that, feeling he had too little room to work in, my father would make his apprentices stand well away from him.

He would merely raise his hand in a simple gesture: at that particular moment he would never utter a word, and no one else would, no one was allowed to utter a word, even the go-between's voice would no longer be raised in song; the silence would be broken only by the panting of the bellows and by the faint hissing of the gold. But if my father never used to utter actual words at this time, I know that he was uttering them in his mind; I could see it by his lips that kept working while he bent over the pot and kept stirring the gold and the charcoal with a bit of wood that would keep bursting into flame, and so had to be constantly replaced by a fresh bit.

What were the words my father's lips were forming? I do not know; I do not know for certain: I was never told what they were. But what else could they have been, if not magical incantations? Were they not the spirits of fire and gold, of fire and air, air breathed through the earthen pipes, of fire born of air, of gold married with fire—were not these the spirits he was invoking? Was it not their help and their friendship he was calling upon in this marriage of elemental things? Yes, it was almost certainly those spirits he was calling upon, for they are the most elemental of all spirits, and their presence is essential at the melting of gold.

The operation that was going on before my eyes was simply the smelting of gold; but it was something more than that: a magical operation that the guiding spirits could look upon with favour or disfavour; and that is why there would be all round my father that absolute silence and that anxious expectancy. I could understand, though I was just a child, that there was no craft greater than the goldsmith's. I expected a ceremony, I had come to be present at a ceremony, and it really was one, though very protracted. I was still too young to be able to understand why it was so protracted; nevertheless, I had an inkling, beholding the almost religious concentration of all those present as they watched the mixing process.

When finally the gold began to melt, I used to feel like shouting, and perhaps we would all have shouted if we had not been forbidden to make a sound: I would be trembling, and certainly everyone else would be trembling as we sat watching my father stirring the mixture, still a heavy paste in which the charcoal was gradually being consumed. The next stage followed swiftly; the gold now had the fluidity of water. The guiding spirits had smiled on the operation!

"Bring me the brick!" my father would say, thus lifting the ban that until then had kept us all silent.

The brick, which an apprentice would place beside the fire, was hollowed out, generously greased with Galam butter. My father would take the pot off the fire, tilt it carefully, and I would watch the gold flowing into the brick, flowing like liquid fire. True, it was only a very sparse trickle of fire, but oh, how vivid, how brilliant! As the gold flowed into the brick, the grease would splutter and flame and give off a thick smoke that caught in the throat and stung the eyes, leaving us all weeping and coughing.

It occurred to me later on that my father could easily have relinquished all the work of smelting the gold to one or other of his assistants: they were not without experience in these matters; they had taken part hundreds of times in the same preparations and they would certainly have brought the work to a successful conclusion. But as I have told you, my father kept moving his lips! We could not hear those words, those secret words, those incantations which he addressed to powers that we should not, that we could not hear or see: this was essential. Only my father was versed in the science of conjuring the spirits of fire, air and gold, and conjuring evil spirits, and that is why he alone conducted the whole operation.

By now the gold would have cooled in the hollow of the brick, and my father would begin to hammer and stretch it. This was the moment when his work as a goldsmith really began. I noticed that before embarking on it he never failed to stroke stealthily the little snake coiled up under the sheep-skin; one can only assume that this was his way of gathering strength for what remained to be done, and which was the most difficult.

But was it not extraordinary, was it not miraculous that on these occasions the little black serpent always coiled up under the sheep-skin? He was not always there, he did not visit my father every day, but he was always present whenever there was gold to be worked.

Moreover, it is our custom to keep apart from the working of gold all influences outside those of the jeweller himself. And indeed it is not precisely because the jeweller alone possesses the secret of his incantations; but also because the working of gold, besides being a task of the greatest skill, is a matter of confidence, of conscience, a task which is not undertaken excepting after due reflection and experiment. Finally, I do not think that any jeweller would renounce the opportunity of performing such a task—I ought to say, such a spectacle!—in which he can display his abilities with a virtuosity that his work as a blacksmith or a mechanic or even as a sculptor is never invested with; even though in these more humble tasks his skill is no less wonderful, even though the statues which he carves in wood with his adze are not insignificant works!

The snake's presence came as no surprise to me; ever since that evening when my father had talked to me about the guiding spirit of our race, it had ceased to surprise me; it was quite natural that the snake should be there: he had knowledge of the future. Did he impart any of that knowledge to my father? It seemed to me quite obvious that he did: did he not always warn him of what was going to happen? But I had another reason for believing implicitly in the powers of the little snake.

The craftsman who works in gold must first of all purify himself, that is, he must wash himself all over and, of course, abstain from all sexual relationships during the whole time. Great respecter of ceremony as he was, it would have been impossible for my father to ignore these rules. Now I never saw him make these preparations; I would see him address himself to his work without any apparent preliminaries. But from that moment it was obvious that, forewarned by his black guiding spirit in a dream of the task that would await him in the morning, my father must have prepared for it as soon as he arose, and had entered his workshop in a state of purity, his body smeared with the magical substances hidden in his numerous pots full of secret potions. So I believe my father never entered his workshop except in a state of ritual purity; and that is not because I want to make him out as being better than he is—he is a man like any other, and has a man's weaknesses—but always when it was a matter of ritual he was uncompromisingly strict.

The woman for whom the trinket was being made, and who would often have looked in to see how the work was getting on, would come for the final time, not wanting to miss anything of the marvellous sight as the gold wire, which my father had succeeded in spinning, was transformed into a trinket. She was here now, devouring with her eyes the fragile golden wire, following its tranquil and inevitable spirals round the little metal cone which gave the trinket its shape. My father would be watching her out of the corner of his eye, and sometimes I would see the corners of his mouth twitch into a smile: the woman's avid attentiveness amused him.

"Are you trembling?" he would say to her.

"*Am* I trembling?" she would ask.

And we would all burst out laughing at her. For she *was* trembling! She was trembling with covetousness for the spiral pyramid in which my father was inserting, among the convolutions, tiny grains of gold. When finally he terminated the work by placing at the summit the largest grain of gold, the woman would jump excitedly to her feet.

Then, while my father was slowly turning the trinket round in his fingers, smoothing it into perfect shape, no one could have displayed such utter happiness as the native woman, not even the praise-singer, whose trade it was to do so, and who, during the whole process of transformation, had kept on singing his praises, accelerating his rhythm, increasing his flatteries as the trinket took shape, and praising my father's talents to the skies.

Indeed, the praise-singer participated in a curious—I was going to say direct, effective—way in the work. He, too, was intoxicated with the joy of creation; he declaimed his rapture, and plucked his harp like a man inspired; he warmed to the task as if he had been the craftsman himself, as if the trinket had been made by his own hands. He was no longer a paid thurifer; he was no longer just the man whose services each and anyone could hire: he had become a man who creates his song under the influence of some very personal, interior necessity.

When my father, after having soldered the large grain of gold that crowned the summit, held out his work to be admired, the go-between would no longer be able to contain himself, and would intone the douga—the great chant which is only sung for celebrated men, and which is danced to only for them.

But the douga is a tremendous chant, a provocative chant, a chant that the go-between would not venture to sing, and that the man for whom it is sung would not venture to dance to, without certain precautions.

My father, forewarned in a dream, had been able to take these precautions as soon as he got up; the praise-singer had taken them as a matter of course when he had made his bargain with the woman. Just as my father had done, he had smeared his body with magic lotions and so had rendered himself invulnerable to the bad spirits which the douga would undoubtedly stir into activity, invulnerable also even to his fellow praise-singers who, jealous perhaps, were only waiting to hear the chant, the note of exaltation and the loss of control which that exaltation entails, to cast their evil spells upon him.

At the first notes of the douga, my father would rise and utter a cry in which happiness and triumph were equally mingled; and brandishing in his right hand the hammer that was the symbol of his profession, and in his left a ram's horn filled with magic substances, he would dance the glorious dance.

No sooner had he finished than workmen and apprentices, friends and customers in their turn, not forgetting the woman for whom the trinket had been created, would flock round him, congratulating him, showering praises on him, and compliment-ing at the same time the go-between, who found himself laden with gifts, gifts that are almost the only resources he has in his wandering life, that he leads after the fashion of the troubadours of old. Beaming, aglow with dancing and the praises he had received, my father would offer kola nuts, that small change of Guinean civility.

All that now remained to be done was to redden the trinket in a little water mixed with chlorine and sea salt. I could go now: the ceremony was over! But often, as I was leaving the workshop, my mother, who might be in the yard pounding millet or rice, would call me.

"Where have you been?" she would ask, although she knew very well where I had been.

"In the workshop."

"Oh, yes, your father was making something out of gold. Gold! It's always gold!"

And she would pound furiously the helpless bowl of rice or millet. "Your father's ruining his health! You see what he's doing."

"He's been dancing the douga," I would reply.

"The douga! The douga won't stop him ruining his eyesight! And you would be better off playing here in the yard instead of going and breathing the dust and smoke in the workshop!"

My mother did not like my father to work with gold. She knew how harmful the soldering of gold can be: a jeweller can wear his lungs out, puffing at his blowpipe, and his eyes suffer by being so close to the intense heat of the forge; and even more perhaps from the microscopic delicacy of the work. But even if there had been no danger in it, my mother still would have disliked this sort of work: she held it in suspicion, for you cannot solder gold without the help of other metals, and my mother used to think that it was not strictly honest to keep the gold which was saved by its alloys, although this was the accepted thing; and she, too, was quite prepared, whenever she took cotton to be woven, to receive in return a piece of cloth of only half the original weight.

III

I OFTEN used to go and spend a few days at Tindican, a small village to the west of Kouroussa. My mother was born at Tindican, and her mother and brothers still lived there. I was always highly delighted to be going there, for they were very fond of me, and my grandmother in particular, for whom my visit was always a great treat, took great pleasure in petting me; and I for my part loved her with all my heart.

She was a tall woman, still with jet-black hair, slim, very erect, and strong; in fact, she was still fairly young and still did her share in the farm work, though her sons, who could cope with it all quite easily themselves, had often tried to make her give it up; but she would not hear of it, and obviously it was in this continual activity that the secret of her youthful vigour lay. She had lost her husband soon after their marriage, and I had never known him. Sometimes she would talk to me about him, but never for very long; almost at once, her voice would be choked by tears, and so I know next to nothing about my grandfather, and I was unable to picture him in my mind's eye, for neither my mother nor my uncles would talk to me about him: in our land, we hardly ever speak about dead people whom we have loved very much; we feel too sick at heart when we remember them.

Whenever I went to Tindican, it was always with my youngest uncle, who used to come to fetch me. He was younger than my mother and was not much more than an adolescent; and so I used to feel that he was still very close to my own age. He was very good-natured, and my mother did not have to tell him to look after me; he was naturally kind, and needed no telling. He would take me by the hand, and I would walk beside him; he, out of consideration for my extreme youth, would take much smaller steps, so that instead of taking two hours to reach Tindican, we would often take at least four. But I scarcely used to notice how long we were on the road, for there were all kinds of wonderful things to entertain us.

I say "wonderful things," because Kouroussa is quite a large town and the life of the countryside and the fields is lost to us; and for a town child, such life is always wonderful. As we wandered along the road, we would startle out of their hiding-places here a hare, there a wild boar, and birds would suddenly rise up with a great rattle of wings; sometimes, too, we would encounter a band of monkeys; and always I would feel a little shock of fright in my heart, as if I myself were more startled than the wild creatures that had been warned by our approach. Observing my rapturous delight, my uncle would collect pebbles and throw them far in front of us, or would beat the tall grasses with a dead branch, the better to stir up the game. I used to imitate him, but never for very long: in the afternoon, the sun burns fiercely down upon the savannah; and I would soon come back to him and slip my hand into my uncle's. And we would wander quietly along again.

"I hope you're not feeling too tired?" my uncle would ask.

"No."

"We can have a little rest if you like."

He would choose a tree—a kapok tree or any tree that gave a sufficiency of shade—and we would sit down. He would tell me the latest news about the farm: calvings, the purchase of an ox, the clearing of land for a new field or the misdemeanours of a wild boar; but it was the births in particular that excited my interest.

"One of the cows has calved," he would say.

"Which one?" I would ask, for I knew each animal by name.

"The white one."

"The one with horns like the crescent moon?"

"That's the one."

"And what sort of calf is it?"

"A fine one, with a white star on his forehead."

"A star?"

"Yes, a star."

And for a little while I would think about that star, I would see it in my mind's eye. A calf with a star on his forehead: that meant he was to be the leader of the herd.

"Oh, but he must be beautiful!" I would say.

"You can't imagine anything so beautiful. His ears are so rosy, you'd almost think they were transparent."

"I want to see him at once. Shall we go and see him as soon as ever we arrive?"

"Of course."

"You'll come with me, won't you?"

"I'll come with you, you little scare-cat."

Yes, I was scared of all big animals with horns. My little playmates in Tindican used to go up to them without the slightest fear, hanging on their horns and even jumping on their backs; but I used to keep my distance. Whenever I had to go off into the bush with a drove of cattle, I would watch them grazing, but I would never go too close to them; I liked them, but I was afraid of their horns. Of course the calves had no horns, but they made sudden, unexpected movements: you couldn't really trust them.

"Come on!" I would say to my uncle. "We've lain here long enough."

I was impatient to get there. If the calf was in the paddock I would be able to stroke him: in the paddock, the calves were always quiet. I would put a little salt on the palm of my hand, and the calf would come and lick the salt; I would feel his tongue gently scraping my palm.

"Let's hurry!" I would cry.

But my legs weren't used to such haste, and I would soon slow down. And we would saunter along, walking as slowly as we liked. My uncle would tell me how the monkey had foiled the panther when it wanted to eat him up, or how the palm-squirrel had kept the hyena waiting all night long for nothing. These were stories I had heard a hundred times, but each time I heard them with renewed pleasure; my laughter used to send up the game all round us.

Before we even reached the outskirts of Tindican, I would see my grandmother coming to meet us. I would drop my uncle's hand and run shouting towards her. She would lift me high in the air, then press me to her bosom, and I used to squeeze her as hard as I could, flinging my arms around her, overcome with happiness.

"How are you, my little man?" she would say.

"I'm fine!" I would cry.

"Now, is that so?"

And she would look me over, feeling me; she would look and see if my cheeks were fat, and she would feel me to see if I was something more than just skin and bones. If she was satisfied in her investigations, she would congratulate me; but if her fingers felt only skin and bone—for I grew very fast, and that made me thin—she would groan.

"Just look at that!" she would say. "Don't they give you anything to eat in town? You're not going back until you've put some flesh on these bones. D'you hear me?"

"Yes, Grandmamma."

"And how are your mother and father and everybody at your place? Are they all well?"

And before she would set me down again, she would wait until I'd told her all the news about everyone at home.

"I hope the journey hasn't worn him out," she would say to my uncle.

"Not at all," he would reply. "We've been crawling along like tortoises, and now he's ready to run like a hare."

Then, more or less reassured, she would take my hand, and we would walk to the village, and with my hands in theirs we would all—my granny, my uncle and myself—make our entry into the village. As soon as we reached the first huts, my grandmother would shout out:

"Folks, here's my little man just arrived!"

The women would come out of their huts and run towards us, exclaiming and laughing: "Why, he's a real little man! That's a real fine little man you've got there!"

Many of them would lift me up to press me to their bosoms. They, too, would carefully examine my appearance—how I was looking and what clothes I was wearing, for they were town clothes, and they had to declare that everything was splendid, and said that my grandmother was very lucky to have a fine little man like me. They came running from all over to greet me; as if the head of the canton in person had come to Tindican; and my grandmother would be glowing with pride and joy.

Stopped like this at every hut, acknowledging the enthusiasm of the village women and giving everyone news of my parents, it used to take at least two hours to make our way over the two hundred yards or so that divided my grandmother's hut from the first huts in the village. And when those good ladies finally did leave us, it would be to supervise the cooking of enormous plates of rice and dishes of chicken which they were to bring us for the festive dinner in the evening.

So even if I was as skinny as a rake when I arrived in Tindican, I could be certain of leaving there, ten days later, as plump as a partridge and bursting with health.

My uncle's compound was a large one. Though it contained far fewer families than our own, and though it did not have the same importance, its proportions were very generous, as things usually are in the country, where there is plenty of room. There were the paddocks for cattle and for goats; there were the granaries for rice and millet, cassava and ground-nuts, as well as for okra, which take the form of little huts raised on stone supports to protect them from the damp. With the exception of these paddocks and granaries, my uncle's compound looked very much as ours did; though its fence was stronger: instead of plaited reeds, they had used sturdy wooden posts cut in the nearby forest; as for the huts, they were built just like ours, but they were more primitive.

My Uncle Lansana, being the eldest, had inherited the compound on my grandfather's death. Actually, my uncle had a twin who might have inherited it, but Lansana had been the first-born; and among our people it is the first-born of twins who is considered the elder. However, it sometimes happens that some of the elder twin's rights are transferred to the younger, for one of the twins always has a more forceful character than the other, and he becomes the heir, even though he may not be the first-born.

Maybe, in my uncles' case, it might have been the second twin who asserted his superiority, for he lacked neither skill nor authority. But such things did not interest him. He had no taste for farming and he was only rarely seen in Tindican. He led a roving existence; it was only by chance or when he made one of his infrequent visits that we knew of his whereabouts; adventure was in his blood. I myself saw him only once: he had come back to Tindican; he was only there a few days but all the time he thought only of getting away again. I remember him as an extremely attractive character who talked a great deal; in fact he never stopped talking, and I could have listened to him for hours on end. He would talk about his adventures, which were curious and disturbing and opened up astonishing vistas to me. He used to load me with presents. Was he putting himself out to please the schoolboy I then was, or was it simply that he was by nature generous? I do not know. When I saw him setting out for fresh adventures, I wept. What was he called? I cannot remember; maybe I never knew. During the few days he remained at Tindican, I called him Bo, and that was what I called my Uncle Lansana also, for that is the name usually given to twins, and this nickname often takes the place of their real one.

My Uncle Lansana had two other brothers, one of whom had recently married; the younger, the one who had come to fetch me from Kouroussa, was engaged, though he was still too young to take a wife. So that there were two families, though they were not very large, dwelling in the compound besides my grandmother and my youngest uncle.

Generally, on my arrival in the afternoon, my Uncle Lansana would still be at work in the fields, and I would go straight to my grandmother's hut, the one I was to stay in throughout my visit.

The inside of this hut closely resembled the one I shared with my mother at Kouroussa; there was even the same sort of calabash as the one my mother had for keeping the milk in, suspended just in the same way by three ropes from the roof so that none of the animals could reach it, and covered with the same sort of lid to prevent the soot from falling in it. The thing that made this hut different, as far as I was concerned, was that there were ears of maize hanging from the rooftop in countless garlands which grew smaller and smaller as they approached the summit; the smoke from the fire kept circling among the ears and so preserved them from attack by termites and mosquitoes. These garlands might have served as a rustic calendar, for as the harvest-time came round again, their number would decrease, until finally there would be none left.

But for the moment I would go into the hut only in order to take my clothes off: my grandmother felt that after walking from Kouroussa, the first thing to do was to give myself a bath. She wanted me at least to start my visit clean, though she had no illusions about how long such cleanliness would last; so she would take me straight away to the wash-place, a small enclosure near the hut, surrounded by a reed fence and paved with large stones. Then she would go back to the hut, take the pot from the fire, and pour the hot water into a calabash. After she had cooled it to the right temperature, she would carry it into the wash-place. There she would soap me from head to foot with black soap, then rub me roughly down with a sponge made of tow from the dried stems of pulpy plants. I would leave the hut, all shining with wet, my blood racing under my gleaming skin, my hair black as pitch, and run to dry myself in front of the fire.

My little playmates would be waiting there for me.

"So you've come back?" they would say.

"I've come back."

"For how long?"

"For a little while."

Then, according to whether I was thin or plump—for to them too, how one looked was of the first importance, and I was usually thin as a rake—I would hear:

"My! *you're* looking well!"

"Oh!" I would modestly reply.

Or:

"You've not got much flesh on you!"

"I'm growing up," would be my dignified reply. "When you're growing up, you don't have much flesh on your bones."

"Y-yes . . . All the same, you're too thin."

And they would fall silent for a while as they each turned over in their minds this strange growth which makes city children thinner than country children. Then one of them would invariably shout:

"You've never seen as many birds as there are in the fields this year!"

But each year it was the same: there were always great flocks of birds laying waste the crops, and we, the children, always had the job of driving them away.

"I've got my sling," I would say.

I had brought it with me: I would never have dreamt of leaving it behind, and here I carried it with me all the time, whether I was watching the cattle grazing or guarding the crops from the top of the look-out posts.

These posts used to play an important part in my visit to Tindican: everywhere there were to be seen these platforms mounted on forked stakes that looked as if they were riding the great flowing seas of the harvest fields. With my little playmates I would climb the ladder to one of them and scare the birds, and sometimes the monkeys that came to raid our fields. At any rate, that is what we were supposed to do, and we did it without grumbling, for it was more of a pleasure than a duty. But it sometimes happened that we became absorbed in other games, and forgot why we were there. And though I did not suffer for this forgetfulness, my playmates often did: their parents were not slow to discover that the crops had not been properly watched, and then, depending on how much damage had been done, the careless watchers had their vigilance improved by a sharp scolding or by the whip. Nevertheless, though suitably chastened, we chattered all the time, exchanging those exciting little secrets that are not for grown-up ears, and which were mostly accounts of childish little thefts, while still keeping an eye on the crops; in any case, our shouts and our singing were generally sufficient to keep the birds away, even the millet-eaters that used to descend in dense flocks on the fields.

My little playmates were very kind to me. They were really wonderful friends, daring—certainly more daring than I was— and even a little reckless: but they would moderate their natural impetuosity out of consideration for the town child I was, and they held in great respect this little city-dweller who used to come and join in their rural games; they were always filled with admiration for my schoolboy clothes.

As soon as I had got dry in front of the fire, I would put them on again. My little playmates would watch me with envious eyes as I slipped on my short-sleeved khaki shirt, my shorts of the same colour, and my sandals. I also had a beret, which I hardly ever wore. But these small splendours were enough to dazzle the eyes of the country children, whose only covering was a brief loincloth. For my part, I envied them their loincloth, which allowed them much more liberty of movement. Those town clothes, which had to be kept clean, were a real nuisance: they got dirty, and were easily torn. When we were climbing up the observation posts, I had to take great care not to catch my trousers on the rough wooden rungs; when we were on the platform at the top, I had to keep away from the fresh-cut sheaves of corn, which were put there to be used for next season's sowing, out of the reach of termites. And if we lit a fire to roast the lizards or the field mice which we killed with our slings, I did not dare approach too close, or attempt to skin the spoils of the hunt: the blood would have marked my clothes, and the fire would have blackened them; I had to stand by and watch the lizards or the field mice being cleaned, and their insides filled with salt before they were placed on the fire; and even while I was eating them, all kinds of precautions were necessary.

So I would gladly have given up those schoolboy garments which were only suitable for town wear; and, in fact, I would very soon have discarded them if I had had anything else to put on, but those were the only clothes I had with me, and no others were given me; here at any rate I could dirty them or tear them without being scolded: my grandmother used to wash them and mend them without any fuss. I had come to run and play and climb up the look-out posts and wander off into the long grass with the flocks and herds, and naturally I could not do these things without some damage to my precious clothes.

At nightfall, my Uncle Lansana would come back from the fields. He would greet me after his own quiet fashion, for he was rather timid and spoke little. Working alone in the fields all day, you get used to being silent; you think of all kinds of things, and then you start all over again, because thoughts are something you can never grasp completely: the mute mystery of things, their how and why predisposes you to silence. It is enough to call such things to mind and to become aware of their inscrutable mystery which leaves behind it a certain light in the eyes. My Uncle Lansana's eyes were singularly piercing when he looked at you;

actually, he very rarely looked at you: he would remain usually rapt in that inner dream which obsessed him endlessly in the fields.

When we were all together at mealtimes I would often turn my eyes towards my uncle, and generally, after a moment or two, I would succeed in catching his eye. There was always a smile behind the gravity of his gaze, for my uncle was goodness itself and he loved me; I really believe he loved me as much as my grandmother did. I would respond to his gently smiling glance, and sometimes, as I always ate very slowly, it would make me forget to eat.

"You're not eating anything," my grandmother would say.

"Yes, I am eating," I would reply.

"That's right," my grandmother would say, "you must eat it all up!" But of course it was impossible to eat up all the meat and rice that had been prepared to celebrate my happy arrival; my little friends used to lend an eager hand with it, too. They had all been invited, and used to go for the food with the frank appetites of young wolves; but there was too much, there was always too much: we could never get to the end of such a meal.

"Look how round my belly is!" I would hear myself saying.

Yes, our little bellies *were* round, and sitting afterwards round the fire, solemnly digesting our food, we might easily have fallen asleep if we had not had such naturally lively dispositions. But we had our palavers to hold, like our elders; we had not seen each other for weeks, sometimes months, and we had so many things to tell each other, so many new stories to relate, and this was the time for them!

Of course we all had our own stories to tell, we knew lots of them, but there would always be some stories that we were hearing for the first time, and those were the ones we were most eager to listen to as we sat round the fire, and it was the tellers of these tales who would get the most applause.

In this fashion my first day in the country would come to a close, unless someone brought out a tom-tom, for this was a special occasion. And in Tindican it was not every evening you heard the tom-tom.

IV

DECEMBER always found me at Tindican. December is our dry season, when we have fine weather and harvest our rice. Year after year I was invited to this harvest, which is always the occasion of great junketings and feastings, and I used to wait impatiently for my uncle to come and fetch me.

Of course, the festival had no set date, since it depended on the ripening of the rice, and this, in turn, depended on the weather, the good will of the heavens. It depended perhaps still more on the good will of the spirits of the soil, whose influence could not be ignored. If their response was favourable, it only remained to beg of them, on the day before the harvest, to provide sunny skies and protection for the harvesters against the danger of snake bites.

When the great day had arrived, the head of each family would rise at dawn to go and cut the first swathe in his fields. As soon as this first sheaf had been cut, the tom-tom would sound, signalling the beginning of the harvest. Such is our custom. I could not have said then why this was done: why the signal was given only after the first swathe had been cut in each of the fields. I only know that such was the custom, and that was enough for me. Like all our customs, this one must have had its own significance, which I could have easily found out from the elders of the village, who kept its secret meaning in the ancestral depths of heart and memory. But at that time I was not old enough or curious enough to ask my elders and betters, and when finally I wanted to do so, I had left Africa behind.

To-day I am inclined to think that these first swathes were cut in order to break the spell of inviolability which one feels at the sight of an unmown field; but I do not remember that these first swathes served any particular purpose once they had been cut: I do not remember them being used as offerings. Sometimes only the spirit of a tradition survives, and so it happens that the merest ghost of an outward ceremony remains. Was that the case here? I cannot say; though I made frequent visits to Tindican, they did not last long enough for me to find out everything. All I know is that the tom-tom used to sound only after the first sheaf had been gathered, and that we used to await the signal eagerly, because we were always in a hurry to get to work, and also because we wanted to leave the rather chilly shadow of the great trees at the edge of the fields, where the morning air used to be piercingly cold.

When the signal had been given, the reapers used to set out, and I would fall into step with them, marching to the rhythm of the tom-tom. The young men used to toss their glittering sickles high in the air and catch them as they fell, shouting aloud for the simple pleasure of hearing their own strong young voices, and sketching a dance step or two on the heels of the tom-tom players. I suppose I should have done well to follow my grandmother's advice and to keep at a safe distance from those lively jugglers. But there was such a vivid freshness in the morning air, such scintillating vivacity in their juggling feats, in the spinning sickles that in the rising sun would blaze and flash with sudden brilliance, and there was such irresistible alacrity in the rhythm of the tom-tom that I could never have kept myself away from them.

Besides, at that particular season it was impossible not to want to join in everything. In our December, the whole world is in flower and the air is sweet: everything is young and fresh; the spring seems linked with the summer, and the countryside that for so long has been drenched in rain and shrouded in baleful mists now lies radiant; the sky has never seemed so blue, so brilliant; the birds are ecstatically singing; there is joy all round us—its gentle explosions are echoed in every heart. It was this season, this beautiful time of the year, that was stirring me so deeply, and the beat of the tom-tom and the festive air of our little procession moved me also. It was the best time of the year, the summer and all it stands for, all it holds and cannot hold—for how could it contain so much profusion?—and it made my heart leap with joy.

When they had arrived at the first harvest-field, the men would line up at the edge, naked to the loins, their sickles at the ready. Then my Uncle Lansana or some other farmer—for the harvest threw people together and everyone lent a hand in each other's harvesting—would invite them to begin work. At once the black torsos would bend over the great golden field, and the sickles would begin the reaping. Now it was not only the breeze of morning that was making the whole field sway and shiver, but the men also, with their sickles.

These sickles kept rising and falling with astonishing rapidity and regularity. They had to cut the stalk between the bottom joint and the lowest leaf, so that only the leaf was left behind; well, they hardly ever missed. Of course, such a degree of accuracy depended on the reaper: he would hold the ear with one hand and incline the stalk to receive a clean blow from the sickle. He would reap the ears one by one, but the swift rise and fall of the sickle was nevertheless amazing. Besides, each man made it a point of honour to reap as accurately and as swiftly as possible; he would move forward across the field with a bunch of stalks in his hand, and his fellow workmen would judge his skill by the number and the size of his sheaves.

My young uncle was wonderfully skilful at rice-cutting: in fact there was no one to touch him at it. I would follow proudly behind him, ready to take each sheaf as he cut it. When I had taken a sheaf from him, I would strip the stalks of their leaves then trim them all to an equal length and pile them up. And I would always take care to do this very gently, for rice is harvested only when it is very ripe, and if it is roughly handled the ears lose the best part of their grains. I did not tie the sheaves, for that was a man's job, but once they had been tied, I was allowed to go and put them on the great pile in the centre of the field.

As the morning drew on, it would become hotter, the air seeming to quiver in a dense heat-haze which was intensified by clouds of dust from the trampled soil and stubble. This was the moment when my uncle would wipe the sweat from his forehead and his chest and ask for his water bottle. I would run and fetch it from under the leaves where it lay, fresh and cool, and offer it to him with the words: "Will you leave some for me?"

"You don't think I would drink it all, do you?"

But I would watch anxiously as, holding the flask high in the air, he quaffed great draughts of the water without touching the flask to his lips.

"There, that's better," he would say, handing the bottle to me. "The dust cakes in your throat."

I would put my lips to the bottle, and at once the coolness of the water would make itself felt throughout my whole body with a kind of fresh interior radiance. But its refreshment was only momentary: it was soon forgotten, and left my body bathed in sweat.

"Take your shirt off," my uncle would say. "It's soaking wet. You shouldn't keep wet things on your chest."

And he would start work again, and I would start following him again, proud to see that we were the leaders.

"Aren't you tired?" I would ask him.

"Why should I be tired?"

"Your sickle moves so quickly."

"It does, doesn't it?"

"We're ahead of all the others."

"Oh? Are we?"

"You know we are!" I would cry. "Why do you say 'Oh, are we?' like that?"

"I don't want to boast, you know."

"No, of course not."

And I would begin to wonder if I should ever be able to do what he was doing one day, and to do it as well as he did.

"Won't you let me reap for a while?"

"What would your grandmother say? A sickle is not a plaything: you have no idea how sharp it is!"

"Yes, I do."

"Now it isn't your job to cut rice. I shouldn't think it ever will be; later on . . ."

But I didn't like to be so easily put off from working in the fields. "Later . . ." Why only "later". . . ? I did not see why I should not become a reaper like the rest of them, a farmer too. Was it because . . .

"Well, are you dreaming?" my uncle would say.

And I would take the bundle of stalks he handed me, strip off the leaves and trim the stalks. Yes, I had been daydreaming: my life did not lie here . . . nor in my father's forge, either. Then what sort of life was I going to lead? And I would tremble at the thought of the unknown existence ahead of me. Wouldn't it have been simpler to follow in my father's footsteps? "School . . . school . . ." I would say to myself. Did I like school all that much? Maybe I did. My uncles . . . Yes, my uncles had followed quite naturally in their father's footsteps, though others had taken a different course: my father's brothers had gone to Conakry [3]; my Uncle Lansana's twin brother was . . . But where *was* he now?

"Well, still daydreaming?" my uncle would ask.

"Yes . . . No . . . I . . ."

"If you go on like this, we'll lose the lead."

"I was thinking about Uncle Bo. Where is he now?"

"God only knows! On his last visit, he was . . . You see, I don't know where he is any more! He's never in the same place: he's like a bird: he can't stay quietly on one tree, he needs the whole sky."

"Will I, too, be like a bird some day?"

"What *are* you talking about?"

"Well, you've just told me that Uncle Bo is like a bird."

"Do you want to become like him?"

"I don't know yet."

"Well, you have plenty of time to make your mind up, anyhow. Meanwhile, take this sheaf."

And he would go on reaping. Even though his body was soaking wet, he always returned to his work with great vigour, as if he were only just beginning. But all the same, the heat was a burden; the air would seem to weigh down upon us; and weariness would gradually begin to creep over us: draughts of cold water were no longer any good, and so we would begin to fight our weariness with singing.

"Sing with us," my uncle would say.

---

3. *Conakry*, capital of Guinea, located on the Atlantic coast.

The tom-tom, which had been following us as we advanced into the field, kept time with our singing. We sang like a choir, often very high, with great bursts of melody, and sometimes very low, so low that we could hardly be heard. And our weariness would disappear, the heat grow less.

If, on such occasions, I paused for a moment and gazed at the reapers, the long, sinuous line of reapers, I would always be struck, delightfully touched, enraptured in fact, by the tenderness, the vast, infinite tenderness in their eyes, by the immense serenity of their gaze—and that does not mean it was remote or preoccupied—as they looked about them from time to time. And yet, although they all seemed to me at such moments "miles away" from what they were doing, though their eyes seemed far away from what they were doing, their skill never faltered; the dark hands and the glittering sickles kept moving with an unbroken, almost abstracted precision.

What was it those eyes were actually gazing at? I do not know. The surrounding country side? Maybe. Maybe it was the distant trees, and the far-off sky. Maybe not. Maybe those eyes were gazing at nothing, fixed on the invisible, and maybe that is what made them appear so tranced, so abstracted. The long wavering line of reapers kept on moving deeper and deeper into the field, laying it bare; wasn't that enough? Wasn't it enough to see the ears of rice bowing before the long, gentle wave of those black bodies? Our husbandmen were singing, and as they sang, they reaped; they were singing in chorus, and reaping in unison: their voices and their gestures were all harmonious, and in harmony; they were one!—united by the same task, united by the same song. They were bound to one another, united by the same soul: each and every one was tasting the delight, savouring the common pleasure of accomplishing a common task.

Was it this delight, this pleasure, even more than the fight against weariness and against the burden of the heat, that urged them on, that filled them to overflowing with rapturous song? Such was obviously the case: and this is what filled their eyes with so much tenderness, that wonderful serenity that used to strike me with such delighted and rather regretful astonishment;

for though I was among them, with them, surrounded by these waves of tenderness, I was not one of them: I was only a schoolboy on a visit—and how I longed to forget that fact!

Actually, I often *did* forget it; I was still very young and was often able to forget myself in the moment; everything that passed through my head—and that was a great deal—was almost always fleeting and less enduring than the clouds that moved across the summer sky; and besides, I was at the age—I shall never grow out of it!—when one lives entirely in the present; and in those days, holding the first position in the long line of reapers seemed to have more importance than anything I would be likely to do in the future. "Make haste!" I would urge my uncle.

"Oh! So you've woken up at last?" he would tease me.

"Yes. We mustn't waste any more time."

"Who's been wasting time? Me?"

"No, but you might if we go on like this: we're not so far ahead now."

"Oh?"

And he would take a look round the field.

"Is that what you call not being so far ahead? Well, I'm pretty sure I've not been wasting my time, but maybe I ought to now. Don't forget I mustn't get too far ahead of the others: it would not be polite."

I do not know how the idea of "rustic" manners—I use the word in its accepted sense of "lacking in delicacy"—came to be associated with the people of the fields. The outward forms of common civility are more scrupulously observed in the country than in the town; there a certain ceremony in manners is observed which the town has no time for. The way of life, of course, is simpler in the country, but a countryman's dealings with his fellow men follow accepted rules. Familiarity is discouraged, perhaps *because* country people are familiar with every detail of each other's lives. In everything I noticed a kind of dignity which was often lacking in town life; no one ever did anything without first having been ceremoniously invited to do so, even though he had a right to do so. The personal liberty of others was in fact always highly respected. And if their minds seemed to work slower in the country that was because they always spoke only after due reflection, and because speech itself was a most serious matter.

At midday, the women, bearing steaming platters of *couscous*,[4] would leave the huts and walk in single file to the field. As soon as we caught sight of them, we would shout our greetings. Midday! It was midday! And work would stop all over the field.

"Come on," my uncle would say.

And I would run along behind him.

"Not so fast!" I would say. "I can't keep up with you."

"Is there a hole in your stomach?" he would ask me. "I could stable an ox in mine, I'm so hungry!"

And our appetites were in fact wonderfully whetted. However strong the sun, however furnace-hot the field with its dust and its quivering haze, it did not interfere with our appetites. We would squat down round the platters, and the hot *couscous,* made even hotter by the spices in it, would disappear, engulfed in great hungry mouthfuls, washed down by bumpers of cool water drawn from huge jars covered with banana leaves.

The break would last until two o'clock, and the men would spend the time sleeping in the shade of the trees or sharpening their sickles. Tireless, the young lads would play games or go and set snares; and though we would as usual make a lot of noise, we would take care not to whistle, because we were not supposed to whistle or pick up dead wood during the time of the harvest: such things would have brought misfortune to the fields.

The afternoon's work was much shorter and the time used to fly. It would be five o'clock before we knew it. The great field would now be shorn of its precious yield, and we would walk back in procession to the village—the tall silk-cotton trees and the wavering smoke from the huts seemed to welcome us from far off—preceded by the indefatigable tom-tom player, and singing at the tops of our voices the Song of the Rice.

---

4. *couscous* (küs′küs), a highly seasoned dish made from coarsely ground meal mixed with salt water, to which vegetables, meat, or fish are added. It is eaten in different forms throughout West Africa.

Overhead, the swallows would already be skimming lower, though the air would still be clear as ever; but they, too, knew when the end of the day was near. We would go home contented, weary but happy. The good spirits had taken care of us: not one of us had been bitten by snakes that our trampling feet might have disturbed. The flowers, which would begin to unfold with the approach of evening, would be spreading their perfume on the air again, so that we walked as if attired in freshly plucked garlands. If we had not been singing so loudly, we might have been able to hear the familiar sounds of the close of day: the shouts and laughter of women mingling with the lowing of cattle returning to their byres. But we were singing, always singing! Ah! How happy we were in those days! .....

VI

I STARTED SCHOOL very early. I began by attending the Moslem school, and a little later I was enrolled in the French school. Neither my mother nor I had any notion how long I would be a student at the latter: had she guessed the number of years I should be there, I am sure she would have kept me at home. But perhaps my father had guessed already . . .

Immediately after breakfast my sister and I would start out for school, carrying our exercise books and notebooks in a satchel made of raffia.

On the way we would be joined by schoolmates, and the nearer we got to the school buildings the larger our little band would grow. My sister would keep with the girls, and I would walk with the boys. And like all little boys we liked to tease the girls and pull their hair; and the girls gave as good as they got, and used to laugh in our faces. But if we pulled their hair, their reprisals did not stop at calling us names: they would fight back with teeth and nails for all they were worth, scratching and kicking and biting as hard as ever they could, though this did not noticeably diminish our fondness for them. The only one I did not touch was my sister, and in return she did not interfere with my activities either. Fanta, one of her friends, also let me alone, though I can't say I did the same to her.

"Why do you pull my hair?" she asked me one day when we were alone in the school yard.

"Why shouldn't I pull it? You're a girl!"

"But I've never done anything to you!"

"No, that's true," I said.

And for a moment I stopped to think. Until that moment, I had not realised that she was the only girl, apart from my sister, who had never hit me. "Why don't you hit me?" I said.

"Because!"

"Because? What sort of an answer's that?"

"Even if you were to pull my hair this minute, I would not hit you."

"All right then, I'm going to pull your hair!"

But what would have been the point in pulling her hair? Boys did that sort of thing only when they were all together. And because I did not carry out my threat she burst out laughing.

"Just you wait till we're going home!" I said. "It won't do you any harm to wait!" She laughed and ran away. But when we were going home, again something prevented me from pulling her hair, and from then on I rarely bothered her. My sister was not long in noticing this.

"You don't pull Fanta's hair any more," she said.

"Why should I pull her hair?" I answered. "She doesn't hurt me."

"Do you think I haven't noticed?"

"Then you know why I don't pull her hair."

"Really?" she asked. "Is that the only reason?"

What was she getting at? I shrugged my shoulders. It was a lot of little-girl nonsense: they did not know what they were talking about most of the time. All girls were like that.

"Shut up talking about Fanta!" I said. "You make me tired."

But she only began shrieking with laughter.

"Listen here," I said, "if you don't stop laughing at me . . ."

She made sure she was well out of my reach, then suddenly started to shout: "Fanta! . . . Fanta! . . ."

"Will you shut up?" I said.

But she just went on louder than ever, and I rushed at her, but she ran away shouting: "Fanta! . . . Fanta! . . ."

I looked all round me to see if I couldn't find a stone to throw at her; but there weren't any. "I'll pay you back for that," said I to myself.

Once in school, we went straight to our seats, boys and girls sitting side by side, our quarrels over; and, as soon as we had sat down, we became all ears, and sat absolutely still, so that the teacher used to give his lessons in an impressive silence. I should just like to have seen what would have happened if we had so much as stirred in our seats. Our teacher moved like quicksilver: he never remained long in the same place; he was here, there and everywhere. His flow of talk would have bewildered less attentive pupils. But we were remarkably attentive, and we found it no strain to be so. Young though we were, we all regarded our school work as something deadly serious. Everything we learned was strange and unexpected; it was as if we were learning about life on another planet; and we never grew tired of listening. Even if it had been otherwise, the silence could not have been more absolute under the strict discipline of a master who seemed to be everywhere at once and who would never have given us an opportunity to let our attention wander or to interrupt. But as I have said, an interruption was out of the question: it simply did not occur to us. And so we tried to attract the teacher's attention as little as possible: for we lived in constant dread of being sent out to the blackboard.

This blackboard was our nightmare. Its dark, blank mirror was the exact reflection of the amount of our knowledge. We knew very little, and the little we knew was very shaky: the slightest thing could upset it. Now if we did not want to be the recipients of several strokes of the cane, we had to go to the blackboard and take the chalk in our hands and pay our debt in kind. Here the tiniest detail was of the utmost importance: the wretched blackboard magnified every mistake. If we made one of our downward strokes not exactly of the same height as the others, we were required either to do an extra lesson on Sunday, or we had to go to the teacher during break, and receive, in the class that was always known as the infants', an unforgettable beating on our bare backsides. Irregular downward strokes used to horrify our teacher: he would examine our exercise books under a magnifying glass, and for each irregularity he discovered we got a stroke. I remember him well, a man like quicksilver; and he wielded his stick with joyous abandon!

This was how things were in the lower classes. In the upper school, there were not so many beatings, but other kinds of punishment, hardly more pleasant, took their place. Indeed, I experienced a great variety of punishments at that school: only my own discomfort lacked variety. Our love of knowledge had to be ineradicable to survive such ordeals.

The easiest form of punishment, for second-year pupils, was sweeping the school yard. Not until then did we realise how vast it was, nor how many guava trees were planted in it. We could have sworn that the guava trees had been put there simply to litter the ground with their leaves, for we certainly never were allowed to taste any of the fruit. In the third and fourth years our punishment was to work in the kitchen-garden; it has since struck me that no cheaper form of labour could have been found. In our last two years, however, while we were studying for our proficiency certificate, the school authorities had such confidence in us—a confidence that we would gladly have done without—that we were entrusted with the herd of cattle which belonged to the school.

This task was no sinecure! You wouldn't have found a less easily managed herd for miles around. If a farmer had a vicious cow, it would be sure to end up in our herd. There was good reason for this: the farmer obviously would only be too anxious to get rid of his awkward beast, and naturally had to sell it at a loss. The school authorities were only too glad to make a profit, and did so. But it was pure stinginess. And so our school owned the most peculiar, the most heterogeneous and the most complete collection of bad-tempered old beasts in existence. If we shouted to them to go to the right, they would of course go to the left.

These beasts used to gallop madly about the bush, as they were constantly plagued by a swarm of flies, and we used to have to chase after them for incredible distances. Curiously enough, they were always more inclined to wander off on their own, or start fighting among themselves, than to forage for food. But this picturesque behaviour was no pleasure to us. We knew that on our return the fullness of their bellies would be carefully inspected to find out how well they had pastured; and woe betide us should the bellies of these rawboned creatures appear inadequately filled!

But woe betide us indeed, if a single head was missing from this devil's own herd! At night, we would run till we were breathless, trying to herd them together; we would lay about them with a big stick, which was not much good, I fear, and certainly did not improve the dispositions of these fantastic beasts. Then we would lead them to water and make them drink vast quantities to make up for the lack of solid stuff in their bellies. We would come back, worn out, with the entire herd. It goes without saying that we would not have dared to come back to the school without having mustered the complete herd. I shudder to think of what one missing head would have cost us!

Such were the dealings we had with our teachers, the black side of our school life: and naturally we could hardly wait for our schooling to be over, for the day when we should receive our famous proficiency certificates that would proclaim to the world that we were "educated." Yet when I think of what the pupils in the top form made us suffer, all that I have said about the "black" side of our school life seems to pale into insignificance. Those older students—I refuse to call them school fellows—who were older and stronger than we were, and less strictly supervised, persecuted us in every conceivable way. They gave themselves superior airs and had an inflated sense of their own importance—they probably felt that they would never enjoy so much power again—and perhaps they were trying to get a little of their own back for the rough handling they themselves had experienced when they were younger: excessively harsh treatment is perhaps not quite the best method of inculcating good behaviour.

I still remember—my hands and my fingertips still remember!
—what used to lie in store for us on our return to school from
the holidays. The guava trees in the school yard would be in full
leaf again, and the old leaves would be strewn around in scattered heaps. In places there were even more than just heaps of
them: it would be like a muddy sea of leaves.

"Get that all swept up!" the headmaster would tell us. "I want
the whole place cleaned up, at once!"

"At once!" There was enough work there, damned hard work,
too, to last us for over a week. Especially since the only tools
with which we were provided were our hands, our fingers, our
nails.

"Now see that it's done properly, and be quick about it," the
headmaster would say to the older pupils, "or you'll have to
answer for it!"

So at an order from the older boys we would all line up like
peasants about to reap or glean a field, and we would set to work
like members of a chain gang. In the school yard itself, it wasn't
too bad: the guava trees were fairly well spaced; but there was
one part where the closely planted trees grew in a hopeless tangle
of leaves and branches. The sun could not penetrate here, and
the acrid stench of decay lingered in the undergrowth even at the
height of summer.

If the work was not going as quickly as the headmaster
expected, the big boys, instead of giving us a helping hand, used
to find it simpler to whip us with branches pulled from the trees.
Now guava wood is regrettably flexible; skilfully handled, the
springy switches used to whistle piercingly, and fall like flails of
fire on our backsides. Our flesh stung and smarted, while tears of
anguish sprang from our eyes and splashed on the rotting leaves
at our feet.

In order to avoid these blows, we used to bribe our tyrants
with the succulent cakes of Indian corn, the *couscous* made of
meat or fish which we used to bring for our midday meal. And if
we happened to have any money on us, the coins changed hands
at once. If we did not do this, if we were afraid of going home
with an empty stomach or an empty purse, the blows were

redoubled. They were administered with such furious generosity and with such diabolical gusto that even a deaf mute would have gathered that we were being flogged not so much to spur us on to work, but rather to lash us into a state of submissiveness in which we would be only too glad to give up our food and money.

Occasionally, one of us, worn out by such calculated cruelty, would have the courage to complain to the headmaster. He would of course be very angry, but the punishment he inflicted on the older boys was always negligible—nothing compared to what they had done to us. And the fact is that however much we complained, our situation did not improve in the slightest. Perhaps we should have let our parents know what was going on, but somehow we never dreamed of doing so; I don't know whether it was loyalty or pride that kept us silent, but I can see now that we were foolish to keep quiet about it, for such beatings were utterly foreign to our nature, to the most fundamental and secret principles of our character, and completely at variance with our passion for independence and equality.

But one day, one of my little schoolmates, Kouyaté Karamoko, who had just been brutally assaulted, declared openly that he had had enough of this sort of thing. Kouyaté was extremely small and thin, so small and thin that we used to tell him jokingly that he couldn't have any stomach, or at least one only as big as a bird's: a gizzard. Moreover, Kouyaté did nothing to develop his little gizzard or whatever it was that served him for a stomach: he only liked sour, acid things, and citrus fruits: at lunch break, he wasn't happy unless he could exchange his *couscous* for guavas, oranges or lemons. But if Kouyaté was to be deprived even of fruit, it was obvious that his gizzard or whatever it was would finally become even smaller: like the stomach of a grasshopper, perhaps. Now the older boys' insistent demands forced Kouyaté into periods of rigorous fasting. That day, his frustrated passion for sour fruit and also the weals on his buttocks, turned Kouyaté into a rebel.

"Yes, I've had enough of it!" he said to me, sniffing through his tears. "D'you hear? I've had enough! I'm going to tell my father."

"You keep quiet," I said. "Telling your father won't do us any good."

"Do you really believe that?"

"Don't forget, the big boys . . ."

But he would not let me finish.

"I'm going to tell him!" he cried.

"Hush, don't shout like that!"

We were working in the same row, and he was the nearest to me in it: I was afraid that this outburst would bring another flogging from the big boys.

"You know what sort of a man my father is, don't you?" he said.

"Yes, of course."

Kouyaté's father was one of the most venerated praise-singers of the district. He was an educated man, welcome everywhere, though he no longer practised his art; he was a kind of emeritus praise-singer, and very proud of his position.

"But your father's an old man now," I said.

"He's tough!" said Kouyaté proudly.

He drew his thin little body up to its full height.

"You make me laugh sometimes!" I said.

Whereupon he began to whimper again.

"Oh, well, do as you like!" I told him.

The next day, Kouyaté had no sooner entered the school yard than he went over to Himourana, the big boy who had thrashed him so mercilessly the day before.

"My father is most anxious to meet the boy who has been kindest to me in the top class, and I thought of you at once. Can you come and share our dinner this evening?"

"You bet I can!" answered Himourana, who was as stupid as he was brutal, and probably as greedy as he was stupid.

That evening, at the appointed time, this big bully Himourana showed up at Kouyaté's compound. Now this compound is one of the best-guarded ones in Kouroussa: it has only one gate, and the fence around it, instead of being made of woven reeds, is constructed of mud bricks, with pieces of broken glass bottles fixed to the top. It could be entered and left only with the permission of the master of the house. Kouyaté's father came in person to open the gate, and when Himourana was inside, he carefully bolted it.

"Would you care to sit down in the courtyard?" he said. "Our whole family is expecting you."

Himourana took a quick look at the pots and pans, which seemed to give ample promise of a succulent repast, and sat down with the rest of the family, eager for the compliments that he felt sure were about to be addressed to him. But Kouyaté got up and pointed at him.

"My father," he said, "this is the big boy who never stops beating me, and takes my food and my money!"

"Well, well," said Kouyaté's father, "that's not a nice thing to say about him. Are you sure you're telling me the truth?"

"I swear by Allah!" said Kouyaté.

"So it must be the truth," said his father.

And he turned towards Himourana.

"Well, young man, it's time you gave an explanation of your strange behaviour. Have you anything to say in your defence? Be quick: I haven't much time to spare, but I don't want to be uncharitable."

It was as if a thunderbolt had dropped at Himourana's feet— he couldn't have been more dumbfounded: he had obviously not heard a word of what Kouyaté's father had said to him. As soon as he had recovered a little from his surprise, his one thought was to get away; this was obviously his best course, but it needed a stupid bully like Himourana to imagine he could escape from such a well-guarded compound. He had not run more than a few steps before he was caught.

"Now, sir," said Kouyaté's father, "listen carefully to what I have to say to you; get this into your head, once and for all: I do not send my son to school to learn how to become the slave of boys like you!"

And thereupon Himourana felt himself lifted in the air by his feet and arms—everything had been carefully planned—and held in a convenient position, while, despite his screams, Kouyaté's father laid into him, belabouring his bare backside with his cattle whip. Then he was allowed to run away, shamefaced, with his tail on fire, like a scalded cat.

Next day, the story of Himourana's beating spread like wildfire. It created a real scandal. Nothing like that had ever happened before, so that we found it hard to realise that it had actually taken place, although we all felt we had been avenged by the action taken by Kouyaté's father. The big boys of the two top classes held a meeting and decided that Kouyaté as well as his sister Mariama would be sent to Coventry,[5] and they ordered all of us to send them to Coventry too; but they did not dare lay a finger on Kouyaté or his sister, and at this even the stupidest among us became aware that they were afraid: we suddenly felt that an era had ended and we prepared to breathe the air of liberty again.

At midday, I went up to Kouyaté, having decided to defy the big boys' orders.

"Careful," said Kouyaté; "they might beat you for this."

"I'm not afraid of them!" I said.

I had some oranges for my midday meal, and I gave them to him.

"Thank you," he said, "but do go away: I'm afraid they'll beat you."

I had no time to reply: I could see several of the big boys coming towards us, and I hesitated an instant, uncertain whether to stand up to them or to run away. I decided to stand up to them. Had I not already begun to do so? But suddenly I felt my head reeling under their blows, and I took to my heels. I did not stop until I had reached the edge of the schoolyard, then I began to cry, more with rage than pain. When I had pulled myself together a little, I saw Fanta sitting beside me.

"What do *you* want?" I said.

"I've brought you a wheat cake," she replied.

I took it and ate it almost without realising what I was doing, though Fanta's mother was renowned as the best cake-maker in the district. I got up and drank some water and washed my face.

5. *sent to Coventry*, ostracized.

Then I came back and sat down again. "I don't like you to come and sit beside me when I'm crying," I said.

"Were you crying?" she asked. "I didn't notice."

I looked at her. She was lying. Why was she lying? Obviously to spare my pride: I smiled at her.

"Do you want another wheat cake?" she asked.

"No," I replied. "I couldn't eat another one: I feel sick with anger. Don't you?"

"Yes," she said.

There were suddenly tears in her eyes.

"Oh, I hate them!" I said. "You can't imagine how much I hate them! Listen: I'm going to leave this school. I'm going to try and grow up fast, then I'll come back, and for every beating I've received I'll pay them back a hundredfold! Yes," I said, "that's what I'll do!"

She stopped crying, and looked up admiringly at me.

That evening, I went and spoke to my father under the veranda. "Father," I said, "I can't go to school any more."

"What?" said my father.

"No," I said, "I can't go back."

But by this time the scandal had had time to go the rounds of the compounds in Kouroussa.

"What's going on in that school?" my father asked.

"I'm afraid of the big boys," I said.

"I thought you weren't afraid of anyone?"

"I am: I'm afraid of the big boys."

"What have they been doing to you?"

"They take everything I've got! They take my money and they take my food."

"Do they, now?" said my father. "And do they beat you?"

"Do they beat me!" I said bitterly.

"Very well, then, I'll come and have a word with those bullies to-morrow. Will that do?"

"Yes, Father."

The next morning my father and his apprentices came with me to the school gate. Each time a big boy approached, my father said to me: "Is that one of them?"

I always said no, even though many of them *had* whipped me and robbed me; I was waiting for my most persistent attacker to appear. When I saw him coming I said in a loud voice: "That's the one who beats me the most!"

At once the apprentices threw themselves upon him and stripped him naked, and began to beat him so hard that my father had in the end to restrain them. Then my father said to the big boy who stood there with a frightened look in his eyes: "I shall have a word with the headmaster about you. I should like to know if the pupils in the top forms of this school are here solely for the purpose of beating up the younger boys and stealing their money."

That day, there was no longer any question of sending Kouyaté and his sister to Coventry: they mingled with us freely, and none of the big boys dared raise his voice in protest or lift a finger to us. Was a new era beginning? It felt like it. The big boys kept to themselves. And as we kept well away from them and were more numerous than they were, it almost looked as if it was the big boys who had been sent to Coventry by us; they looked embarrassed. Indeed, they were in a rather unpleasant situation: their parents had not known about their tyrannical cruelty; if they got to know about it, and there was now every likelihood that the whole thing would become public, the big boys would have to endure all kinds of scoldings and punishments.

In the afternoon, at the end of school, my father came as he had said he would. The headmaster was in the schoolyard, surrounded by teachers. My father went up to him, and, without even stopping to wish him good day, said: "Do you know what's been going on in this school?"

"Everything is going as it should," said the headmaster.

"It is, is it?" said my father. "Are you not aware of the fact that the big boys beat the little ones, that they steal their money and take their food? Are you blind, or do you not wish to see what's going on?"

"I'll thank you to mind your own business!" said the headmaster.

"And is this not my own business?" said my father. "Is it none of my business when my own son is being treated like a slave in your school?"

"Certainly not."

"You should not have said that," said my father.

And he went right up to the headmaster.

"Do you think you'll beat me up as your apprentices beat up one of my pupils this morning?" cried the headmaster.

And he hit out with his fists; but although he was stronger, he was fat and his fat impeded rather than helped him; and my father, who was thin, but active and supple, had no difficulty in dodging his blows and setting about him in no uncertain fashion. My father got him down on the ground and was punching him for all he was worth: I don't know what might have happened if the teachers had not dragged him off.

The headmaster was feeling his jaw and didn't say a word. My father dusted himself down, then took me by the hand. He went out of the schoolyard without a word to anyone, and I marched proudly back to our compound with him. But towards evening, when I went for a walk in the town, I could hear folks saying as I passed by: "Look! That's the schoolboy whose father went and beat up the headmaster in his own schoolyard!"

And suddenly I didn't feel nearly so proud. This scandal was not the same sort of thing as Kouyaté's father had started. It had taken place in front of the teachers and the pupils, and the headmaster himself had been the victim. No, this wasn't at all the same sort of thing; and I imagined that now I would be expelled. I ran back to our compound and said to my father: "Why did you beat him? Now they won't want me back at school, I know."

"I thought you said that you didn't want to go back to school?" said my father.

And he laughed out loud.

"But, Father, it's no laughing matter!" I said.

"You go to sleep and forget all about it, you little silly. If we don't hear the put-put of a certain motor bicycle outside the gate of the compound tomorrow, I shall complain to the district supervisor."

But my father did not need to make this complaint, and I was not expelled, for, the next day, a little before nightfall, the headmaster's motor bike chugged up to the gate of our compound. The headmaster came in, and everybody, my father included, went to meet him, and greeted him amiably with: "Good evening, sir."

He offered the headmaster a chair, and my father and he sat down, while, at a sign from my father, the rest of us withdrew. The interview seemed to be a very cordial one; indeed it must have been, for from then on, my sister and I took part in no more forced labour at school.

Yet the scandal could not be hushed up entirely. A few months later the headmaster was forced to resign owing to a petition signed by all of the parents. But meanwhile the rumour had got around that he was using some of the bigger lads as house-boys for the convenience of his wives. These pupils had been boarded with him so that they might enjoy special attention, and their board had been paid for with cattle. I don't know all the ins and outs of the affair; I only know that this was the last straw that broke the camel's back, and that we were never again bullied by the big boys. . . . . .

IX

I WAS FIFTEEN when I left home for Conakry, where I was going to pursue a course of technical studies at the École Georges-Poiret, now known as the Technical College.

I was leaving my parents for the second time. The first time was immediately after I had passed my scholarship examination, when I had acted as interpreter to an officer who had come to map the land in our district and in part of the neighbouring Sudan. But on this second occasion, I was taking much lengthier leave of them.

For a whole week, my mother had been gathering together provisions for me. Conakry is about four hundred miles from Kouroussa, and to my mother it was an unknown if not unexplored land, where God alone knew if I would get enough to eat. And so she collected together *couscous,* meat, fish, yams, rice and potatoes. The previous week my mother had already undertaken a tour of the most celebrated marabouts,[6] consulting them about my future and making many sacrifices. She had offered up an ox in memory of her father and had invoked the aid of her ancestors' spirits, in order that good fortune might attend me on a voyage which, in her eyes, was rather like departing for a savage land; the fact that Conakry is the capital of Guinea only served to accentuate the strange character of the place where I was going.

On the eve of my departure, all the marabouts and witch doctors, friends and notables, and, it must be said, whoever cared to cross our threshold, all attended a magnificent feast in our compound. For my mother believed that on this occasion no one should be turned away; on the contrary, representatives of all classes of society had to attend the feast, so that the blessing I was to take with me would be complete. Moreover, this was the reason why the marabouts had requested such large quantities of food. And so each guest, after having eaten his fill, would seize me by the hand and bless me, saying: "May good fortune favour you! May your studies be fruitful! And may the Lord protect you!"

As for the marabouts, they used much lengthier phrases. They would begin by reciting a few quotations from the Koran, adapting them to the occasion; then, having completed their invocations, they would utter the name of Allah; whereupon they would bless me.

I passed a wretched night. I was very depressed, a little upset, and I woke up several times. Once I seemed to hear groans. I guessed immediately that it was my mother. I got up and went to her hut: my mother was tossing on her bed and quietly lamenting. Perhaps I should have gone to her and tried to console her, but I did not know how she would take it; maybe she would not have liked to think she had been found weeping and wailing; and I withdrew with a heavy heart. Is this what life was going to be like? Were tears a part of everything we did?

---

6. *marabouts* (mar′ə büts), Mohammedan holy men.

My mother woke me at dawn, and I got up at once. I saw that her face was strained, but she was determined to keep control of herself and I said nothing. I pretended that her apparent calm had really convinced me. My luggage was piled up in the hut. Carefully wrapped and in a prominent position was a large bottle.

"What is in the bottle?" I asked.

"Do not break it," said my mother.

"I'll look after it."

"Take great care of it. And every morning, before you begin your studies, take a little sip of it."

"Is it supposed to be good for the brain?"

"It is indeed. It's the best there is: it comes from Kankan."

I had already drunk some of this liquid: my teacher had made me drink some when I was sitting my scholarship examination. It is a magic potion that possesses many qualities: it is particularly good for developing the brain. It is a curious mixture: our marabouts have small boards on which they write prayers taken from the Koran. When they have written down the text, they erase it by washing the board: the washing-water is carefully collected, and, with the addition of honey, forms the main part of the elixir. If it was bought in the town of Kankan, which is a strongly Mohammedan town, and the holiest of our native places; and bought, moreover, at a very high price, it must be a particularly potent beverage. My father, for his part, had given me the evening before a he-goat's horn containing talismans; I was to wear this horn all the time, as a protection against evil spirits.

"Run and say your good-byes now," said my mother.

I had to go and say farewell to the elders of our compound and of the neighbouring compounds. I went with a heavy heart. I had known these men and women since my tenderest years, I had always known them, I had watched them living in this very place, and watched them disappear from it too: my father's mother had disappeared. And would I ever see again these people to whom I was now saying farewell? Overcome by doubts, I felt suddenly as if I was taking leave of the past itself. And indeed, was not that just what I was doing? Was I not leaving behind me here a part of my life?

When I came back to my mother and saw her standing in tears beside my luggage, I, too, began to weep. I implored her not to accompany me to the station, for it seemed to me that if she did I should never be able to tear myself away from her arms. She nodded her consent. We embraced for the last time and I almost ran out of the hut. My sisters and brothers and the apprentices carried my luggage.

My father quickly caught up with me and took my hand, as he used to when I was a little boy. I slowed down: I felt weak, and cried as if my heart was broken.

"Father," I said.

"I am listening," he replied.

"Am I really going away?"

"What else could you do? You know quite well that you have to go."

"Yes," I said.

And I began to cry again.

"Come, come, my little one! You're a big boy now, aren't you?"

But his very presence, his very kindness—and even more, the fact that he was holding my hand—took away the last vestiges of courage. He understood.

"I shall not go any farther," he said. "We shall say good-bye to each other here: it would not do if we burst into tears at the station, in front of your friends. And I do not want to leave your mother alone just now. Your mother is very upset. I am too! We are all terribly upset. But we must be brave. Be brave, my son. My brothers will look after you. But work hard. Work as you used to work here. We have made many sacrifices for you; they must not be for nothing. Do you hear me?"

"Yes," I said.

He remained silent for a moment, then went on: "You see, I had no father to look after me, as you had. At least, not for very long: when I was twelve years old I became an orphan; and I had to make my own way in life. It was not easy. The uncles in whose care I was left treated me more like a slave than a nephew. Not that I was a burden to them for very long: they hired me out to the Syrians almost at once. I was simply a domestic drudge, and I had to hand over everything I earned to my uncles. But even so it did not diminish their cruelty and greed. I always had to keep my own counsel and work hard to make a name for myself. You . . . But I have said enough. Seize your opportunity. And make me proud of you. I ask no more of you. Will you do it?"

"I will, Father."

"Good! Good . . . Well, be brave, son. Good-bye."

"Father!"

He held me close; he had never held me so close before.

"Good-bye, little one, good-bye."

Abruptly he let me go and walked away very fast—perhaps he did not want to let me see his tears. I went on along the road to the station. My eldest sister, my brothers, Sidafa and the younger apprentices went with me carrying my luggage. As we walked along, we were joined by friends; Fanta joined us too. And it was rather as if I was on my way to school again: all my companions were there, but there had never been so many before. Was I not, indeed, on my way to school?

"Fanta," I said, "we are on the way to school."

But the only answer she gave was a faint smile, and that was the only answer my words received. I was indeed on the way to school, but I was alone; I was already alone. . . . There had never been so many of us, but never had I felt so alone. Although it was perhaps worst for me, we all shared the pain of parting. We spoke little. And soon we were standing on the railway platform, waiting for the train, but we had hardly said one word to each other.

Several praise-singers had come to celebrate my departure. I had no sooner reached the station than they began to beset me with their flatteries. "Already thou art as wise as the White Man," they sang. "Thou art verily as wise as the White Man. In Conakry, thou shalt take thy place even among the most illustrious." Such excessive praises had the effect of subduing, rather than of inflaming my vanity. What did I know, after all? I was still very far from "wise." The friends who were with me were as wise as I was! I should have liked to ask the praise-singers to stop, or at least to moderate their flattery; but that would have been contrary to custom, so I remained silent. Perhaps their flatteries were after all not altogether useless: they made me determined to take my work seriously. True, I had always done so; but now I felt myself obliged to bring to pass, one day, everything that the praise-singers were chanting, if, on my return, I did not wish to look a fool.

These flatteries had an additional effect: they kept me from thinking of the sadness I felt. They had made me smile—before they began to embarrass me—but, even though my companions, too, had felt how ridiculous they were—it was natural that they should feel how ridiculous they were—they allowed nothing of this to appear on their faces; perhaps we are so accustomed to the hyperboles of our praise-singers that we no longer take very much notice of them. But what about Fanta? No, Fanta must have taken all those flatteries for the truth. Fanta . . . Fanta never thought of smiling: her eyes were filled with tears. Dear Fanta! . . . Despairingly, I cast a glance at my sister. She must surely know how I felt; she always felt as I did. But I saw she was simply looking after my luggage; she had already told me several times to keep my eye on it, and when our eyes met she told me again.

"Don't worry," I said. "I'll keep an eye on it."

"Do you remember how many cases there are?"

"Of course."

"Good. Now don't lose any. Remember you are staying the first night at Mamou. The train stops for the night at Mamou."

"You don't have to explain everything to me. I'm not a child."

"No, but you don't know what sort of people they'll be down there. Keep your luggage beside you, and count it from time to time. You understand? Keep your eye on it."

"Yes," I said.

"And be careful with strangers. D'you hear me?"

"I hear you."

But already I had stopped listening to her and to the songs of the praise-singers. My sadness suddenly returned. My little brothers had slipped their little hands into mine, and I kept thinking how warm and soft their hands were; I kept thinking, too, that the train would soon be here, and that I should have to let go their hands and leave their tender warmth, leave their gentleness; and I began to feel afraid of seeing the train appear, I began to hope it would be late. Sometimes it was late; perhaps it would be late to-day. I looked at the clock. It *was* late! . . . But suddenly it appeared and I had to let go of their hands and leave their gentle pressure behind, as if it was the whole of my life.

They passed my luggage to me through the window, and I put it all over the seats. My sister gave me some last words of advice that were as useless as all the others she had given me: and everyone had something nice to say to me, Fanta and Sidafa especially. But in all that waving of hands and scarves that accompanied the train's departure, I only really saw my brothers, who ran the length of the platform, the length of the train, shouting good-bye. At the point where the platform ended, my sister and Fanta joined them, waving their head-scarves. And then, suddenly, they disappeared from sight, long before the first bend of the track, for a sudden mist enveloped them, and tears blinded my eyes. . . . For a long time I lay prostrate in a corner of my compartment, with my luggage strewn all round me, and with that final sight ever before my eyes: my young brothers, my sister, Fanta. . . . ▶

Adebisi Fabunmi
Oshogbo,
1966. Lino-cut.

Matei Markwei / *Ghana*
(c. 1923–   )

LIFE IN OUR VILLAGE

In our little village
When elders are around,
Boys must not look at girls
And girls must not look at boys
5 Because the elders say
That is not good.

Even when night comes
Boys must play separately,
Girls must play separately.
10 But humanity is weak
So boys and girls meet.

The boys play hide and seek
And the girls play hide and seek.
The boys know where the girls hide
15 And the girls know where the boys hide—
So in their hide and seek,
Boys seek girls,
Girls seek boys,
And each to each sing
20 Songs of love.

Tsegaye Gabre Medhen /

Ethiopia

(1935–   )

HOME-COMING SON

Look where you walk, unholy stranger—
this is the land of the eighth harmony
in the rainbow: Black.
It is the dark side of the moon
5 brought to light;
this is the canvas of God's master stroke.

Out, out of your foreign outfit, unholy stranger—
feel part of the great work of art.
Walk in peace, walk alone, walk tall,
10 walk free, walk naked.
Let the feelers of your motherland
caress your bare feet,
let Her breath kiss your naked body.
But watch, watch where you walk, forgotten stranger—
15 this is the very depth of your roots: Black.

"Home-Coming Son" by Tsegaye Gabre Medhen. Reprinted by permission of Dr. R. Pankhurst, director, Institute of Ethiopia.

Where the tom-toms of your fathers vibrated
in the fearful silence of the valleys,
shook in the colossus bodies of the mountains,
hummed in the deep chests of the jungles.
20 Walk proud.
Watch, listen to the calls of the ancestral spirits, prodigal son—
to the call of the long-awaiting soil.
They welcome you home, home. In the song of birds
you hear your suspended family name,
25 the winds whisper the golden names of your tribal warriors,
the fresh breeze blown into your nostrils
floats their bones turned to dust.
Walk tall. The spirits welcome
their lost-son-returned.
30 Watch, and out of your foreign outfit, brother,
feel part of the work of art.
Walk in laughter, walk in rhythm, walk tall,
walk free, walk naked.
Let the roots of your motherland caress your body,
35 let the naked skin absorb the home-sun and shine ebony.

William Modisane[1] / *South Africa*
(1923–   )

THE DIGNITY OF BEGGING

THE MAGISTRATE raises his eyes above the documents and plunges them like daggers into my heart. His blue eyes are keen: my heart pounds like the bass of a boogie-woogie.

"I'm sick to death of you . . . heartily sick. There's not a native beggar on the streets whose full story I don't know," the magistrate says. "I've watched some of you grow up. There isn't one I haven't tried to rehabilitate many times. Some I was forced to send to gaol, but they always come back . . . they come back to the goose that lays the golden egg."

These are fighting words. The magistrate sounds as though he's going to put us away for a few weeks. My only regret is that Richard Serurubele has to share my fate. If only the magistrate knew that he is not a parasite like the rest of us, that he's what is called an exploited beggar. He was crippled by an automobile accident, and since then his parents have made capital out of it. They use him to beg so they can balance the family budget. They never show him the comfort of love. Relentlessly they drive him, like an animal that has to work for its keep and feed. He is twenty-one. Dragging one foot along, he is an abject sight who has all the sadness of the world in his face. He looks many times older than my mother-in-law.

"The Dignity of Begging" by William Modisane from AFRICAN VOICES, AN ANTHOLOGY OF NATIVE AFRICAN WRITING, compiled by Peggy Rutherfoord. Published by Drum Publications Ltd. Reprinted by permission of Drum Publications Ltd.
1. *Modisane* (mō di sä′nä).

"You beggars make it difficult for me to do my duty, and in spite of my failure to rehabilitate you, I always believe in giving you another chance. . . . A fresh start, you might call it. But I'm almost certain that you'll be back here in a few days."

The magistrate is getting soft, I can see my freedom at a distance of an arm's stretch. Here is my chance to put on my act. A look of deep compunction and a few well-chosen words can do the trick. I clear my throat and squeeze out a tear or two.

"Your honour, most of us beg because we've been ostracized by our families; they treat us as though we were lepers," I say, wiping off a tear. "They want us to look up to them for all the things we need. They never encourage us to earn our own keep. Nobody wants to employ us, people are more willing to offer us alms rather than give us jobs. All they do is show us pity. . . . We don't want to be pitied, we want to be given a chance to prove that we're as good as anybody else."

I can see from the silence in the court that everybody is deceived. . . . Everybody is filled with a sense of self-reproach. The magistrate is as mute as the undertaker's parlour. I can read pity on the faces of all the people in the court; perhaps the most pathetic is my own. I am magnificent . . . an answer to every film director's dream. I know I have said enough . . . enough to let us out, that is.

"I understand you have matriculated, your name is Nathaniel, isn't it?" He turns a page of the report prepared by a worker in the Non-European Affairs Department. "Yes, here we are. Nathaniel Mokgomare, the department recommends that you be sent to a place where you will be taught some useful trade. I want you to report to Room 14 at the department's building to-morrow morning."

This is not what I had bargained for; my brilliant idea has boomeranged. Why must I take a job when I can earn twice a normal wage begging? After all, what will horses do if I take a job? I *must* uphold the dignity of begging. Professional ethics forbid all beggars from working.

"As for you, Richard Serurubele, I'll let you go this time, but mark my words: the next time you appear before me, I'll have you sent to the Bantu Refuge.[2] Now get out of here, both of you."

If the magistrate had seen the big grin on my face as we leave the court, he would have thrown my deformed carcass in gaol and deliberately lost the key. He does not see it though.

With the exception of a few loose ends everything has gone according to schedule, but my friend Serurubele is just about the most miserable man on earth. The trouble with him is he lacks imagination, but then of course, not everybody is as bright as I am. He always seems to be looking at the dull side of life, a vice coupled with an appalling brand of honesty most bishops would swear didn't exist.

"One of these days I'm going to kill myself," Serurubele says. "I can't go on like this, I'm tired of living off other people. Why did this have to happen to me? Tell me, Nathan. Why?"

How this man expects me to answer a question like this is beyond me. For one unguarded moment I almost tell him to send his Maker a telegram and ask Him all about it, but my gentler nature sees the harm such an answer might do.

"I don't know," I say, abruptly. "Things like this just happen; it's not in us to question why. Nature has a way of doing things, but even then she gives something in return. . . . at least I think so. . . . But how should I know, anyway?"

This is the one time I cannot find something concrete to say; I want to show him that there is compensation for his disability, but I just cannot lay my hands on it. This, I remember, is what made me leave home.

I left because my parents did not understand. They almost made a neurotic out of me; but to-day I wonder if it wasn't my own sensitivity which gave their actions then their seemingly absurd proportions. They seemed afraid to walk about freely; everybody sat down as if the house was full of cripples. I was treated like a babe in arms. All the things I wanted were brought to me, I was not even allowed to get myself water to drink. This

---

2. *the Bantu Refuge,* one of the tracts of land allotted by the South African government to the African tribes. They are similar in many respects to America's Indian reservations.

excessive kindness gradually began to irritate me. . . . It became a constant reminder that I didn't belong, that I was an invalid. It then became apparent that they would soon put the food into my mouth which they had already chewed for me, and push it down my throat. These thoughts of inadequacy drove me from home.

A new life opened for me. I got myself a wife, two bouncing boys and a property at Pampoenfontein, also a room at Sophiatown [3] complete with piano. Within two years I had begged well over a few hundred pounds. The money has been used wisely. Only one problem confronts me now, I want enough money to provide for my old age. . . . The two boys are also to be considered.

"For Christ's sake, Nathaniel," Serurubele says, "what's wrong with you. Why are you always so wrapped up in your thoughts. . . . this is where I stay, remember?"

I say good-bye to him and go to my room. After having something to eat I settle down to some hard thinking. There are all sorts of insurances and societies, unions and what have you, which protect workers. Why not a beggars' union? I could rally all the beggars of the city into one union with some professional name like "The United Beggars' Union," into whose funds every beggar would contribute ten shillings [4] a week. In the city of Johannesburg alone, there are over a hundred beggars and if they could all be talked over, a capital of about two-thousand-four-hundred pounds could be realized in one year.

What a brilliant idea . . . an inspiration of genius. Sometimes I feel depressed that the world has not had the vision to realize the potentialities of my genius . . . possibly it cannot accommodate Einstein and myself in the same generation. Anyway, so much for that.

---

3. *Sophiatown,* the Colored *location* in Johannesburg. Under South Africa's system of *apartheid* (See footnote on page 22.), whites, blacks, and Coloreds (people of mixed ancestry) must all live in their own districts. The districts for non-whites are called *locations*. Sophiatown was a particularly notorious slum, which has since been destroyed in urban renewal. **4.** *ten shillings,* about $1.40.

I could promise to offer each a bonus of ten pounds a year. That would be smart. . . . No beggar could resist such an offer. Maybe I should promise to buy each a property somewhere cheap, say, buy one property a year for the needy ones like Serurubele, equip him with third-rate tools and interest him in turning out junk that nobody will care to give a second look at. The scheme would be costly, but at least it would go far in enlisting their confidence. Only one would get the property; the others would wait patiently until I get religion.

The following morning I'm at Room 14 bright and early. A white man with a bored expression on his face is sitting behind a big mahogany desk. I tell him my name. He takes some paper and writes on it. He tells me to go to the address written on the paper.

The faint showers that were falling outside have become heavier, and as I go out I say something nasty about the weather. A brilliant idea strikes me as a well-dressed lady is walking towards me. She looks like a mobile gold mine ready to be tapped. . . . in fact, I can almost see the gold nuggets in her teeth. I put on a gloomy face, bend lower than usual and let my deformed carcass shiver. She stops and looks at me as if she's responsible for my deformity.

"Why, you poor boy, you're freezing to death," she says, with melodrama. "Here, go buy yourself something to eat."

I feel the half-crown piece [5] in my hand and give her the usual line of how the good Lord will bless her, and send her tons and tons of luck: but from the way she's dressed, she appears to have had more than her share of luck.

I play this trick all the way to the address I'm given, and by the time I get there, I count well over ten half-crowns. Not bad, I say to myself; at this rate I can become the richest and most famous beggar in the city. To think the department wants to pin me behind a desk! The idea is criminal, to say the least.

One of these days when I'm on my annual leave, I hope to write a book on begging, something like a treatise on the subject.

---

5. *half-crown piece,* two shillings and sixpence, about thirty-four cents.

It will be written with sensitivity and charm, brimful with sketches from life, and profusely illustrated with coloured photographs, with easy-to-follow rules on the noblest and oldest occupation in the world: Begging! It will be a text-book for all aspiring beggars, young and old, who will reap a wealth of knowledge from my personal experiences and genius. In fact, I think it will be the only one of its kind in world literature. Even millionaires will take up begging as a pastime to colour their humdrum existence.

It will naturally begin with a history of the art from its ancient crudity of maiming children as a preparation in their education, right up to the contemporary age of beggars who are driven to the city in the latest American cars. . . . beggars with a bank balance big enough to impress the Receiver of Revenue. I can almost see it on the best-seller list for several months. This reverie almost causes me to lose my way.

I find the place and go in. My heart just misses a beat when I see the large number of people inside. Some, if not most, are deformed monstrosities like myself. What could be sweeter? I can see my plan taking shape.

The man in charge starts explaining the elementary principles of the typewriter. I pretend to be interested and ask many unnecessary questions, but intelligent enough to impress him. By five o'clock I'm running over the keyboard like a brilliant amateur.

On my way home I go via Serurubele's corner. He is still there and looking as miserable as ever. I suggest that we go home. I lure him to my room and when we get there I begin playing a certain tarantella like Rubinstein, only my rendering is in a major flat. Either my piano recital is good or my friend just loves bad sounds.

"You can have a house like this and everything that goes with it; it's yours for the taking. Why beg for other people when you can do it for yourself?"

"I've got to help with the rent and the food," he says. "How do you think I'm going to get a house like this? I can't just wish for it."

"You don't have to, you must plan and work for it like I did. I have a plan that will give it to you in less than a year. . . . Listen."

I then start explaining to him about the society with particular emphasis on the good it will do to all beggars. I see his teeth sparkling behind thick lips. I put him in charge of organizing them for our first meeting.

Last night I dreamt I was at the race course and I saw the winning double as plain as I see my twisted leg. I raid my savings in the room and make my way to Turffontein. When I get there I start scouting around for policemen. None are about and a soothing satisfaction comes with the realization that I shall not bother myself with police badges. I put a pound win on two and seven, a double in the first leg. As I'm making my bet, a man with eyes as big and lethargic as an owl's is standing next to me and beaming like a blushing groom.

I'm too nervous to watch the race, so I decide to walk about and appreciate the scenery. Suddenly I feel as though someone is staring at me. I turn round and look straight at Miss Gallovidian, a welfare worker, who has the uncanny habit of showing up at the most unexpected places. I don't need a fortuneteller to tell me I'm in trouble. She has a notorious record of having safely deposited more than twelve beggars in the Refuge. My only chance is to get out of here before she can find a beefy policeman. I'm walking to the gate when I hear people talking about two and seven. I even forget the trouble Miss Gallovidian is going to bring me. I run as fast as a man with a twisted leg can to the Bookie. Only six tickets were sold, the loud speaker was saying, only I'm not interested.

As the Bookie is handing me the money Blushing Groom seems even happier than I am. His crooked teeth, which are dulled by tobacco, click every time the Bookie counts a hundred. His greasy lips are watering while a pair of bloodshot eyes are blinking with a dull brilliance. It hurts my eyes to look at him. I have hardly put the money in my pocket, when gruesome pats me on the back and says, nice and loud: "We made it!"

I must have been a fool not to have been wise as to why Blushing Groom was acting the perfect chaperon.

"That's fine," I say. "What have *we* made?"

"Don't be bashful," he says, "we caught the richest double. Come, this calls for a celebration." He extends a hand, and all the time he's smiling as if his wife has given birth to quadruplets.

"Look, pal," I say. "It's a good try. I couldn't have done better myself. This is the perfect set-up, isn't it? Well, I've got news for you: I caught that double alone, I don't know you and I don't care to. Go get yourself another piece of cheese. . . . I'm not that easy."

This ape suddenly stops smiling and looks at me like I had the plague. His broad, flat nose starts puffing out steam like an angry Spanish bull (only I'm not in the mood to make fancy passes like a toreador). All in all, he looks positively fierce, like the animal in the simile.

"Six-hundred and seventy pounds is a lot of money," he shouts. "Nobody's going to cheat me out of my share. You being a cripple. . . ."

"Shut up!" I yell. "Never call me that again, you . . . You!" I swing a right cross to his face, but this ape is smart. He blocks it and lands a hard one on my chin. I rock back and land flat on my sitters, while jungle tom-toms beat out a solid conga in my head. After a while my head clears and I get up, burning with rage. If I only had the strength, I would tear this ape apart.

Blushing Groom has put on quite a show; we have a good audience. Some white folks are threatening to beat his brains out. . . . I sincerely hope they do.

Suddenly I see a police badge jostling its way through. This is no place for me! I dash and start zigzagging through the people. A junior confusion starts, with everybody trying to give way. I run a few minutes, stumble and fall on my face. The policeman bends down and grabs me firmly by the arm and whispers: "Look, John, let's not have trouble. Come along quietly and everything will be just fine."

Under the circumstances I have no choice but to submit. My mother always told me never to resist arrest, let alone striking a uniformed officer of the law. Me and my money part company after Blushing Groom had preferred charges. My submission causes me to spend a not-so-glorious weekend at the Bantu Refuge. My transfer there being arranged by the thoughtful sergeant in the charge office, who out of pure love could not have me thrown in with hardened criminals . . . what with the place filled with housebreakers, extortioners, professional pickpockets and a generous assortment of other unsavoury characters. Frankly, I hoped he would mind his own business. I might even have started a crap game and made me some money.

"I am almost certain that you will be back here in a few days," the magistrate had said. Somebody ought to tell him he has a great future . . . reading palms. He looks at me and a grin spreads over his pancake-like face. This place must be short of magistrates; why has it got to be the same one all the time?

"Beggars who play the horses are a dangerous nuisance. They misuse the kindness that is shown to them."

Just my luck: now I have to listen to a lecture on morals. The magistrate looks pleased with himself, and I don't like it. Miss Gallovidian looks at me and smiles like a proud victress. She probably expects a promotion for this. I'm called on to the stand.

Some man with a thin face asks me to raise my right hand and swear to tell the truth. After saying my piece, the prosecutor starts questioning me as if he's promised thirty per cent of Blushing Groom's cut. After his session with me, he calls Blushing Groom to the stand.

"Do you know this man?" the prosecutor says.

"No, sir."

"How was it then you put up ten shillings to bet the horses with him?"

"I was losing all morning when I decided to try somebody's guesses. I met him, and we started talking."

"Did anybody see you talking to him?"

"I don't know, but somebody must have."

"Then what happened?"

"I asked him if he had a tip. He said he had one straight from the horse's mouth . . . A sure thing, he said. I then asked him if

I could put up ten shillings. He agreed. I was afraid to make the bet, so I gave him the money and walked over to the Bookie's stand with him where he placed a pound win on two and seven."

"Why were you afraid to make the bet?"

"I thought he was luckier than I was . . . besides, I had been losing all morning."

"Why did you strike him?"

"He was trying to cheat me out of my share, and tried to hit me when he couldn't."

The magistrate looks at me with something like contempt in his eyes. I won't have to put on a show for him this time. I might just as well kiss half my money good-bye. Blushing Groom's story is watertight.

"I'm thoroughly disappointed with you," the magistrate says. "I didn't know you were a thief too. I don't believe you could have made that bet alone; beggars haven't got so much money. I believe his story, things like this do happen. The money will be shared equally between the two of you."

"I don't believe you could have made that bet alone." What a cheek! I'll have that hobo know I make more money in one week than he does in a month. I don't believe you. . . . Good God!

I feel like committing mass murder as the court hands Blushing Groom three hundred and thirty-five pounds of my money. This prehistoric beast has a swell racket. A few more jobs like this and he can retire and buy himself a villa on the Riviera.

Blushing Groom is magnificent, inspiring awe. He is completely uncompromising, thoroughly unscrupulous, without qualms or a conscience. He has wholly realized the separateness of good and evil and attained a purity in evil worthy of honest appraisal. He would not allow himself to be swayed from cheating me by my being a cripple. If I were allowed to choose a brother, he would be my only choice.

I take my share of the money and clear out before the magistrate and Miss Gallovidian cook up another charge against me. On my way home I find it difficult to resist the temptation of stopping at some busy corner and doing my stuff. I might make up for some of the money, but I just happen to be wearing my best and have been a beggar long enough to know that people don't give money away to beggars who are dressed better than they. People who give alms to beggars do so to establish their superiority over the receiver, and like I said: I'm not an apprentice beggar.

When I get home I find a letter from my wife.

"Our son, Tommy, is sick. Please come home. . . ."

I become afraid and anxious for my Tommy, and even the kind words of my outsize landlady fail to move me.

I had to wait for something like this to show me the folly of my ways. A man's place is next to his wife and family. I had hoped that some day I would be able to provide my boys with a decent education, to grow them like normal boys, not just sons of a helpless cripple. . . . to find a place for them in the sun. I might be a big shot beggar but as a husband and father, I stink.

"If I should not see my friend Serurubele, will you. . . ."

"Yes, I'll explain to him. I'll always have your room for you if you should ever want it again."

Deep down I know that I will want it again. I have three hundred and thirty-five reasons why I should. Blushing Groom and the gullible public of Johannesburg will live in my mind for ever. . . . I have to come back. I owe it to the profession. ▶

Ezekiel Mphahlele[1] / *South Africa*
(1919–   )

THE MASTER OF DOORNVLEI[2]

THE EARLY SUMMER RAIN was pouring fiercely. In the mud-and-grass church house a bird flitted from one rafter to another, trapped. All was silent in the church except for a cough now and again that punctuated the preacher's sermon. Now and then, to relieve the gravity of the devotional moment, a few members of the congregation allowed themselves to be ensnared by the circling movements of the bird.

But only a few of them. Most of the people had their eyes fixed on the elderly preacher, as if they were following the motion of every line on each lip as he gave his sermon. In any case, he did not have a booming voice, like his deacon's (a point on which the old man was often plagued by a feeling of inferiority). So his listeners always watched his lips. One or two older women at the back screwed up their faces to see him better.

A nine-year-old boy was particularly charmed by the lost bird, and his eyes roved with it. Then he felt pity for it and wished he could catch it and let it out through the window which it missed several times. But the preacher went on, and his listeners soared on the wings of his sermon to regions where there was no labour or sweat and care.

Suddenly the boy saw the bird make straight for a closed window and hit against the glass and flutter to the floor. It tried

1. *Mphahlele* (mə fä lä′lā). 2. *Doornvlei* (dürn′vlā).

to fly but could not. He went to pick it up. He hugged it and stroked it. He looked about, but the people's faces looked ahead, like stolid clay figures. Why are they so cold and quiet when a bird is in pain? he asked himself.

It lay quiet in his hand, and he could feel the slight beat of the heart in the little feathered form.

"And so, brothers and sisters," the preacher concluded, "the Holy Word bids us love one another, and do to others as we would that they do to us. Amen." He asked his flock to kneel for prayer.

At this time Mfukeri,[3] the foreman of Doornvlei Farm on which the makeshift church was built, came in. He looked around and spotted his target—a puny wisp of a boy with scraggy legs, the boy with the bird in his hand.

When he took the boy out the people continued to kneel, unperturbed, except for the raising of a head here and there; perhaps just to make sure who the victim was this time. As the two went out the boy's rather big waistcoat that dangled loosely from his shoulders, flapped about.

It was common for Mfukeri to butt in at a prayer session to fetch a man or woman or child for a job that needed urgent attention. The congregants were labour tenants, who in return for their work earned the few square yards of earth on which they lived, and a ration of mealie-meal,[4] sugar, and an occasional piece of meat.

When they complained about such disturbances to the farmer, Sarel Britz, he said: "I'm just to my labourers. I favour nobody above the rest. Farm work is farm work; I often have to give up my church service myself."

The boy tried to protect the bird. He could not keep it on his person, so he put it under a tin in the fowlrun before he went about the work Mfukeri had directed him to do. The rain continued to pour.

The following day the boy took ill with pneumonia. He had got soaked in the rain. On such days the little mud-and-grass

---

3. *Mfukeri* (mə fū kä′rē). **4.** *mealie-meal,* corn meal.

houses of the labourers looked wretched: as if they might cave in any time under some unseen load. The nearest hospital was fifty miles away, and if the workers wanted to see the district surgeon, they would have to travel twenty-five miles there and back. The district surgeon could only be seen once a week.

The boy ran a high temperature. When he was able to speak he asked his mother to go and see how his bird fared in the fowlrun. She came back to tell him that the bird had been found under a tin, dead. That same night the boy died.

When the news went round, the workers seemed to run berserk.

"It has happened before . . ."

"My child—not even ten yet . . . !"

"Come, let's go to Sarel Britz . . . !"

"No, wait, he'll be angry with us, very angry . . ."

"We can also get angry . . ."

"Yes, but the White man is very powerful . . ."

"And truly so—where do we get work if he drives us off the farm . . . ?"

"He wants our hands and our sweat—he cannot do that . . ."

"He beats us, and now he wants to kill us . . ."

"Send him back to Rhodesia—this Mfukeri . . . !"

"Yes, we don't do such things on this farm . . ."

"By the spirits, we don't work tomorrow until we see this thing out . . . !"

"Give us our trek-passes [5] . . . ! Save our children . . .!"

"Ho friends! I am not going with you. I have children to look after . . . !"

"That is why we are going to Sarel Britz . . . !"

"Come, friends, let's talk first before we march to the master of Doornvlei."

Tau Rathebe, who could read and write, rallied the workers to

---

5. *trek-passes.* Under South African law, blacks must carry an identification card, or "pass," and produce it on demand, or else be subject to arrest. By witholding their passes, white employers can keep their black laborers in virtual slavery.

an open spot not far from the main gate. Grim and rugged farm workers; shaggy; none with extra flesh on him; young and old, with tough sinewy limbs. Those who were too scared to join the march kept in the bushes nearby to watch. Women remained behind.

The men were angry and impatient. "We want Mfukeri away from Doornvlei, or we go, trek-pass or none!" was the general cry, echoed and re-echoed.

And they marched, as they had never done before, to the master's house.

Britz and Mfukeri were standing on the front verandah, waiting. It was to be expected: the foreman had already gone to warn Britz. Apart from what knowledge he had about Tau Rathebe, it was plain from the early morning that the workers were not prepared to work.

"What is it, men?"

"The people want Mfukeri sent away," said Tau. "He has been using his *sjambok* [6] on some workers, and now old Petrus Sechele's son is dead, because Mfukeri took him out in the rain. I've warned him about this before."

"I'll think about it. You're asking me to do a difficult thing; you must give me time to think."

"How long?" asked Tau.

Sarel Britz felt annoyed at the implied ultimatum and Tau's insolent manner; but he restrained himself.

"Till noon today. Just now I want you to go to your work. I'm just, and to show it, Mfukeri is not going to the fields until I've decided."

They dispersed, each to his work, discontented and surly. When Mfukeri left Sarel Britz in conference with his mother, the usually smooth and slippery texture on the foreman's face, peculiar to Rhodesian Africans, looked flabby.

"I've told him not to use the *sjambok,* but he insists on doing it, just because I forbid it," said Britz when he had gone.

"Reason?" Marta Britz asked.

---

6. *sjambok* (shäm′bok), a heavy leather whip.

"Just to make me feel I depend on him."

"He never behaved like this when your father was alive. Once he was told he must do a thing or mustn't he obeyed."

There was a pause during which mother and son almost heard each other's thoughts.

"You know, Mamma, when I was at university—on the experimental farm—I knew many Black and Coloured folk. Thinking back on the time, now, makes me feel Pa was wrong."

"Wrong about what?"

"About Kaffirs [7] being children."

"But they are, my son. Your father himself said so."

"No, one has to be on the alert with them. One can't afford to take things for granted."

"How are they grown up?"

Sarel went and stood right in front of her. "Yes, Ma, they're fully grown up; some of them are cleverer and wiser than a lot of us Whites. Their damned patience makes them all the more dangerous. Maybe Mfukeri's still somewhat a child. But certainly not the others. Take today, for instance. A coming together like this has never been heard of on a White man's farm. And they've left everything in the hands of their leader. No disorder. They're serpent's eggs, and I'm going to crush them." He paused.

"I didn't tell you that Mfukeri has been keeping an eye on this Tau Rathebe. We've found out he was deported from Johannesburg. Somehow slipped into this farm. And now he's been having secret meetings with three or four of our Kaffirs at a time, to teach them what to do like today."

"So! Hemel!" [8]

"So you see, Ma, Papa was wrong. I'm going to keep a sharp eye on the swine. But first thing, I'm ready to drive Rathebe away; out with him tomorrow."

At noon the master of Doornvlei made his double decision known: that Tau Rathebe was to leave the farm the following morning, and that Mfukeri had been warned and would be given another chance—the last.

---

7. *Kaffirs,* black South Africans, a term of abuse. 8. *Hemel!* Heavens!

This caused a stir among the labourers, but Tau Rathebe asked them to keep calm.

They wanted to leave with him.

"No. The police will take you as soon as you leave Doornvlei. You can't go from one farm to another without a trek-pass," he reminded them.

He left Doornvlei . . .

Sarel Britz felt confused. He kept repeating to himself what he had said to his mother earlier. These are no children, no children . . . they are men . . . I'm dealing with the minds of men . . . My father was wrong . . . All my boyhood he led me to believe that black people were children . . . O Hemel, they aren't . . . ! He had begun to see the weakness of his father's theory during his university years, but it was the incident with Rathebe that had stamped that weakness on his mind.

Harvest time came, and Doornvlei became a little world of intense life and work. The maize triangle of South Africa was buzzing with talk of a surplus crop and the threat of low prices.

"A big crop again, Mfukeri, what do you say?" said Britz.

"Yes, baas," [9] he grinned consent, "little bit better than last year."

"You know you're a good worker and foreman, Mfukeri. Without you I don't know how I'd run this farm."

"Yes, baas. If baas is happy I'm happy."

"Since Rathebe left there's peace here, not so?"

"Yes, baas, he makes too much trouble. Long time I tell baas he always meet the men by the valley. They talk a long time there. Sometime one man tell me they want more money and food. I'm happy for you, baas. The old baas he say I must help you all the time because I work for him fifteen years. I want him to rest in peace in his grave."

Britz nodded several times.

The Rhodesian foreman worked as hard as ever to retain the master's praise. He did not spare himself; and the other workers had to keep up with his almost inhuman pace.

---

9. *baas* (bäs), master. [*Afrikaans*]

"Hey you!" Mfukeri shouted often. "You there, you're not working fast enough." He drove them on, and some worked in panic, breaking off mealie cobs and throwing them with the dexterity of a juggler into sacks hanging from the shoulder. Mfukeri did not beat the workers any more. On this Sarel Britz had put his foot down. "Beat your workers and you lose them," his father had often said. But every servant felt the foreman's presence and became jittery. And the army of black sweating labourers spread out among the mealie stalks after the systematic fashion of a battle strategy.

Sometimes they sang their songs of grief and hope while reaping in the autumn sun. Sometimes they were too tired even to sing of grief; then they just went on sweating and thinking; then there was a Sunday afternoon to look forward to, when they would go to the village for a drink and song and dance and lovemaking.

Sarel Britz became sterner and more exacting. And his moods and attitude were always reflected in his trusty Mfukeri. Britz kept reminding his tenants that he was just; he favoured no one above the others; he repeated it often to Mfukeri and to his mother. He leant more and more on his foreman, who realized it and made the most of it.

Back at university the students had had endless talks about the Blacks. Britz had discussed with them his father's theory about allowing the Black man a few rungs to climb up at a time; because he was still a child. Most of his colleagues had laughed at this. Gradually he accepted their line of thinking: the White man must be vigilant.

Often when he did his accounts and books, Sarel Britz would stop in the middle of his work, thinking and wondering what he would do if he lost much of his labour, like the other farmers. What if the towns continued to attract the Black labourer by offering him jobs once preserved for the White man. Would the Black workers continue to flow into the towns, or would the law come to the farmer's rescue by stopping the influx?

Sarel Britz lived in this fear. At the same time, he thought, it would break him if he paid his workers more than forty shillings [10] a month in order to keep them. A mighty heap of troubles rose before his eyes, and he could almost hear the shouts and yells of labour tenants from all the farms rising against their masters . . .

The threat became more and more real to Britz. But Mfukeri consoled him. Britz had lately been inviting him to the house quite often for a chat about doings on the farm. If only that Kaffir didn't know so much about the farm so that he, Britz, had to depend on him more than he cared to . . . "Come to the house tonight, Mfukeri, and let's talk," he said, one afternoon in late autumn.

"All right, baas."

Mfukeri went to see his master. He wondered what the master had to say. He found him reclining comfortably on his chair. Mfukeri could not dare to take a chair before he was told to sit down—in the same chair he always sat on.

"Thank you, baas."

After a moment of silence, "What do you think of me, Mfukeri?"

"Why do you ask me, baas?"—after looking about.

"Don't be afraid to say your mind."

"You're all right, baas."

"Sure?"

"Yes, baas." They smoked silently.

"You still like this farm?"

"Very much, baas."

"I'm glad. You're a good foreman—the only man I trust here."

Mfukeri understood Britz. He wanted to assure his master that he would never desert him, that he was capable of keeping the tenants together. Hadn't he spied cleverly on Tau Rathebe and avoided an upheaval?

The foreman felt triumphant. He had never in his life dreamt he would work his way into a White man's trust. He had always felt so inferior before a White man that he despised himself. The

---

10. *forty shillings*, about $5.60.

more he despised himself the sterner and more ruthless he became towards his fellow-workers. At least he could retain a certain amount of self-respect and the feeling that he was a man, now that his master looked so helpless.

As the foreman sat smoking his pipe, he thought: "How pitiable they look when they're at a Black man's mercy . . . I wonder now . . ."

"All right, Mfukeri," said the master. The Rhodesian rose and stood erect, like a bluegum tree, over the White man; and the White man thought how indifferent his servant looked; just like a tree. To assert his authority once more Britz gave a few orders.

"Attend to that compost manure first thing tomorrow morning. And also the cleaning up of the chicken hospital; see to that fanbelt in the threshing machine."

"Yes, baas, goodnight."

He was moving towards the door when Britz said, "Before I forget, be careful about Donker mixing with the cows. It wasn't your fault, of course, but you'll take care, won't you?"

"Yes." He knew his master regarded his bull Donker as inferior stock, and felt hurt.

It was a bewildered Britz the foreman left behind. The farmer thought how overwhelming his servant was when he stood before him. Something in him quaked. He was sensitive enough to catch the tone of the last "baas" when Mfukeri left: it was such an indifferent echo of what "baas" sounded like years before.

Mfukeri kept a bull with a squatter family on a farm adjoining Doornvlei. Labour tenants were not allowed to keep livestock on the farm on which they themselves worked, because they were paid and received food rations. Mfukeri's friend agreed to keep Donker, the bull, for him. It was a good bull, though scrub.

Two days later Sarel Britz was roused from his lunch-hour sleep by noise outside. He ran out and saw workers hurrying towards a common point. In a few moments he found himself standing near Mfukeri and a group of workers. In front of the barn Britz's pedigree stallion, Kasper, was kicking out at Donker, Mfukeri's bull. Donker had the horse against the barn wall, and was roaring and pawing the earth.

Kasper kicked, a quick barrage of hoofs landing square on the bull's forehead. But the stocky Donker kept coming in and slashing out with his short horns. Normally, there would be ecstatic shouting from the workers. They stood in silence weaving and ducking to follow the movements of the fighters. They couldn't express their attitude towards either side, because they hated both Britz and Mfukeri; and yet the foreman was one of them.

The stallion tried to turn round, which was almost fatal; for Donker charged and unleashed more furious lightning kicks. Master and foreman watched, each feeling that he was entangled in this strife between their animals; more so than they dared to show outwardly. Sarel Britz bit his lower lip as he watched the rage of the bull. He seemed to see scalding fury in the very slime that came from the mouth of the bull to mix with the earth.

He didn't like the slime mixing with the sand: it looked as if Donker were invoking a mystic power in the earth to keep his forehoofs from slipping. Once the hoofs were planted in the ground the bull found an opening and gored Kasper in the stomach, ripping the skin with the upward motion of the horn.

Sarel Britz gave a shout, and walked away hurriedly.

When Mfukeri saw Kasper tottering, and his beloved bull drawing back, an overwhelming feeling of victory shot through every nerve in him. What he had been suppressing all through the fight came out in a gasp and, with tears in his eyes, he shouted: "Donker! Donker!"

There was a murmur among some of the onlookers who said what a pity it was the horse's hoofs weren't shod; otherwise the ending would have been different.

Kasper was giving his last dying kicks when Britz came back with a rifle in his hand. His face was set. The workers stood aside. Two shots from the rifle finished off the stallion.

"Here, destroy the bull!" he ordered Mfukeri, handing him the gun. The foreman hesitated. "I said shoot that bull!"

"Why do you want me to shoot my bull, baas?"

"If you don't want to do it, then you must leave this farm, at once!"

Mfukeri did not answer. They both knew the moment had come. He stood still and looked at Britz. Then he walked off, and coaxed his bull out of the premises.

"I gave him a choice," Sarel said to his mother, telling her the whole story.

"You shouldn't have, Sarel. He has worked for us these fifteen years."

Sarel knew he had been right. As he looked out of the window to the empty paddock, he was stricken with grief. And then he was glad. He had got rid of yet another threat to his authority.

But the fear remained. ▶

Jacob Afolabi Untitled (Oshogbo), 1964. Lino-cut.

Abioseh Nicol / *Sierra Leone*

(1920–   )

LIFE IS SWEET AT KUMANSENU

THE SEA AND THE WET SAND to one side of it; green tropical forest on the other; above it the slow tumbling clouds. The clean round blinding disc of sun and the blue sky, covered and surrounded the small African village, Kameni.

A few square mud houses with roofs like helmets, here thatched and there covered with corrugated zinc where the prosperity of cocoa and trading had touched the head of the family.

The widow Bola stirred her palm oil stew and thought of nothing in particular. She chewed a Kola nut rhythmically with her strong toothless jaws and soon unconsciously she was chewing in rhythm with the skipping of Asi, her grand-daughter. She looked idly at Asi as the seven-year-old brought the twisted palm-leaf rope smartly over her head and jumped over it, counting in English each time the rope struck the ground and churned up a little red dust. Bola herself did not understand English well, but she could count easily up to twenty in English for market purposes. Asi shouted six and then said nine, ten. Bola called out that after six came seven. And I should know, she sighed. Although now she was old and her womb and breasts were withered, there was a time when she bore children regularly every two years. Six times she had borne a boy child and six times they had died. Some had swollen up and with weak

From THE TRULY MARRIED WOMAN, by Abioseh Nicol, published by the Oxford University Press.

plaintive cries had faded away. Others had shuddered in sudden convulsions, with burning skins, and had rolled up their eyes and died. They had all died. Or rather he had died, Bola thought, because she knew it was one child all the time whose spirit had crept up restlessly into her womb to be born and to mock her.[1] The sixth time Musa, the village magician whom time had transformed into a respectable Muslim, had advised her and her husband to break the bones of the quiet little corpse and mangle it so that it couldn't come back to torment them alive again. But she held on to the child, and refused to let them handle it. Secretly she had marked it with a sharp pointed stick at the left buttock before it was wrapped in a mat and they had taken it away. When, the seventh time she had borne a son, and the purification ceremonies had taken place, she had turned it slyly to see whether the mark was there. It was. She showed it to the old woman who was the midwife and asked her what that was, and she had forced herself to believe the other who said it was an accidental scratch made whilst the child was being scrubbed with herbs to remove placental blood. But this child had stayed. Meji, he had been called. And he was now thirty years of age and a second-class clerk in Government offices in a town ninety miles away. Asi, his daughter, had been left with her to do the things an old woman wanted a small child for, to run and take messages to the neighbours, to fetch a cup of water from the earthenware pot in the kitchen, to sleep with her and be fondled.

She threw the washed and squeezed cassava leaves into the red boiling stew, putting in a finger's pinch of salt, and then went indoors, carefully stepping over the threshold to look for the dried red pepper. She found it, and then dropped it, leaning against the wall with a little cry. He turned round from the window and looked at her with a twisted half smile of love and sadness. In his short-sleeved, open-necked white shirt and grey gaberdine trousers, a gold wrist watch and brown suede shoes, he

---

1. *one child . . . to mock her.* Among West African peoples the belief exists of a spirit-child who does not live to maturity but returns to its mother's womb in a series of rebirths.

looked like the pictures in African magazines of a handsome clerk who would get to the top because he ate the correct food, or regularly took the correct laxative, which was being advertised. His skin was greyish brown and he had a large red handkerchief tied round his neck.

"Meji, God be praised," Bola cried. "You gave me quite a turn. My heart is weak and I can no longer take surprises. When did you come? How did you come? By lorry, by fishing boat? And how did you come into the house? The front door was locked. There are so many thieves nowadays. I'm so glad to see you, so glad," she mumbled and wept, leaning against his breast.

Meji's voice was hoarse, and he said: "I am glad to see you too, Mother," beating her back affectionately.

Asi ran in and cried "Papa, Papa," and was rewarded with a lift and a hug.

"Never mind how I came, Mother," Meji said, laughing, "I'm here, and that's all that matters."

"We must make a feast, we must have a big feast. I must tell the neighbours at once. Asi, run this very minute to Mr. Addai, the catechist, and tell him your papa is home. Then to Mami Gbera to ask her for extra provisions, and to Pa Babole for drummers and musicians. . . ."

"Stop," said Meji raising his hand. "This is all quite unnecessary. I don't want to see *anyone,* no one at all, I wish to rest quietly and completely. No one is to know I'm here."

Bola looked very crestfallen. She was proud of Meji, and wanted to show him off. The village would never forgive her for concealing such an important visitor. Meji must have sensed this because he held her shoulder comfortingly and said: "They will know soon enough. Let us enjoy each other, all three of us, this time. Life is too short."

Bola turned to Asi, picked up the packet of pepper and told her to go and drop a little into the boiling pot outside, taking care not to go too near the fire or play with it. After the child had gone, Bola said to her son, "Are you in trouble? Is it the police?"

He shook his head. "No," he said, "it's just that I like returning to you. There will always be this bond of love and affection between us, and I don't wish to share it. It is our private affair and that is why I've left my daughter with you," he ended up irrelevantly, "girls somehow seem to stay with relations longer."

"And don't I know it," said Bola. "But you look pale," she continued, "and you keep scraping your throat. Are you ill?" She laid her hand on his brow. "And you're cold, too."

"It's the cold wet wind," he said, a little harshly. "I'll go and rest now if you can open and dust my room for me. I'm feeling very tired. Very tired indeed. I've travelled very far today and it has not been as easy journey."

"Of course, my son, of course," Bola replied, bustling away hurriedly but happily.

Meji slept all afternoon till evening, and his mother brought his food to his room, later took the empty basins away. Then he slept again till morning.

The next day, Saturday, was a busy one, and after further promising Meji that she would tell no one he was about, Bola went off to market. Meji took Asi for a long walk through a deserted path and up into the hills. She was delighted. They climbed high until they could see the village below in front of them, and the sea in the distance, and the boats with their wide white sails. Soon the sun had passed its zenith and was half way towards the west. Asi had eaten all the food, the dried fish and the flat tapioca pancakes and the oranges. Her father said he wasn't hungry, and this had made the day perfect for Asi, who had chattered, eaten, and then played with her father's fountain pen and other things from his pocket. They soon left for home because he had promised they would be back before dark; he had carried her down some steep boulders and she had held on to his shoulders because he had said his neck hurt so and she must not touch it. She had said: "Papa, I can see behind you and you haven't got a shadow. Why?"

He had then turned her round to face the sun. Since she was getting drowsy, she had started asking questions, and her father had joked with her and humoured her. "Papa, why has your watch stopped at twelve o'clock?" "Because the world ends at noon." Asi had chuckled at that. "Papa, why do you wear a scarf always round your neck?" "Because my head would fall off if I didn't." She had laughed out loud at that. But soon she had fallen asleep as he bore her homewards.

Just before nightfall, with his mother dressed in her best, they had all three, at her urgent request, gone to his father's grave, taking a secret route and avoiding the main village. It was a small cemetery, not more than twenty years or so old, started when the Rural Health Department had insisted that no more burials take place in the backyards of households. Bola took a bottle of wine and a glass and four split halves of Kola, each a half sphere, two red and two white. They reached the graveside and she poured some wine into the glass. Then she spoke to the dead man softly and caressingly. She had brought his son to see him, she said. This son whom God had given success, to the confusion and discomfiture of their enemies. Here he was, a man with a pensionable clerk's job and not a farmer, fisherman or a mechanic. All the years of their married life people had said she was a witch because her children had died young. But this boy of theirs had shown that she was a good woman. Let her husband answer her now, to show that he was listening. She threw the four Kola nuts up into the air and they fell on the grave. Three fell with the flat face upwards and one with its flat face downwards. She picked them up again and conversed with him once more and threw the Kola nuts up again. But still there was an odd one or sometimes two.

They did not fall with all four faces up, or with all four faces down, to show that he was listening and was pleased. She spoke endearingly, she cajoled, she spoke sternly. But all to no avail. Then she asked Meji to perform. He crouched by the graveside and whispered. Then he threw the Kola nuts and they rolled a little, Bola following them eagerly with her sharp old eyes. They all ended up face downwards. Meji emptied the glass of wine on the grave and then said that he felt nearer his father at that moment than he had ever done before in his life.

It was sundown, and they all three went back silently home in the short twilight. That night, going outside the house near her son's room window, she found, to her sick disappointment, that he had been throwing away all the cooked food out there. She did not mention this when she went to say goodnight, but she did sniff and say that there was a smell of decay in the room. Meji said he thought there was a dead rat up in the rafters, and he would clear it away after she had gone to bed.

That night it rained heavily, and sheet lightning turned the darkness into brief silver daylight, for one or two seconds at a time. Then the darkness again and the rain. Bola woke soon after midnight and thought she could hear knocking. She went to Meji's room to ask him to open the door, but he wasn't there. She thought he might have gone out for a while and been locked out by mistake. She opened the door quickly, holding an oil lamp upwards. He stood on the verandah, curiously unwet, and refused to come in.

"I have to go away," he said hoarsely, coughing.

"Do come in," she said.

"No," he said, "I have to go, but I wanted to thank you for giving me a chance."

"What nonsense is this?" she said. "Come in out of the rain."

"I did not think I should leave without thanking you."

The rain fell hard, the door creaked and the wind whistled.

"Life is sweet, Mother dear, good-bye, and thank you."

He turned round and started running.

There was a sudden diffuse flash of lightning and she saw that the yard was empty. She went back heavily, and fell into a restless sleep. Before she slept she said to herself that she must see Mr. Addai next morning, Sunday, or, better still, Monday, and tell him about this in case Meji was in trouble. She hoped Meji would not be annoyed. He was such a good son.

But it was Mr. Addai who came instead, on Sunday afternoon, quiet and grave, and saw Bola sitting on an old stool in the verandah, dressing Asi's hair in tight thin plaits.

Mr. Addai sat down and, looking away, he said: "The Lord giveth and the Lord taketh away." And soon half the village were sitting round the verandah and in the yard.

"But I tell you, he was here on Friday and left Sunday morning," Bola said. "He couldn't have died on Friday."

Bola had just recovered from a fainting fit after being told of her son's death in town. His wife, Asi's mother, had come with the news, bringing some of his property. She said Meji had died instantly at noon on Friday and had been buried on Saturday at sundown. They would have brought him to Kameni for the burial. He had always wished that. But they could not do so in time as bodies did not last much after a day.

"He was here, he was here," Bola said, rubbing her forehead and weeping.

Asi sat by quietly. Mr. Addai said comfortingly, "Hush, hush, he couldn't have been, because no one in the village saw him."

"He said we were to tell no one," Bola said.

The crowd smiled above Bola's head, and shook their heads. "Poor woman," someone said, "she is beside herself with grief."

"He died on Friday," Mrs. Meji repeated, crying. "He was in the office and he pulled up the window to look out and call the messenger. Then the sash broke. The window fell, broke his neck and the sharp edge almost cut his head off; they say he died at once."

"My papa had a scarf around his neck," Asi shouted suddenly.

"Hush," said the crowd.

Mrs. Meji dipped her hand into her bosom and produced a small gold locket and put it round Asi's neck, to quieten her. "Your papa had this made last week for your Christmas present. You may as well have it now."

Asi played with it and pulled it this way and that.

"Be careful, child," Mr. Addai said, "it was your father's last gift."

"I was trying to remember how he showed me yesterday to open it," Asi said.

"You have never seen it before," Mrs. Meji said, sharply, trembling with fear mingled with anger.

She took the locket and tried to open it.

"Let me have it," said the village goldsmith, and he tried whispering magic words of incantation. Then he said, defeated,

"It must be poor-quality gold; it has rusted. I need tools to open it."

"I remember now," Asi said in the flat complacent voice of childhood.

The crowd gathered round quietly and the setting sun glinted on the soft red African gold of the dangling trinket. The goldsmith handed the locket over to Asi and asked in a loud whisper: "How did he open it?"

"Like so," Asi said and pressed a secret catch. It flew open and she spelled out gravely the word inside. "ASI"

The silence continued.

"His neck, poor boy," Bola said a little wildly, "that is why he could not eat the lovely meals I cooked for him."

Mr. Addai announced a service of intercession after vespers that evening. The crowd began to leave quietly.

Musa, the magician, was one of the last to leave. He was now very old and bent. In times of grave calamity, it was known that even Mr. Addai did not raise objection to Musa being consulted.

He bent over further and whispered in Bola's ear: "You should have had his bones broken and mangled thirty-one years ago when he went for the sixth time and then he would not have come back to mock you all these years by pretending to be alive. I told you so. But you women are naughty and stubborn."

Bola stood up, her black face held high, her eyes terrible with maternal rage and pride.

"I am glad I did not," she said, "and that is why he came back specially to thank me before he went for good."

She clutched Asi to her. "I am glad I gave him the opportunity to come back, for life is sweet. I do not expect you to understand why I did so. After all, you are only a man." ▶

Rui Nogar / *Mozambique*
(20th cent.)

POEM OF THE CONSCRIPTED WARRIOR

Translated from the Portuguese by
Philippa Rumsey

He went there
Afraid
Of being afraid.

(Oh Our Lady of Anything
5 In my village
I left my wife behind.)

He went there
With the shame
Of feeling ashamed.

10 (Perhaps I might even kill children;
I have two children, oh Lord . . .)

"Poem of the Conscripted Warrior" by Rui Nogar, translated by Philippa Rumsey, from AFRICAN WRITING TODAY edited by Ezekiel Mphahlele. Reprinted by permission of Penguin Books Ltd.

He went there
Involuntarily
He went there
15 And the courage was not his own
And the hate was not his own
Not his own
Not at all
But he went
20 Infected with blood lust
He killed killed killed
Until one day
Oh! irony
On that day
25 There was sun
There was hope
There was his wife
There were his children his mother a letter
There was so much
30 But all crumbled away
All
In the treacherous cackling
Of the grenades
With yellow beaks
35 And red tails . . .

Grace A. Ogot / *Kenya*
(1930–   )

THE RAIN CAME

THE CHIEF was still far from the gate when his daughter Oganda saw him. She ran to meet him. Breathlessly she asked her father, "What is the news, great Chief? Everyone in the village is anxiously waiting to hear when it will rain." Labong'o held out his hands for his daughter but he did not say a word. Puzzled by her father's cold attitude Oganda ran back to the village to warn the others that the chief was back.

The atmosphere in the village was tense and confused. Everyone moved aimlessly and fussed in the yard without actually doing any work. A young woman whispered to her co-wife, "If they have not solved this rain business today, the chief will crack." They had watched him getting thinner and thinner as the people kept on pestering him. "Our cattle lie dying in the fields," they reported. "Soon it will be our children and then ourselves. Tell us what to do to save our lives, oh great Chief." So the chief had daily pleaded with the Almighty through the ancestors to deliver them from their great distress.

Instead of calling the family together and giving them the news immediately, Labong'o went to his own hut, a sign that he was not to be disturbed. Having replaced the shutter, he sat in the dimly lit hut to contemplate.

It was no longer a question of being the chief of hunger-stricken people that weighed Labong'o's heart. It was the life of

"The Rain Came" by Grace A. Ogot from MODERN AFRICAN STORIES, edited by Koemy and Mphahlele. Reprinted by permission of the author.

his only daughter that was at stake. At the time when Oganda came to meet him, he saw the glittering chain shining around her waist. The prophecy was complete. "It is Oganda, Oganda, my only daughter, who must die so young." Labong'o burst into tears before finishing the sentence. The chief must not weep. Society had declared him the bravest of men. But Labong'o did not care any more. He assumed the position of a simple father and wept bitterly. He loved his people, the Luo,[1] but what were the Luo for him without Oganda? Her life had brought a new life in Labong'o's world and he ruled better than he could remember. How would the spirit of the village survive his beautiful daughter? "There are so many homes and so many parents who have daughters. Why choose this one? She is all I have." Labong'o spoke as if the ancestors were there in the hut and he could see them face to face. Perhaps they were there, warning him to remember his promise on the day he was enthroned when he said aloud, before the elders, "I will lay down my life, if necessary, and the life of my household, to save this tribe from the hands of the enemy." "Deny! Deny!" he could hear the voice of his forefathers mocking him.

When Labong'o was made chief he was only a young man. Unlike his father he ruled for many years with only one wife. But people mocked him secretly because his only wife did not bear him a daughter. He married a second, a third and a fourth wife. But they all gave birth to male children. When Labong'o married a fifth wife, she bore him a daughter. They called her Oganda, meaning "beans," because her skin was very smooth. Out of Labong'o's twenty children, Oganda was the only girl. Though she was the chief's favourite, her mother's co-wives swallowed their jealous feelings and showered her with love. After all, they said, Oganda was a girl whose days in the royal family were numbered. She would soon marry at a tender age and leave the enviable position to someone else.

Never in his life had he been faced with such an impossible

---

1. *the Luo,* an agricultural people living in the flat land around Lake Victoria in western Kenya.

decision. Refusing to yield to the rain-maker's request would mean sacrificing the whole tribe, putting the interests of the individual above those of the society. More than that. It would mean disobeying the ancestors, and most probably wiping the Luo people from the surface of the earth. On the other hand, to let Oganda die as a ransom for the people would permanently cripple Labong'o spiritually. He knew he would never be the same chief again.

The words of Nditi, the medicine-man, still echoed in his ears. "Podho, the ancestor of the Luo, appeared to me in a dream last night and he asked me to speak to the chief and the people," Nditi had said to the gathering of tribesmen. "A young woman who has not known a man must die so that the country may have rain. While Podho was still talking to me, I saw a young woman standing at the lakeside, her hands raised above her head. Her skin was as a tender young deer's. Her tall slender figure stood like a lonely reed at the river bank. Her sleepy eyes wore a sad look like that of a bereaved mother. She wore a gold ring on her left ear and a glittering brass chain around her waist. As I still marvelled at the beauty of this young woman, Podho told me, 'Out of all the women in this land, we have chosen this one. Let her offer herself a sacrifice to the lake monster! And on that day, the rain will come down in torrents. Let everyone stay at home on that day, lest he be carried away by the floods.' "

Outside there was a strange stillness, except for the thirsty birds that sang lazily on the dying trees. The blinding midday heat had forced the people into their huts. Not far away from the chief's hut two guards were snoring away quietly. Labong'o removed his crown and the large eagle-head that hung loosely on his shoulders. He left the hut and, instead of asking Nyabogo the messenger to beat the drum, he went straight and beat it himself. In no time the whole household had assembled under the *siala* tree where he usually addressed them. He told Oganda to wait a while in her grandmother's hut.

When Labong'o stood to address his household his voice was hoarse and tears choked him. He started to speak but words refused to leave his lips. His wives and sons knew there was danger, perhaps their enemies had declared war on them. Labong'o's eyes were red and they could see he had been weeping. At last he told them, "One whom we love and treasure will be taken away from us. Oganda is to die." Labong'o's voice was so faint that he could not hear it himself. But he continued, "The ancestors have chosen her to be offered as a sacrifice to the lake monster in order that we may have rain."

For a moment there was dead silence among the people. They were completely stunned; and as some confused murmur broke out Oganda's mother fainted and was carried off to her own hut. But the other people rejoiced. They danced around singing and chanting, "Oganda is the lucky one to die for the people; if it is to save the people, let Oganda go."

In her grandmother's hut Oganda wondered what the whole family was discussing about her that she could not hear. Her grandmother's hut was well away from the chief's court and much as she strained her ears, she could not hear what they were saying. "It must be marriage," she concluded. It was an accepted custom for the family to discuss their daughter's future marriage behind her back. A faint smile played on Oganda's lips as she thought of the several young men who swallowed saliva at the mere mention of her name.

There was Kech, the son of an elder in a neighbouring clan. Kech was very handsome. He had sweet, meek eyes and roaring laughter. He could make a wonderful father, Oganda thought. But they would not be a good match. Kech was a bit too short to be her husband. It would humiliate her to have to look down at Kech each time she spoke to him. Then she thought of Dimo, the tall young man who had already distinguished himself as a brave warrior and an outstanding wrestler. Dimo loved Oganda, but Oganda thought he would make a cruel husband, always quarrelling and ready to fight. No, she did not like him. Oganda fingered the glittering chain on her waist as she thought of Osinda. A long time ago when she was quite young Osinda had given her that chain and, instead of wearing it around her neck several times, she wore it round her waist where it could permanently stay. She heard her heart pounding so loudly as she thought of him. She whispered, "Let it be you they are discussing, Osinda the lovely one. Come now and take me away. . . ."

The lean figure in the doorway startled Oganda who was rapt in thought about the man she loved. "You have frightened me, Grandma," said Oganda laughing. "Tell me, is it my marriage you were discussing? You can take it from me that I won't marry any of them." A smile played on her lips again. She was coaxing her grandma to tell her quickly, to tell her they were pleased with Osinda.

In the open space outside the excited relatives were dancing and singing. They were coming to the hut now, each carrying a gift to put at Oganda's feet. As their singing got nearer Oganda was able to hear what they were saying: "If it is to save the people, if it is to give us rain, let Oganda go. Let Oganda die for her people and for her ancestors." Was she mad to think that they were singing about her? How could she die? She found the lean figure of her grandmother barring the door. She could not get out. The look on her grandmother's face warned her that there was danger around the corner. "Mother, it is not marriage then?" Oganda asked urgently. She suddenly felt panicky, like a mouse cornered by a hungry cat. Forgetting that there was only one door in the hut, Oganda fought desperately to find another exit. She must fight for her life. But there was none.

She closed her eyes, leapt like a wild tiger through the door, knocking her grandmother flat to the ground. There outside in mourning garments Labong'o stood motionless, his hands folded at the back. He held his daughter's hand and led her away from the excited crowd to the little red-painted hut where her mother was resting. Here he broke the news officially to his daughter.

For a long time the three souls who loved one another dearly sat in darkness. It was no good speaking. And even if they tried, the words could not have come out. In the past they had been like three cooking-stones, sharing their burdens. Taking Oganda away from them would leave two useless stones which would not hold a cooking-pot.

News that the beautiful daughter of the chief was to be sacrificed to give the people rain spread across the country like wind. And at sunset the chief's village was full of relatives and friends who had come to congratulate Oganda. Many more were on their way, coming, carrying their gifts. They would dance till morning to keep her company. And in the morning they would prepare her a big farewell feast. All these relatives thought it a great honour to be selected by the spirits to die in order that the society might live. "Oganda's name will always remain a living name among us," they boasted.

Of course it was an honour, a great honour, for a woman's daughter to be chosen to die for the country. But what could the mother gain once her only daughter was blown away by the wind? There were so many other women in the land, why choose her daughter, her only child? Had human life any meaning at all? —other women had houses full of children while Oganda's mother had to lose her only child!

In the cloudless sky the moon shone brightly and the numerous stars glittered. The dancers of all age groups assembled to dance before Oganda, who sat close to her mother sobbing quietly. All these years she had been with her people she thought she understood them. But now she discovered that she was a stranger among them. If they really loved her as they had always professed, why were they not sympathetic? Why were they not making any attempt to save her? Did her people really understand what it felt like to die young? Unable to restrain her emotions any longer, she sobbed loudly as her age-group got up to dance.

They were young and beautiful and very soon they would marry and have their own children. They would have husbands to love and little huts for themselves. They would have reached maturity. Oganda touched the chain around her waist as she thought of Osinda. She wished Osinda were there too, among her friends. "Perhaps he is ill," she thought gravely. The chain comforted Oganda—she would die with it around her waist and wear it in the underground world.

In the morning a big feast of many different dishes was prepared for Oganda so that she could pick and choose. "People don't eat after death," they said. The food looked delicious but

Oganda touched none of it. Let the happy people eat. She contented herself with sips of water from a little calabash.

The time for her departure was drawing near and each minute was precious. It was a day's journey to the lake. She was to walk all night, passing through the great forest. But nothing could touch her, not even the denizens of the forest. She was already anointed with sacred oil. From the time Oganda received the sad news she had expected Osinda to appear any moment. But he was not there. A relative told her that Osinda was away on a private visit. Oganda realized that she would never see her dear one again.

In the afternoon the whole village stood at the gate to say good-bye and to see her for the last time. Her mother wept on her neck for a long time. The great chief in a mourning skin came to the gate barefooted and mingled with the people—a simple father in grief. He took off his wrist bracelet and put it on his daughter's wrist, saying, "You will always live among us. The spirit of our forefathers is with you."

Tongue-tied and unbelieving Oganda stood there before the people. She had nothing to say. She looked at her home once more. She could hear her heart beating so painfully within her. All her childhood plans were coming to an end. She felt like a flower nipped in the bud never to enjoy the morning dew again. She looked at her weeping mother and whispered, "Whenever you want to see me, always look at the sunset. I will be there."

Oganda turned southwards to start her trek to the lake. Her parents, relatives, friends and admirers stood at the gate and watched her go. Her beautiful, slender figure grew smaller and smaller till she mingled with the thin dry trees in the forest.

As Oganda walked the lonely path that wound its way in the wilderness, she sang a song and her own voice kept her company.

> *"The ancestors have said Oganda must die;*
> *The daughter of the chief must be sacrificed.*
> *When the lake monster feeds on my flesh,*
> *The people will have rain;*
> *Yes, the rain will come down in torrents.*

The wind will blow, the thunder will roar.
And the floods will wash away the sandy beaches
When the daughter of the chief dies in the lake.
My age-group has consented,
My parents have consented,
So have my friends and relatives;
Let Oganda die to give us rain.
My age-group are young and ripe,
Ripe for womanhood and motherhood;
But Oganda must die young,
Oganda must sleep with the ancestors.
Yes, rain will come down in torrents."

The red rays of the setting sun embraced Oganda and she looked like a burning candle in the wilderness.

The people who came to hear her sad song were touched by her beauty. But they all said the same thing: "If it is to save the people, if it is to give us rain, then be not afraid. Your name will forever live among us."

At midnight Oganda was tired and weary. She could walk no more. She sat under a big tree and, having sipped water from her calabash, she rested her head on the tree trunk and slept.

When she woke up in the morning the sun was high in the sky. After walking for many hours she reached the *tong*, a strip of land that separated the inhabited part of the country from the sacred place—*kar lamo*. No lay man could enter this place and come out alive—only those who had direct contact with the spirits and the Almighty were allowed to enter this holy of holies. But Oganda had to pass through this sacred land on her way to the lake, which she had to reach at sunset.

A large crowd gathered to see her for the last time. Her voice was now hoarse and painful but there was no need to worry any more. Soon she would not have to sing. The crowd looked at Oganda sympathetically, mumbling words she could not hear. But none of them pleaded for her life. As Oganda opened the gate a child, a young child, broke loose from the crowd and ran towards her. The child took a small ear-ring from her sweaty

hands and gave it to Oganda, saying, "When you reach the world
of the dead, give this ear-ring to my sister. She died last week.
She forgot this ring." Oganda, taken aback by this strange
request, took the little ring and handed her precious water and
food to the child. She did not need them now. Oganda did not
know whether to laugh or cry. She had heard mourners sending
their love to their sweethearts, long dead, but this idea of sending
gifts was new to her.

Oganda held her breath as she crossed the barrier to enter the
sacred land. She looked appealingly at the crowd but there was
no response. Their minds were too preoccupied with their own
survival. Rain was the precious medicine they were longing for
and the sooner Oganda could get to her destination the better.

A strange feeling possessed the princess as she picked her way
in the sacred land. There were strange noises that often startled
her and her first reaction was to take to her heels. But she
remembered that she had to fulfil the wish of her people. She was
exhausted, but the path was still winding. Then suddenly the path
ended on sandy land. The water had retreated miles away from
the shore, leaving a wide stretch of sand. Beyond this was the
vast expanse of water.

Oganda felt afraid. She wanted to picture the size and shape of
the monster, but fear would not let her. The people did not talk
about it, nor did the crying children who were silenced at the
mention of its name. The sun was still up but it was no longer
hot. For a long time Oganda walked ankle-deep in the sand. She
was exhausted and longed desperately for her calabash of water.
As she moved on she had a strange feeling that something was
following her. Was it the monster? Her hair stood erect and a
cold paralysing feeling ran along her spine. She looked behind,
sideways and in front, but there was nothing except a cloud of
dust.

Oganda began to hurry but the feeling did not leave her and
her whole body seemed to be bathing in its perspiration.

The sun was going down fast and the lake shore seemed to
move along with it.

Oganda started to run. She must be at the lake before sunset.

As she ran she heard a noise coming from behind. She looked back sharply and something resembling a moving bush was frantically running after her. It was about to catch up with her.

Oganda ran with all her strength. She was now determined to throw herself into the water even before sunset. She did not look back but the creature was upon her. She made an effort to cry out, as in a nightmare, but she could not hear her own voice. The creature caught up with Oganda. A strong hand grabbed her. But she fell flat on the sand and fainted.

When the lake breeze brought her back to consciousness a man was bending over her. "O . . . !" Oganda opened her mouth to speak, but she had lost her voice. She swallowed a mouthful of water poured into her mouth by the stranger.

"Osinda, Osinda! Please let me die. Let me run, the sun is going down. Let me die. Let them have rain."

Osinda fondled the glittering chain around Oganda's waist and wiped tears from her face. "We must escape quickly to an unknown land," Osinda said urgently. "We must run away from the wrath of the ancestors and the retaliation of the monster."

"But the curse is upon me, Osinda, I am no good for you any more. And moreover the eyes of the ancestors will follow us everywhere and bad luck will befall us. Nor can we escape from the monster."

Oganda broke loose, afraid to escape, but Osinda grabbed her hands again. "Listen to me, Oganda! Listen! Here are two coats!" He then covered the whole of Oganda's body, except her eyes, with a leafy attire made from the twigs of *bwombwe*. "These will protect us from the eyes of the ancestors and the wrath of the monster. Now let us run out of here." He held Oganda's hand and they ran from the sacred land, avoiding the path that Oganda had followed.

The bush was thick and the long grass entangled their feet as they ran. Half-way through the sacred land they stopped and looked back. The sun was almost touching the surface of the water. They were frightened. They continued to run, now faster, to avoid the sinking sun.

"Have faith, Oganda—that thing will not reach us."

When they reached the barrier and looked behind them, trembling, only a tip of the sun could be seen above the water's surface.

"It is gone! It is gone!" Oganda wept, hiding her face in her hands.

"Weep not, the daughter of the chief. Let us run, let us escape."

There was a lightning flash in the distance. They looked up, frightened.

That night it rained in torrents as it had not done for a long, long time. ►

Adebisi Fabunmi Takoradi sea port (Oshogbo), 1966. Lino-cut.

Lenrie Peters / *Gambia*
(1932–   )

HOMECOMING

The present reigned supreme
  Like the shallow floods over the gutters
Over the raw paths where we had been,
  The house with the shutters.

5 Too strange the sudden change
  Of the times we buried when we left
The times before we had properly arranged
  The memoirs that we kept.

Our sapless roots have fed
10 The wind-swept seedlings of another age.
Luxuriant weeds have grown where we led
  The Virgins to the water's edge.

There at the edge of the town
  Just by the burial ground
15 Stands the house without a shadow
  Lived in by new skeletons.

That is all that is left
  To greet us on the homecoming
After we have paced the world
20 And longed for returning.

"Homecoming" from SATELLITES by Lenrie Peters. Reprinted by permission of Heinemann Educational Books Ltd.

PARACHUTE

Parachute men say
The first jump
Takes the breath away;
Feet in the air disturbs
5 Till you get used to it.

Solid ground
Is now where you left it.
As you plunge down
—Perhaps head first—
10 As you listen to
Your arteries talking,
You learn to sustain hope.

Suddenly you are only
Holding an open umbrella
15 In a windy place.
As the warm earth
Reaches out to you,
Reassures you
The vibrating interim is over,

"Parachute" from SATELLITES by Lenrie Peters. Reprinted by permission of Heinemann Educational Books Ltd.

20 You try to land
Where green grass yields,
And carry your pack
Across the fields.

The violent arrival
25 Puts out the joint.
Earth has nowhere to go:
You are at the starting point;

Jumping across worlds
In condensed time—
30 After the awkward fall,
We are always at the starting point.

Richard Rive / *South Africa*
(1931–   )

AFRICAN SONG

MUTI KNEW when he felt angry. There would be something hard in his throat, and he would clench the hands tightly so that the veins stood out. But this time he knew that he was not angry but afraid. His mouth felt dry and there was a clamminess in the palms of his hands. Somehow Muti could feel, or rather sense that they were going to meet the Police. Yet when the blue uniforms entered the dilapidated meeting-place he was as surprised as if he had not expected them. He stared as if bewitched as they marched in and covered all entrances. And Muti knew it was not an anger he felt but a deep fear which he could not understand. He was far more afraid of the blue uniforms and glistening buttons than of the fact that he had no pass.[1] There were useless regrets now that he had come to the meeting, useless regrets that he had not first learnt the ways of the Big City and got a pass. He only felt a numbness and a terror. His tongue felt enormous and his mouth felt dry. Muti eyed Mpisa and noticed how calmly he took it. But his uncle had a pass and Muti had none. Muti could almost feel Mpisa imploring him to keep calm. But how could one keep calm when there were Policemen at the door, and Policemen at the window. Some his own colour and some who were white?

---

1. *no pass.* Under South African law, blacks must carry an identification card, or "pass," and produce it on demand, or else be subject to arrest.

And then everyone was standing and Muti watched fascinatedly as the people sang; but still he sat because he had no pass. And what Muti knew must happen was happening because the blue uniforms were coming nearer, as this one shuffled in his pocket for a pass; and that one had terror in his eyes because he knew he had not one; and still another was calm like Mpisa. And still the people sang. And Muti felt a great calm come over him like a warrior feels before battle, and he clambered clumsily to his feet.

And already this one was led away because he had no pass and that one lifted the hand in protest. But one must not lift the hand in protest. And still the people sang. And Muti was filled with the wonder of it all and was not afraid of the prison walls and the blue uniforms. And then in a hoarse voice Muti also began singing the song of Africa, and not one Muti sang but a hundred Mutis, ten thousand Mutis, and they all sang the song that was Africa.

And as they sang there was a deep calm.

> *And this is what they sang.*
> *Nkosi Sikelel' Afrika* . . . . .

which means God bless Africa. God bless the sun-scorched Karoo [2] and the green of the Valley of a Thousand Hills. God bless the mountain streams that chatter impudently when they are high in the hills and are young, but roll lazily from side to side like old women in the Great Plains. And the dry pans which twist their tortured bosoms to the hot skies. And the mighty waters that hurl themselves against her shores and mockingly retreat only to come again with a new energy as if to engulf the mielies [3] and the land and the villages and the towns, even great Africa itself. God bless the cataracts that taunt the solemn rocks, and the African sky that spits blood in the evening. And the timeless hills

---

2. *Karoo.* A *karoo* is a dry tableland. The Great Karoo is a plateau three or four thousand feet high, in the southern part of the Cape province in South Africa. **3.** *mielies* (mē′lēs), corn. [*Afrikaans*]

where the shy roebuck rears its tragic eyes and the dassie [4] sips in silent pools. And the blue krantzes [5] where man has still to breathe. God bless this Africa of heat and cold, and laughter and tears, and deep joy and bitter sorrow. God bless this Africa of blue skies and brown veld,[6] and black and white and love and hatred, and friend and enemy.

For where there was rich laughter there is now sorrow and indifference. And where the eyes were shot with joy for the richness of the soil, there is now a gloom, for the mielies are no longer thick on the stalk. And before the milk lapped the sides of the calabashes, but now they are dry and the milk does not spill over the sides. And even those in the Great Cities who had laughter in their eyes and remembered their ancestors, and the land and the people, now speak in whispers and no longer remember their ancestors, and the land and the people. For now the land is without joy.

There is a heavy mist over all the land, and the mist is thick so that the eye can hardly see through, but where it does lift, one can see sorrow and weariness which only Africa can understand. For the ancient koppies [7] are weary, and the veld is no longer gay, and the people are tired, and the mielies bend their heads and weep.

God bless this Africa, this Africa which is part of us. God protect this Africa. God have mercy upon Africa.

> *And still they sang.*
> *Maluphakonyisw' Upshondo Lwayo* . . . . .

which is lift up our descendants. And Muti thought of himself and wondered if he were a better man than his father, and his father's father and the many before him. For he felt like the Great Bird that flies higher and higher till it is a brother to the sun and can see the land even before the White man came. And

---

4. *the dassie,* an African rabbit. **5.** *krantzes,* cliffs. **6.** *veld,* a grassland, with scattered trees. **7.** *koppies,* hills.

then Muti climbed higher like the Bird and saw the land even before the White man came.

But Muti did not understand. Where were the cities and the towns and the villages? And the buildings and the shops? And where were the ones who lived in the cities and the towns? And the White ones and the Black ones? For Muti saw nothing but the burning veld and the flat koppies and the hardy renosterbos.[8] And when he searched even further for his own people, he found them at last, and then his heart burst with pride. For he saw proud warriors with plumes of ostrich feathers, and shaking armlets which clicked as they raised the hands. And these warriors were huge ones and proud, and lifted high the legs and stamped upon the earth so that the ground shook. For they danced the dance of the young men and it was a vigorous dance and required much strength. And they were fearsome to behold.

And Muti also saw the small ones that hide in the sand and the bushes. But these one must not look upon for they hunt the crab and the shellfish and eat the flesh of the dassie. And Muti felt no man should look upon them and so he turned away his head as if he did not see, and gazed upon the warriors. And he heard them roar out, "He is one who sees everything. No he is a lion for he hunts alone and kills many!" And that is what Muti heard them shout and it pleased him.

And then like the Great Bird, Muti saw the workers in the field, and the huts and the women threading the beads. And the beads were of many colours like the stones which the sun splits, red and yellow and orange. And Muti admired their hair which was stiff with the clay of the river, and he saw they were buxom and pleasant to behold. And there were cows and fat-tailed sheep. And there was much beer and much laughter and plenty to eat.

But Muti also saw the days that were lean, when the gourds were empty and the animals panted heavily. And then there was much throwing of bones and this one was sacrificed and that maiden must spill her blood for the gods were angry.

---

8. *renosterbos,* the rhinoceros bush, a small South African shrub, thought to be a favorite food of the rhinoceros.

And Muti was filled with a shame lest those warriors should see him. And he wanted to hide his face lest the tillers of the soil might see him, or the crab-hunters laugh derisively. What if they saw how frightened he was because he had no pass. But they could not feel frightened because they did not know the ways of the White Ones. And then Muti did not feel so ashamed.

> *And still the people sang.*
> *Yiwa Nemithandazo yayo nyi Sikelele* . . . . .

And this means hear our prayers and bless them. And now Muti again saw the look on the face of the Old-one and felt the sadness in her heart. And like one in a dream he saw from afar and heard from afar.

"I am going away, my Mother."

And she had said nothing but only stared at him with ageless eyes.

"I have decided to go away, my Mother."

And she had stared and said nothing.

"I will find work and make much money, for there is not much money in the soil. And when I find work I will have much money in my hands so that you will laugh, my Mother. And then," and he had winked slyly, "then there will be a wife."

And then she had sighed as if from a great distance and said, "It is well."

But he felt it was not well and he wanted her to ask why it was not well, why he left the land of the fathers, and the fields and the cow, but she only said,

"It is well."

"But I shall not go to Johannesburg, my Mother, for that place is not good. I shall go to some other place." And she said,

"I have a brother in Cape Town, he will be good to you."

And then he said,

"It is good, I will not go to Johannesburg." For he was filled with a great anger and said aloud, "And am I a mole that I must climb into the ground and dig the earth?"

But she said,

"No you are not a mole, you are a man."

And then he laughed and slapped his thighs and was pleased that she had said that, and he said,

"Ho, Mother, you are indeed a good one."

But when he went for the pass he was not a man for the White one in the office was angry and his face was red so that one could count the wrinkles. And at first Muti felt that the White man was angry because he was leaving the land of his fathers, and the fields and the cow. But when the White man asked him to go to the Great City, Muti did not want to, for there one becomes a mole.

But there are ways to get a pass if one has money, and so Muti sold the cow, and then Muti came to Cape Town.

Ho but this is a beautiful place, and the Great Water is bigger than many dams. And there are people who travel far on the Great Waters. And if one works well and has a pass one can also go on the Great Water to the land of the White ones. And there is a big mountain that is flat like a Karoo koppie but higher than many kraals.[9]

And Muti remembered the bull-necked White man and was afraid because he still had no pass. But there are ways to get a pass if one has money, and at the meeting would be his own people, and Mpisa would be there who knew the ways of the City and could speak the language of the White ones.

But Mpisa told him to be careful until he had a pass, especially of those in the blue uniforms, and that was why there was a clamminess in his throat when they entered the meeting.

> *And still the people sang.*
> *Yiza Moya, Yiza Moya, Oyingcwele* . . . . .

And still Muti sang these words which mean forward spirit, forward spirit which art holy. And as he sang he felt as if he could burst with pride and love. For he felt proud of this Africa,

---

9. *kraals* (kräls), native villages.

but his pride was tinged with a shame, and his love was not a true love. And as he sang he had a wonderful vision of the Africa of years hence, maybe ten years, maybe a hundred, though his vision was of two kinds, and this was the first vision.

He saw the face of a Black man and the face was grinning so that he could count the teeth. And the Black man was laughing in the face of another and this other man was a White man. But there was no malice in the laughter and the White one nodded and grinned back. And there was much merriment and slapping of backs. And then the vision changed to the Great Cities. And there were houses of plenty and shops laden with the produce of the earth, and there were many people passing up and down without any fear in their faces. And Muti almost laughed for the wonder of it when he saw how they did the work that men and women always do, only this time black men and women were also doing such work, and white men and women also, and brown men and women. And they ate and drank and cooked the foods and made merry, and everyone was full of laughter, and Muti himself laughed with the sheer wonder of it that the black and the white and the brown could so laugh together.

And then Muti saw the fields, and the maize was thick and the grapes hung in clusters on the vine, and there stood a black man with a hoe in his hand straightening his back, and he spoke to a white man, who lifted his work-soiled hands to scan the horizon. And there was much more than laughter, an understanding of the soul, of the land. And this was the first vision.

But there was a second vision. And now Muti saw a black face that was filled with smouldering anger, and there were tiny wrinkles around the eyes and mouth which were not good. And this time the mouth was clenched tightly and one could not count the teeth. For this time it looked into a white face that turned away. And then Muti had a vision of the Great Cities. But this cannot be, for everywhere there were black faces, and the policemen were black, and the people were black, and the one who takes your money was black, and the women who were hurrying, and the men. But where were the others? The white ones and the brown ones? And Muti was filled with a great disbelief. And a great sorrow overcame him when he saw that they were hardly there, but the few who remained were doing the things that black men used to do. And on the land there were no white ones, and in the Great Cities there were no white ones, and Muti was still filled with the disbelief.

And this was the second vision of Muti.

Nkosi Sikelele Thina Lusapho Lwakho . . . . .

And still the people sang these words which mean God bless us Thy children. God bless the children of Africa, for Africa is old but still a child; for she is old in sorrow and suffering but young in laughter and merriment. For the world does not understand Africa, even as a mother that flings the child from her breast. And the land suffers, and the people suffer and the children. God bless the children of Africa whose eyes are not so bright and in whose voices there is not much laughter, for the children are part of Africa, the children are Africa.

Go and see the child in the fields where the maize bends its head. Can you not see that the eye is dimmer and the mouth that of an old man? Can you not see that the soul is wizened and that the laughter is full of sad meaning? For Africa is old in its youth, and grey in its childhood. For even the baby is old in suffering and knows when the breast is dry and the calabash is empty, and the dust is thick on the bed of the river. And the father grunts and turns away the head. And the children have seen the tears in the eyes of the mother and they have also wept silently although they still do not understand. And these are the children of Africa, who are old men and women, but laugh with the voice of youth.

God bless the children in the Great Cities, for they have no beards but are as men. And there is sadness in Africa for the children who no longer play in the streams but follow the ways of the Great Cities. And the laughter of the veld is lost in the sorrow of the towns, and the little ones swagger and laugh insolently. And there is a knife in the hand and hatred in the eye, and mistrust, for the ways of the Great Cities are not good.

God bless us Thy children, make us also ageless but make us part of Africa. God bless our descendants who will be the people of Africa. God bless the cities, and the towns, and the villages. God make us to see a great light so that the ways of man may become better ways. God bless the people and the children, and the veld, and the koppies and the krantzes. God bless Africa.

And still the people sang and the blue uniforms came nearer and Muti knew that he had no pass. But still as they sang Muti's face was lit up with a great light.

God Bless Africa . . . . .
And another man who had no pass was led silently away.
Maluphakonyisw' Upshondo Lwayo . . . . .
And Muti felt as if he could burst with all the pride and love.
Hear our prayers and bless them . . . . .
And still the uniforms came nearer and the brass buttons glowed as the lamps caught them.
Yiza Moya, Yiza Moya, Oyingcwele . . . . .
Forward spirit, Forward spirit, which art holy.
Nkosi Sikelele . . . . .
And Muti could hardly contain himself for the love he felt for his people.
Thina Lusapho Lwakho . . . . .
God bless us Thy children, with a hoarse voice and a body that trembled all over. And then, as the blue uniforms stood before him, the last triumphant note.
Nkosi Sikelel' Afrika!

▶

NO ROOM AT SOLITAIRE

Now FANIE VAN DER MERWE [1] had every right to be annoyed. Here he stood, owner of the only hotel in Solitaire, wiping glasses in an empty bar on Christmas Eve. The owner of the only canteen till Donkergat, and facing empty tables and chairs. Well, not quite empty, because old Dawie Volkwyn [2] sat sullen and morose at the counter. But then Dawie Volkwyn always sat sullen and morose at the counter. Fanie couldn't remember when Dawie had not sat on the very same stool opposite the kitchen door. To have the only canteen for miles around empty on Christmas Eve.

It was obviously done for spite. Oom Sarel [3] always did things for spite. Take the case of Marietjie Louw [4] when she went out with Dawie. His argument with Fanie had started with politics. Oom Sarel had sat at the counter, the way he always sat, holding forth on every subject. God's gift to South African politics, Fanie had mumbled under his breath. Fanie had kept calm until Oom Sarel had said that Kaffirs [5] could not be educated beyond Std. II. [6] Fanie had been annoyed, very annoyed, and had quoted the case of Witbooi's [7] cousin. Now Witbooi's cousin had reached Std. VI at a school in Cape Town. Oom Sarel had insisted that it was unheard of, and if it were so it was deliberately done by the missionaries or the English or something like that. Fanie had added that Witbooi's cousin could read and write in Afrikaans [8]

1. *Fanie van der Merwe* (fä′nē vän dir mir′və). 2. *Dawie Volkwyn* (dä′vē vülk′vän). 3. *Oom Sarel* (üm sä′rel). The word *Oom* means "uncle" and is loosely applied to any older man. 4. *Marietjie Louw* (mä′rē kē lōv). 5. *Kaffirs,* black South Africans, a term of abuse. 6. *Std. II.* Std. II is roughly equivalent to the fourth grade in American schools, Std. VI to the eighth grade. 7. *Witbooi* (vit′bü ē). 8. *Afrikaans,* the Dutch dialect spoken in South Africa.

even better than some of the white bywoners.[9] Oom Sarel had become very red about the neck and had said he would not drink in a bar owned by a Communist. Then he had walked out. Now many had walked out before, but Oom Sarel was different. He owned Bo-Plaas, the richest maize farm in the District, and had already been to Johannesburg twice and sometimes visited Hermanus in the Cape for his holidays.

So it was obviously done for spite. Otherwise why should Oom Sarel have a Christmas Eve braaivleis [10] and invite everyone in Solitaire except Fanie van der Merwe and, well, and Dawie Volkwyn? The free boerewors [11] and brandy were given to lure away all his customers. Louw Viljoen and Daantjie Pretorius and Jan Mostert and them. Fanie would have loved to be there. He would have closed the bar and given Witbooi the evening off. But then, he had been pointedly ignored.

So now he halfheartedly wiped glasses on Christmas Eve and surveyed the deserted canteen. Only Dawie. But then no one ever invited Dawie anywhere. Though in spite of his drinking and bad reputation with women, Dawie Volkwyn knew life. And when he had had sufficient brandy, he would belch, lean back comfortably, narrow his eyes, and hold forth on religion, politics, the English, why the world was going to the dogs, and Marietjie Louw. He was certain that Marietjie was a little more than interested in him, but her father thought Dawie too old at fifty. Marietjie herself must be well over forty, and there was no prospect of a husband in sight.

"Ja,[12] Dawie," said Fanie sitting opposite him, "so goes the world." Dawie made no reply, so Fanie opened a bottle of brandy and filled two glasses. They drank in silence, each occupied with his own thoughts.

Fanie filled again. "It is hard when there is no business."

Another long silence, while they sipped their brandy. After the third glass Dawie replied.

---

9. *bywoners* (bā vô′nirs), sharecroppers. **10.** *braaivleis* (brīv′lās), a barbecue. **11.** *boerewors* (bür′vürs), a type of sausage. **12.** *Ja* (yä), yes.

"I hear Oom Sarel slaughtered two oxen."

"Ja."

"And three lambs, and fowls and geese."

"*Ja.*"

"And Oom Sarel bought all the wine and brandy from Cohen in Donkergat."

"*Ja,*" repeated Fanie fatalistically. He began to have serious doubts about the ability of Witbooi's cousin to read and write in Afrikaans. He would have to ask his kitchen boy. Witbooi's cousin was beginning to mess up his business.

"I never could have thought my bar would be empty on Christmas Eve."

"So goes the world."

Fanie poured Dawie another drink.

"Well here's to Christmas. *Veels geluk.*" [13]

"*Veels geluk.*"

"A long time ago in Bethlehem."

"Ja," said Dawie, looking far back in time, far beyond his fifty years. "It was a long time ago."

"But He will return."

"It says so in the Book."

"*Ja.*"

"In Revelations."

"He will come in all His glory."

"And the trumpets shall sound."

"But I've been thinking, Fanie."

"*Ja?*"

"When He first came they didn't know Him."

"So?"

"It stands so in the Book."

"I know."

"How will we know Him when He comes again?"

"You are speaking dangerous things."

"What if He is not a White man?"

"He is a White man!"

---

13. *Veels geluk* (vels ge′lük), congratulations.

"I know," Dawie said weakly.

They slipped back into silence and Fanie automatically refilled the glasses.

"How will we recognize Him?"

"There will be signs, Dawie."

"Like what?"

"It stands in the Book."

Fanie hoped that Louw Viljoen, Jan Mostert, and Daantjie Pretorius would still come in for a quick one, even if Oom Sarel's wine was free. So he bought it from Cohen in Donkergat. Sheer spite.

"Fanie, I'm not a religious man."

"I know, Dawie."

"I'm not a church-going man."

"I know."

"But I like to ask questions."

"Ja."

"How will we know Him when He comes again?"

"It stands in the Book."

"What does it say?"

"You must read it in the Book."

"I'm not a reading man."

"Ja." Fanie felt that the conversation was leading nowhere, and decided to revert to the subject of Witbooi's cousin. "Do you believe Kaffirs can read?"

"I don't know, Fanie."

"If they went to school in Cape Town?"

"Maybe."

"That's what I told Oom Sarel."

"And so?"

"Called me a kaffir-boetie." [14]

"Wragtig." [15]

"And a Communist."

"That is bad."

---

14. *kaffir-boetie* (käf′fər bŭ′tē), a white person who is sympathetic to blacks. **15.** *Wragtig* (räg′tē), truly.

"So I told him about Witbooi's cousin."

"Ja?"

"You know him?"

"No."

"He passed Std. VI."

"That can be."

"Then Oom Sarel walked out on me."

Both men moodily sipped at their glasses. Dawie wondered whether Marietjie Louw was also at Bo-Plaas and if she was thinking of him. Fanie hoped Louw Viljoen and Daantjie Pretorius would drop in after the braaivleis. After all he liked Louw.

"Baas." [16]

Louw was argumentative, but one could get on with him.

"Baas!"

"Ja, Witbooi?"

"There is a man with a woman outside who want to see the baas."

"Tell them to come in."

"Baas, they are from my people."

"Tell them to go to hell." He turned back to Dawie. "Kaffirs are becoming more and more cheeky."

"That is true."

"A lazy bunch of good-for-nothings."

"I agree with you."

"But that doesn't mean some can't read and write."

"True."

"In Afrikaans."

"That is so."

"Take Witbooi's cousin."

"Ja. Witbooi's cousin."

The kitchen boy reappeared, greatly agitated.

"Baas, the man say it is serious."

"Chase them away."

"I tried to, baas."

"Tell them I'll come with my shotgun."

---

16. *Baas* (bäs), master.

"It's no use, baas."

"Get rid of them."

"I try again, baas."

Fanie removed a fresh bottle of brandy from the shelf and removed the tinsel expertly with his teeth. He twisted the corkscrew in and pulled. He refilled the two glasses, feeling much better, even jovial.

"Now take Witbooi's cousin."

"Ja."

"Now there's a clever Kaffir."

"Must be."

"He works in an office in Cape Town."

"Ja?"

"Writes letters for his boss."

"Wragtig!"

"And at the end of the month he sends out accounts."

"Some of these people can do it."

"But Oom Sarel can't understand."

"Oom Sarel is difficult."

Witbooi tapped Fanie lightly on the sleeve.

"Please, baas, come and see."

"What?"

"The man and woman at the back door."

"Didn't you chase them away?"

"I can't, baas."

"Verdomp! [17] Bring my shotgun!"

"Ja, baas."

"Kom, Dawie, let's get rid of them."

Dawie was reluctant to shift from the half-full bottle of brandy, but had to be careful not to annoy Fanie. He climbed unsteadily to his feet and swayed behind the hotelkeeper through the canteen and kitchen.

In the doorway stood a bearded man of an indefinite age, holding a donkey by a loose rein. A black woman sat groaning on the stoep. [18]

---

17. *Verdomp* (vir dômp′), damn! 18. *Stoep* (stüp), a veranda.

"Ja?" said Fanie.

"My wife, she is sick."

"So what is wrong?"

"She is sick, baas."

"But what is the matter?"

"She is going to have a child."

"I am not a verdomde [19] midwife."

"I look for a doctor, baas."

"Yes?"

"There is no one in the dorp." [20]

"So what can I do?"

"They all at Bo-Plaas, baas."

"So?"

"I need help, baas, my wife is sick."

"Go to Bo-Plaas."

"She is sick, baas."

"Come on, get away."

"Please, baas."

"Voertsek!" [21] Fanie turned on his heels, followed by Dawie. They settled down to their disturbed drink.

"As if I'm a verdomde midwife."

"Kaffirs are getting more cheeky."

"They come to me of all people."

"Wragtig."

"I run a hotel, I don't deliver babies."

"That's the worst of these people."

Suddenly Fanie's eyes gleamed with a sadistic delight. "I hope they go to Bo-Plaas."

"Ja."

"That would put Oom Sarel in his place."

"That would."

"And the woman must give birth right there."

"Ja, that would be very funny."

"Please, my baas."

---

19. *verdomde* (vir dôm'də), damned. 20. *dorp* (dôrp), town. 21. *Voertsek!* (vùrt'sek), get away, a term of abuse.

Fanie turned around, annoyed at Witbooi.

"They're still here, baas."

"Huh?"

"They won't go away."

"Chase them."

"They want a place to rest."

"There's no room."

"In one of the shelters, baas."

"There's no place."

"The woman is very sick."

Fanie downed his brandy at one gulp and then drank two more in quick succession. "There's no room!" he repeated, then stared, amazed, at Dawie, who had begun to laugh hysterically in a high-pitched giggle.

"And what do you find so funny?"

"There's no room," Dawie repeated, "no room in the inn."

"And so?"

"Can't you see, man?"

"No."

"It's Christmas Eve."

"Allewereld!" [22]

"The Kaffir had a donkey."

"Ja, ja!" Fanie burst out in a guffaw, but there was a false ring. He choked, spluttered, and then burst into a fit of coughing. He recovered and laughed till the tears streamed down his cheeks. Dawie laughed dutifully.

"No room at the inn."

"Ja, that is very funny."

Fanie was suddenly silent. Dawie stifled a half-hearted attempt to laugh.

"Come, let's go and see," Fanie said suddenly.

"The Kaffir?"

"Ja."

"All right."

---

22. *Allewereld!* (äl′lə wə relt), literally, the whole world; an exclamation.

"Bring the brandy along."

"And the glasses."

They got up unsteadily and walked to the back door. Fanie looked ash gray under his leathery skin. There was no one at the door.

"Witbooi!"

No reply.

"Witbooi! !"

The servant appeared suddenly, as if from nowhere.

"Baas?"

"Where's the man?"

"I don't know, baas."

"You're lying."

"It's true, baas."

"Where are they?"

"The woman is very sick."

"So where did they go?"

"I put them in the stable, baas."

"Hemelsnaam!" [23]

"Allewereld!"

Fanie and Dawie slowly looked at each other and then, at the same time, timidly looked toward the sky to see whether there was a bright star. ▶

---

23. *Hemelsnaam!* (he′məls näm), an exclamation; literally, Name of heaven!

James D. Rubadiri / *Malawi*
(1930–   )

STANLEY MEETS MUTESA

Henry Morton Stanley, the American journalist who in 1871
found the Scotch missionary David Livingstone on the shores
of Lake Tanganyika in central Africa, continued his explora-
tions in later years. On his next expedition in 1875 he visited
King Mutesa of Buganda, a region northwest of Lake Victoria
and now a part of Uganda, and won admission for Christian
missionaries to that area. This eventually led to the establishment
of a British protectorate there.

Such a time of it they had;
The heat of the day
The chill of the night
And the mosquitoes that followed.
5   Such was the time and
They bound for a kingdom.

The thin weary line of carriers
With tattered dirty rags to cover their backs;
The battered bulky chests
10   That kept on falling off their shaven heads.
Their tempers high and hot
The sun fierce and scorching
With it rose their spirits

"Stanley Meets Mutesa" by James D. Rubadiri from AFRICAN VOICES,
AN ANTHOLOGY OF NATIVE AFRICAN WRITING, edited by Peggy
Rutherfoord. Reprinted by permission of Drum Publications (PTY.) Ltd.

With its fall their hopes
15 As each day sweated their bodies dry and
Flies clung in clumps on their sweat-scented backs.
Such was the march
And the hot season just breaking.

Each day a weary pony dropped,
20 Left for the vultures on the plains;
Each afternoon a human skeleton collapsed,
Left for the Masai [1] on the plains;
But the march trudged on
Its Khaki leader in front
25 He the spirit that inspired.
He the light of hope.

Then came the afternoon of a hungry march,
A hot and hungry march it was;
The Nile and the Nyanza
30 Lay like two twins
Azure across the green countryside.
The march leapt on chaunting
Like young gazelles to a water hole.
Hearts beat faster
35 Loads felt lighter
As the cool water lapt their sore soft feet.
No more the dread of hungry hyenas
But only tales of valour when
At Mutesa's court fires are lit.
40 No more the burning heat of the day
But song, laughter and dance.

The village looks on behind banana groves,
Children peer behind reed fences.
Such was the welcome

---

1. *Masai* (mä sī′), a nomadic people of East Africa.

45 No singing women to chaunt a welcome
Or drums to greet the white ambassador;
Only a few silent nods from aged faces
And one rumbling drum roll
To summon Mutesa's court to parley
50 For the country was not sure.

The gate of reeds is flung open,
There is silence
But only a moment's silence—
A silence of assessment.
55 The tall black king steps forward,
He towers over the thin bearded white man
Then grabbing his lean white hand
Manages to whisper
"Mtu mweupe karibu"
60 White man you are welcome.
The gate of polished reed closes behind them
And the West is let in.

Mabel Segun / *Nigeria*
(20th cent.)

THE PIGEON-HOLE

How I wish I could pigeon-hole myself
and neatly fix a label on!
But self-knowledge comes too late
and by the time I've known myself
5   I am no longer what I was.

I knew a woman once
who had a delinquent child.
She never had a moment's peace of mind
waiting in constant fear,
10   listening for the dreaded knock
and the cold tones of policeman:
"Madam, you're wanted at the station."
I don't know if the knock ever came
but she feared on right till
15   we moved away from the street.
She used to say,
"It's the uncertainty that worries me—
if only I knew for certain . . ."

If only I knew for certain
20   what my delinquent self would do . . .
But I never know
until the deed is done
and I live on fearing,
wondering which part of me will be supreme—
25   the old and tested one, the present
or the future unknown.
Sometimes all three have equal power
and then
how I long for a pigeon-hole.

CONFLICT

Here we stand
infants overblown,
poised between two civilisations,
finding the balance irksome,
5 itching for something to happen,
to tip us one way or the other,
groping in the dark for a helping hand
and finding none.
I'm tired, O my God, I'm tired,
10 I'm tired of hanging in the middle way—
but where can I go?

"Conflict" by Mabel Segun. Copyright © 1962 by Mabel Segun. From REFLECTIONS: NIGERIAN PROSE AND VERSE edited by Frances Ademola, published by African Universities Press. Reprinted by permission of the author.

NEGRITUDE

Considered as a literary movement, *Negritude* had its beginning in Paris in 1934 with the founding of the journal *L'Étudiant Noir* ("The Black Student"). The group of young students that founded it included Léopold Sédar Senghor (1906–   ) from Senegal, Léon Damas (1912–   ) from French Guiana, and Aimé Césaire (1913–   ) from the island of Martinique in the French West Indies. These young men argued for a reappraisal of African culture, with the aim of rediscovering and developing its authentic content. The proponents of *Negritude* stressed the immediacy and universality of their approach to African culture. Césaire understood *Negritude* to be "the simple recognition of the fact of being a Negro and the acceptance of its cultural and historical consequences." Senghor defined it as "the sum total of all the cultural values of Africa." [1] The principal themes employed by these poets and those writers that followed them, like David Diop (1927–1960) from Senegal, include the slave trade, colonialism, the feelings of the African exile for his home, the sufferings of black people everywhere in the world.

English-speaking African writers like David Rubadiri (1930–   ) from Malawi and Ezekiel Mphahlele (1919–   ) from South Africa have been sharply critical of *Negritude,* feeling that its result would be to cramp the creative spirit. While not embracing it wholeheartedly, other English-speaking writers like the Nigerians John Pepper Clark (1935–   ), Wole Soyinka (1935–   ), and Amos Tutuola (1920–   ) have employed many of the themes and adopted many of the outlooks of the French-speaking poets of the *Negritude* school.

---

1. From the *Encyclopedia of World Literature in the 20th Century,* edited by Wolfgang Bernard Fleischmann. New York: Frederick Ungar Publishing Co., 1969.

Léopold Sédar Senghor /

Senegal

(1906–   )

PRAYER TO THE MASKS

Masks! O Masks!
Black mask red mask, you black and white masks
Masks with the four points from which the Spirit blows
I greet you in the silence!
5 And not you the last, lion-headed Ancestor
    You guard this place forbidden to all laughter of woman, to
            every smile that fades
    You give forth this air of eternity wherein I breathe the breath of
            my Fathers.
    Masks with maskless faces, bereft of every dimple as of every
            wrinkle
    Who have fashioned this image, this face of mine leaning over
            the altar of white paper
10 In your image, hear me!
    Behold, Africa of the empires is dying—it is the agony of a
            pitiable princess
    And also Europe to whom we are bound by the navel.
    Fix your immutable eyes upon your children who are
            commanded
    Who give their lives like the poor man his last garment.
15 May we answer Present at the rebirth of the World
    As the leaven which is necessary to the white flour.

For who would teach rhythm to the dead world of machines and
    of cannons?
Who would raise the cry of joy to awaken the dead and the
    orphans at dawn?
Speak, who would restore the memory of life to the man with
    gutted hopes?
20 They call us the men of cotton, of coffee, of oil
They call us the men of death.
We are the men of dance, whose feet regain vigor in striking the
    hard earth.

NIGHT OF SINE[1]

Woman, rest on my brow your soothing hands, your hands softer
    than fur.
Up above the swaying palm trees scarcely rustle in the high night
    breeze.
Not even a lullaby.
Let the rhythmic silence cradle us.
Let us listen to its song, let us listen to the beat of our dark
5   blood, let us listen
To the deep pulse of Africa beating in the midst of forgotten
    villages.

"Night of Sine" (Nuit de Sine) by Léopold Sédar Senghor from THE
AFRICAN ASSERTION edited by Austin J. Shelton. (Originally published in ANTHOLOGIE DE LA NOUVELLE POESIE NEGRE ET
MALGACHE.) Reprinted by permission of the publishers, The Odyssey
Press and Presses Universitaires de France.
1. *Sine.* The region of Sine-Saloum, so called because it lies between
the Sine and the Saloum rivers in Senegal, was the home of Senghor's
tribe.

Now the weary moon sinks toward her bed in the quiet sea
Now the bursts of laughter grow sleepy, the story-tellers
      themselves
Are nodding their heads like babies on the backs of their mothers
Now the feet of the dancers grow heavy, and heavy the voices of
10   the alternating choruses.

This is the hour of stars and of the night who dreams
And reclines on the hill of clouds, wrapped in her long milky
      cloth.
The roofs of the huts gleam tenderly. What do they say, so
      confidentially, to the stars?
Inside, the fire dies out among intimate smells bitter and sweet.

Woman, light the lamp of clear oil, that the Ancestors may
      gather about and talk like parents when children are
15   sleeping.
Let us listen to the voices of the Ancients of Elissa.[2] Like us,
      exiled,
They did not want to die and let the torrent of their seed be lost
      in the desert sands.
Let me listen in the smoky hut where welcome spirits visit,
My head on your breast which is warm like a *dang* [3] just taken
      steaming from the fire,
Let me breathe the smell of our Dead, let me recall and repeat
20   their living voice, let me learn to
Live before descending, deeper than a diver, into the lofty depths
      of sleep.

---

2. *the Ancients of Elissa.* Senghor's family came from the village of Elissa
in Portuguese Guinea. **3.** *dang,* a variety of couscous, a dish made from
coarsely ground flour, sometimes with the addition of meat or vegetables.

BE NOT AMAZED

Be not amazed beloved, if sometimes my song grows dark,
If I exchange the lyrical reed for the Khalam or the tama [1]
And the green scent of the ricefields, for the swiftly galloping
      war drums.
I hear the threats of ancient deities, the furious cannonade of the
      god.
Oh, tomorrow perhaps, the purple voice of your bard will be
5   silent for ever.
That is why my rhythm becomes so fast, that the fingers bleed on
      the Khalam.
Perhaps, beloved, I shall fall tomorrow, on a restless earth
Lamenting your sinking eyes, and the dark tom-tom of the
      mortars below.
And you will weep in the twilight for the glowing voice that sang
      your black beauty.

"Be Not Amazed," by Léopold Sédar Senghor, from MODERN POETRY
FROM AFRICA, ed. Moore and Beier. Reprinted by permission of
Penguin Books Ltd. and Editions du Seuil. (Originally published in *Chants
Pour Naett*.)

1. *Khalam . . . tama*. The *Khalam* is a type of lute. The *tama* is a small
drum, held in the armpit, and played with a stick. The pressure of the
arm on a system of tighteners allows subtle variations of tone.

Wole Soyinka / *Nigeria*

(1935–   )

FADO[1] SINGER

My skin is pumiced to a fault
I am down to hair-roots, down to fibre filters
Of the raw tobacco nerve
Your net is spun of sitar[2] strings
5 To hold the griefs of gods: I wander long
In tear vaults of the sublime
Queen of night torments, you strain
Sutures of song to bear imposition of the rites
Of living and of death. You
10 Pluck strange dirges from the storm
Sift rare stones from ashes of the moon, and ride
Night errands to the throne of anguish
Oh there is too much crush of petals
For perfume, too heavy tread of air on mothwing
15 For a cup of rainbow dust
Too much pain, oh midwife at the cry
Of severance, fingers at the cosmic cord, too vast
The pains of easters for a hint of the eternal.

"Fado Singer" from IDANRE AND OTHER POEMS by Wole Soyinka.
First published in 1967 by Methuen & Co. Ltd. © Wole Soyinka 1967.
Reprinted by permission of Hill and Wang, Inc. and Methuen & Company,
Ltd., London.

1. *fado* (fä'dü), a mournful Portuguese folk song. 2. *sitar,* an Indian
guitar with a long neck and varying number of strings.

I would be free of your tyranny, free
20 From sudden plunges of the flesh in earthquake
Beyond all subsidence of sense
I would be free from headless rides
In rock reams and volcanic veins, drawn by dark steeds
On grey melodic reins.

SEASON

Rust is ripeness, rust
And the wilted corn-plume;
Pollen is mating-time when swallows
Weave a dance
5 Of feathered arrows
Thread corn-stalks in winged
Streaks of light. And, we loved to hear
Spliced phrases of the wind, to hear
Rasps in the field, where corn leaves
10 Pierce like bamboo slivers.
Now, garnerers we,
Awaiting rust on tassels, draw
Long shadows from the dusk, wreathe
Dry thatch in woodsmoke. Laden stalks
15 Ride the germ's decay—we await
The promise of the rust.

"Season" from IDANRE AND OTHER POEMS by Wole Soyinka. First published in 1967 by Methuen & Co., Ltd. © Wole Soyinka 1967. Reprinted by permission of Hill & Wang, Inc., and Methuen & Company, Ltd., London.

I THINK IT RAINS

I think it rains
That tongues may loosen from the parch
Uncleave roof-tops of the mouth, hang
Heavy with knowledge.
5 I saw it raise
The sudden cloud, from ashes. Settling
They joined in a ring of grey; within
The circling spirit.
O it must rain
10 These closures on the mind, binding us
In strange despairs, teaching
Purity of sadness.
And how it beats
Skeined transparencies on wings
15 Of our desires, searing dark longings
In cruel baptisms.
Rain-reeds, practised in
The grace of yielding, yet unbending
From afar, this, your conjugation with my earth
20 Bares crouching rocks.

Efua T. Sutherland / *Ghana*
(1924–   )

EDUFA

CHARACTERS

ABENA, *Edufa's sister*
EDUFA
SEGUWA, *a matronly member of the household*
AMPOMA, *Edufa's wife*
KANKAM, *Edufa's father*
CHORUS *of women from the town*
SENCHI, *Edufa's friend*
SAM, *an idiot servant*

> SCENE: *The courtyard and inner court of* EDUFA's *expensive house. The two areas are linked by wide steps. The inner court is the ground floor of the house. Here, towards the back, and slightly off centre, a slim pillar stands from floor to ceiling. Back of this pillar is a back wall. There are also two flanking walls, left and right. Short flights of steps between back and side walls lead into* EDUFA's *rooms on the left, and guest rooms on the right. A door in the right wall, close to the courtyard steps, leads into the kitchen. There are three, long, boxlike seats, which match the colour of the pillar. Two of these are close to the courtyard steps, against the side walls; one is right of the pillar.*

From PLAYS FROM BLACK AFRICA edited by Frederic M. Litto. Copyright © 1968 by Hill & Wang, Inc. "Edufa" © Efua Theodora Sutherland 1967. Reprinted by permission of Hill & Wang, Inc., and the author.

An atmosphere of elegant spaciousness is dominant.

For Act Three, the seats are shifted to more convenient positions, and light garden chairs, a trestle table, and a drinks trolley are moved in.

People in the audience are seated in EDUFA's *courtyard. The gate by which they have entered is the same one the chorus and other characters use as directed in the play.*

Music for the four songs, transcribed by Dr. E. Laing, will be found at the end of the play.

PROLOGUE

ABENA *is sitting on a side seat, her head in her lap, her cloth wrapped round her for warmth. She is gazing into a small black water-pot which stands on the step below her. Another pot, red, stands on the floor beside her. She tilts the black pot, measuring its contents with her eyes. Then she looks up, sighs wearily, and rubs her eyes as if she can no longer keep sleep away.*

ABENA *(beginning slowly and sleepily).*

Night is long when our eyes are unsleeping.

Three nights long my eyes have been unsleeping,

Keeping wakeful watch on the dew falling,

Falling from the eaves . . .

She glances anxiously round the inner court, rises, goes towards the steps leading to EDUFA's *rooms, hesitates, and turns back.*

And dreaming.

Dreamlike views of mist rising

Above too much water everywhere.

I heard tonight

A voice stretched thin through the mist, calling.

Heard in that calling the quiver of Ampoma's voice.

Thought I saw suddenly in the restless white waters

The laterite red of an anthill—jutting

And rocking.
A misty figure on its topmost tip,
Flicking her fingers like one despairing.
I panicked, and came to this door, listening,
But all was silence—
Night is so deceiving when our eyes
Are robbed too long of sleep.

> *She returns to her seat, puts her head back on her knees,
> and is soon singing.*

O child of Ama,[1]
Child of Ama in the night
Is wandering,
Crying, "Mm-m-m-m,
How my mother's pondering."
O child of Ama,
Why is she wandering,
Why wandering,
Why wandering in the night
Like the dying?
Meewuo!

> *She keeps up the last bars of the song for a while, patting
> the black pot with one hand and her own arm with the other,
> in a manner suggestive of self-consolation. Presently, she
> looks into the sky again.*

But my last night of wakefulness is over. *(She rises, tipping
the black pot.)* The last drop of dew has fallen. There's enough
dew water in the pot. *(She picks up the pot and tilts the red
one.)* And here is stream water from the very eye of the spring
where the red rock weeps without ceasing. *(Gesturing towards
EDUFA's rooms)* My brother Edufa, your orders are done,
though I obey without understanding. . . . *(Walking about)*
Here in this house, where there was always someone laughing,
suddenly no one feels like smiling. I've never known such
silence in my brother's house. Mm? It is unnatural. From rising
until sleep claimed us again at night, people came through our

---

1. *O child of Ama.* For the music to the following song, see page 384.

gate, for who doesn't know my brother Edufa in this town? Benevolent one, who doesn't love him? Old and young, they came. They brought laughter. Those who brought sadness returned with smiles, comforted.

Why then does brother shut our gate to stop such flow of friends? Mm? True that Ampoma, his wife, is unwell; but if she is unwell, should we not open our gate? She is not mortally ill; but even so, just let it be known, and sympathy and comforting gifts would flow in from every home. So much does the whole town hold her dear. *(Yawning)* Oh well . . . I don't even know what it is that ails her. Their door is barred, and my brother says nothing to me. *(Yawning again)* Ha! Tired. *(She picks up the red pot also, carrying the two pressed against her body.)* Well . . . I place these at his door . . . *(She places them at the top of the steps.)* . . . and make my way . . . to . . . . *(Yawning)* sleep. I don't know why I should be so sad.

She crosses, humming her song, and goes out through the kitchen door.

ACT ONE

SCENE I

EDUFA's *hands reach out and pick up the pots. He is heard issuing instructions urgently to someone inside.*

EDUFA. Pour first the dew water, and then the stream water, over the herbs in the bathroom. Quickly. Then bring out fire for the incense.

Outside the courtyard walls a chorus of women is heard performing.

CHORUS *(chanting to the rhythm of wooden clappers).*

Our mother's dead,[1]
Ei! Ei—Ei!
We the orphans cry,

---

1. *Our . . . dead.* For the music to the following song, see page 385.

Our mother's dead,
O! O—O!
We the orphans cry.

> *The chanting repeats. As the voices, the clack-clack accompaniment, and the thudding of running feet recede,* SEGUWA *comes hurriedly out of* EDUFA'S *rooms. She listens as she crosses to the kitchen, and is clearly disturbed by the performance. Her brief absence from the court is filled in by the chanting, which becomes dominant once again as the chorus returns past the house. She comes back, carrying a brazier in which charcoal fire is burning in a small earthen pot. She hesitates by the kitchen door, still preoccupied with the performance outside. At the same time* EDUFA *rushes out in pyjamas and dressing gown. He carries a box of incense and has the air of a man under considerable mental strain.*

EDUFA. Why are they doing a funeral chant? They are not coming towards this house? *(To* SEGUWA*)* You've spoken to no one?

SEGUWA *(with some resentment)*. To no one. My tongue is silenced. *(Pause)* It must be for someone else's soul they clamour.

> *The chanting fades.*

EDUFA *(composing himself)*. No, they are not coming here. *(Pause)* Put the fire down. (SEGUWA *places the fire close to the central seat.* EDUFA *rips the box open and flings incense nervously on the fire.)* Keep the incense burning while Ampoma and I bathe in the herbs.

SEGUWA. It seems to me that the time has come now to seek some other help. All this bathing in herbs and incense burning—I don't see it bringing much relief to your wife, Ampoma, in there.

EDUFA. Doubting?

SEGUWA. I'm not saying I doubt anything. You have chosen me to share this present burden with you, and I'm letting my mouth speak so that my mind can have some ease. It is I myself who say I'm hardy, but how can I help having a woman's bowels?

EDUFA. Calm yourself. I cannot give in to any thoughts of hopelessness. Where is your faith? I thought I could trust it.

SEGUWA. You can trust my secrecy; that I have sworn; though what I have sworn to keep secret, now frets against the closed walls of my skull. I haven't sworn to have faith against all reason. No, not in the face of your wife's condition in that bedroom there. Let's call for help.

EDUFA *(with indications of despair)*. From whom? We are doing everything we can. Also, it is Ampoma's wish that no one should be allowed to see her.

SEGUWA. And is she dead that we should be bound to honour her wishes? She is not herself. In her present state we can expect her to say childish things. The sick are like children. Let me call for help.

It is almost unnatural that even the mother who bore her should be kept ignorant of her sickness, serious as it now is. Ah, poor mother; if we could but see her now. She is probably pampering the children you've sent to her, keeping them happy, thinking she is relieving her daughter for rest and fun with you, her husband. *(Bitterly)* How you are deceived, Mother.

EDUFA. Don't fret so much. Calm yourself, will you?

SEGUWA. It is your wife who needs calming, if I may say so.

EDUFA. You've promised to stand with me in this trouble. You will, won't you? Your service and your courage these last few days have given me strength and consolation. Don't despair now. Ampoma is getting better.

SEGUWA. Better? Ho, ho. After fainting twice last night? *(Shrugs)* Ah, well, just as you say. I promised to stand with you and will. But may God help us all, for the bridge we are now crossing is between the banks of life and the banks of death. And I do not know which way we're facing. *(Pause)* Where is the incense? I'll keep it burning.

EDUFA *(relieved)*. Your kindness will not be forgotten, believe me, when we can smile again in this house. *(He gives her the box. She sprinkles more incense on the fire.)* See that the gate is barred.

AMPOMA *has appeared unnoticed at the top of the steps and is standing there unsteadily. There is a look of near insanity about her.* SEGUWA *sees her first and lets out a stifled scream.*

EDUFA *(hurrying to her)*. Oh, Ampoma. You shouldn't leave your bed. You shouldn't come out here.

AMPOMA *(weakly)*. The sun is shining on the world, and I am . . . falling. *(She totters.)*

SEGUWA. Hold her! She'll fall.

EDUFA *(only just saving AMPOMA from falling)*. Is the gate barred?

SEGUWA *(with uncontrolled irritation)*. O God! I cannot understand it. *(She picks up a wrap AMPOMA has dropped on the steps and starts towards the gate, but gives up in confusion, and returns to the incense-burning.)*

AMPOMA *(moving and compelling EDUFA, who is supporting her, to move with her)*. I have come out into the bright sun. There is no warmth in my bed. And no comfort. Only darkness.

EDUFA. Sit, then. Let us sit together here. *(He urges her tenderly to the seat near the kitchen door, takes the wrap from SEGUWA, and arranges it round AMPOMA's shoulders.)* You want to be in the sun? That means you are getting well. You are. Tell yourself you are. Make your soul will your strength back again. *(Pause)* In a little while we will bathe in the herbs, and later today, at the junction between day and night, we will bathe again, the final time. Tomorrow . . . tomorrow, you will feel much better. I promise you.

AMPOMA *(dreamily)*. Tomorrow? When . . . is tomorrow? *(She droops and quickly buries her face in the nape of EDUFA's neck.)*

EDUFA *(confused)*. Tomorrow . . .

AMPOMA *(breaking free)*. Oh, no! I cannot have them straying.

   SEGUWA *picks up the wrap she flings away and hovers anxiously in the background.*

EDUFA *(helplessly)*. What? Who?

AMPOMA. Like two little goats. I'm leaving them. I? Two little goats struggling on the faraway hillside. I see their eyes glowing in the dark, lonely. Oh, my little boy! And you, my girl with breasts just budding! What hands will prepare you for your wedding? *(She sobs quietly.)*

SEGUWA. She is talking of her children. Thank God they are not here to see this sight.

EDUFA *(to* AMPOMA*)*. Don't talk as if all were ending. All is not ending. It cannot end. *(To* SEGUWA*)* Put on more incense. *(He guides* AMPOMA *back to the seat.)*

AMPOMA *(on the way)*. My bed is so full of a river of my own tears, I was drowning there. *(Helplessly)* Why do we weep so much? *(They sit.)*

EDUFA. Dreams. You only dreamed these things. Sickness plagues the mind with monstrous fantasies. Pay no heed to them. Think only of reality. . . . Think of me. Is not your bed that sunny place in which we plant our children? There has never been anything but warmth and happiness there, and never will be, as long as I live and love you so.

AMPOMA. Don't speak of it. I have strayed into the cold. Yet, how good that I should not be the one to live beyond your days. I could not live where you are not. I could not live without you, my husband.

EDUFA. Ah, loving wife.

AMPOMA. Yes. That is the truth. I have loved you.

EDUFA. You have. And I have you still to fill my days with joy. *(He puts his arm round her protectively.)*

AMPOMA *(looking at him sadly)*. I am dying too young, don't you think? Look at me. *(She rises abruptly.)* What am I saying? We knew this day could come. Am I listening to the lure of his voice at this final stage? Weakening at the closeness of his flesh? *(To* EDUFA*)* Help me. Take your arm away from me. Why do you restrain me at your peril?

EDUFA. Come inside. You've been out here too long already.

AMPOMA *(more calmly, moving again, halting now and then)*. Let me talk with you a little longer in the sun before I step into the dark, where you cannot see me. Soon my pledge will be honoured. I am leaving our children motherless in your hands. Let me hear you say you love them, though I know you do.

EDUFA. I love them, Ampoma.

AMPOMA. And will you keep them from harm? Protect them?

EDUFA. How else would I be worthy of the sacred name of father? How worthy of your trust, brave woman? No harm shall come to the children that I can prevent.

AMPOMA. I fear the harm that might come to them from another woman's dissatisfied heart.

EDUFA. Ampoma, what are you saying? Another woman? I swear that in this, as in nothing else, true triumph is mine. You inspire devotion, incomparable one. There is no other woman beside you.

AMPOMA. The dead are removed. Time must, and will, soften pain for the living. If you should marry another woman, will she not envy my children because you have them with your own love and mine combined?

EDUFA. Poor Ampoma. In what unfamiliar world is your mind wandering that you speak so strangely?

AMPOMA. Promise me that you will never place them in another woman's power. Never risk their lives in the hands of another. Promise me that, and I will die without that unbearable fear here in my heart.

EDUFA. You will not die. But if it will calm you to hear it, I do promise.

AMPOMA. That you will not marry again?

EDUFA. That no other woman will cross my inner door, nor share my bed. This house will never even harbour a woman not of my own blood, at whom my eye could look without restraint.

AMPOMA. Swear it.

EDUFA. I swear it.

AMPOMA *(calmly walking away from him)*. Over me the sun is getting dark. *(With great agitation)* My husband! Watch the death that you should have died. *(She frets from place to place as if escaping from him.)* Stay over there in the sun. Children! My children! If I could cross this water, I would pluck you back from the mountainside. Children! Hold my hand! *(She stretches out her hand to the vision that she alone can see.)*

EDUFA (*catching hold of her*). Oh, wife of my soul. You should never have made that fatal promise.

AMPOMA. That I loved you? My love has killed me. (*Faintness comes over her. She falls into* EDUFA'*s arms.*) Children! And . . . Mother . . . Mother.

> EDUFA *takes her in, almost carrying her.* SEGUWA, *not quite knowing how to help, follows them.*

CHORUS (*heard again in the distance*).

Our mother's dead,
Ei! Ei—Ei!
We the orphans cry,
Our mother's dead,
O! O—O!
We the orphans cry.

> *The voices travel farther into the distance.*

SCENE III

SEGUWA (*returning*). This is what we are living with. This weakness that comes over her and all this meandering talk. Talk of water and of drowning? What calamitous talk is that? When will it end? How will it end? We are mystified. How wouldn't we be? Oh, we should ask Edufa some questions; that is what I say. You should all ask Edufa some questions. (*She goes to the fire, throws in more incense, and withdraws from it as if she hates it.*)

I wish I could break this lock on my lips.
Let those who would gamble with lives
Stake their own.
None I know of flesh and blood
Has right to stake another's life
For his own.
Edufa! You have done Ampoma wrong,
And wronged her mother's womb.
Ah, Mother! Mother!
The scenes I have witnessed in here,

In this respected house,
Would make torment in your womb.
Your daughter, all heart for the man
She married, keeps her agonies from you.
Ah, Mother! Mother!
Edufa has done Ampoma wrong.
Tafrakye!
Some matters weight down the tongue,
But, Mother, I swear
Edufa does Ampoma wrong,
He does her wrong.
> *She returns angrily to the incense burning.*

SCENE IV

KANKAM *enters through the gate. Hearing his footsteps,* SEGUWA *turns round in alarm. She is torn between surprise and fear when she notices who has arrived.* KANKAM *stops on the courtyard steps.*

SEGUWA *(approaching him hesitantly)*. Grandfather!

KANKAM *(quietly)*. Yes. It is me. Three years, is it? Three years since I walked out of that same gate, a disappointed father. Three years. Well . . . tell him I am here.

SEGUWA. Tell Edufa?

KANKAM. Yes, the man whom nature makes my son.

SEGUWA. Oh, Grandfather, do I dare? So troubled is his mood, he has ordered his gate shut against all callers.

KANKAM *(with power)*. Call him.

SEGUWA *(nervously)*. As for me, I'm willing enough to call him, but——

KANKAM *(an angry tap of his umbrella emphasizing his temper)*. Call him! It was I who bore him.

SEGUWA *(on her knees, straining to confide)*. Oh, Grandfather, help him; help him. God sent you here, I'm sure. I could tell you things—no . . . I couldn't tell you. Oh, please forget your quarrel with him and help us all. What shall I say? Hmm. His wife, Ampoma, is sick, sick, very sick.

KANKAM. So he bars his door, just in case anyone looks in to offer help. *(Calling with authority)* Edufa! Edufa!

SEGUWA *(hurrying).* I will call him. He was bathing. *(She meets EDUFA coming out of his rooms.)*

EDUFA *(seeing his father and recoiling).* You? What do you want? *(His eyes shift uneasily as KANKAM stares hard at him. He comes down the steps.)* What do you want? Three years ago you declared me not fit to be your son and left my house. Had my position not been well evaluated in this town, you might have turned tongues against me as the man who drove his own father out of his home. What do you want now?

KANKAM *(walking deliberately to the seat near the kitchen).* Yes. It has burnt down to loveless greetings between father and son, I know. What do I want? I will tell you presently. *(He sits.)* Don't let us fail, however, on the sacredness of courtesy. Had I entered the house of a total stranger, he would have given me water to drink, seeing I'm a traveller. *(EDUFA is embarrassed, but at that moment SEGUWA is already bringing water from the kitchen.)* I happen to be your father, and you a man in whose house water is the least of the things that overflow.

SEGUWA *gives the water to KANKAM, who pours a little on the floor stylistically for libation, drinks, and thanks her. She returns to the kitchen.*

EDUFA *(awkwardly).* Well?

KANKAM. Sit down, son. Sit. *(EDUFA sits uneasily on the opposite seat.)* What do I want, you say? *(Very deliberately)* I want the courage that makes responsible men. I want truthfulness. Decency. Feeling for your fellowmen. These are the things I've always wanted. Have you got them to give? *(EDUFA rises, angry.)* I fear not, since you have sold such treasures to buy yourself the importance that fools admire.

EDUFA. If you have come only to tempt me to anger, then leave my house.

KANKAM. Oh, stop blabbering. I left before, and will do so again, but it isn't any absurd rage that will drive me out.

EDUFA. What do you want, I say?

KANKAM *(with terrible self-control)*. The life of your wife, Ampoma, from you.

EDUFA *(very nervous)*. And you mean by that? *(KANKAM only stares at him.)* What makes me keeper of her life?

KANKAM. Marriage . . . and her innocent love. *(A chilly pause)* Oh, I know it all, Edufa. You cannot hide behind impudence and lies, not with me. Diviners are there for all of us to consult. *(EDUFA winces.)* And deeds done in secret can, by the same process, be brought to light.

EDUFA. You know nothing. Diviners! Ho! Diviners? What have diviners got to do with me?

KANKAM. That, you must tell me. I believe in their ancient art. I know, at least, that Ampoma is sick and could die. It has been revealed to me that she could die. And why? That you might live.

EDUFA. Absurd. It is not true. . . . Ampoma is a little ill, that's all. She has fever . . . that's all. . . . Yes . . . that's all. You are deceived.

KANKAM. Deceived. That I am. Am I not? Look at me and tell me it is not true. *(EDUFA's eyes shift nervously.)* He cannot. How could he? *(Pause)* I went to my own diviner to consult him about my health. He spread his holy patch of sand, lit candles, and over his sacred bowl of water made incantation, and scrawled his mystic symbols in the sand.

I'll tell you what he saw in his divination, for it was all about you, my son. *(Advancing on EDUFA)* Four years ago you went to consult one such diviner.

EDUFA. Do you want me to take you seriously? You cannot believe all this, you who educated me to lift me to another plane of living.

KANKAM. That's all right, my man. Most of us consult diviners for our protection. All men need to feel secure in their inmost hearts.

EDUFA. I am not all men. I am emancipated.

KANKAM. As emancipated as I'll show. Your diviner saw death hanging over your life—a normal mortal condition, I would think. But what happened, coward, what happened when he said you could avert the danger by the sacrifice of another life?

EDUFA. He lies.

KANKAM. Who? Has that not been heard before? Has that not been said to many of us mortal men? Why were you not content, like all of us, to purge your soul by offering gifts of cola and white calico to the needy, and sacrificing a chicken or a sheep or, since you can afford it, a cow?

EDUFA. Are you all right, Father?

KANKAM. Beasts are normal sacrifices, but surely you know they are without speech. Beasts swear no oaths to die for others, Edufa. *(Pause)* Were you not afraid, being husband and father, that someone dear to your blood might be the one to make the fatal oath over that powerful charm you demanded and become its victim?

EDUFA. This is intolerable. I will hear no more. *(He makes for his rooms.)*

KANKAM *(with quiet menace, barring his way).* You will hear it all, unless you'd rather have me broadcast my story in the marketplace and turn you over to the judgement of the town. *(EDUFA stops, sensitive to the threat.)* My diviner does not lie. The very day itself when all this happened was clearly engraved in sand.

EDUFA *(huffily).* All right, all-seeing, prove it. *(He sits.)*

KANKAM *(standing over him).* It had been raining without relief since the night before. Dampness had entered our very bones, and no one's spirits were bright. But you were, of all of us, most moody and morose; in fact, so fractious that you snapped at your wife for merely teasing that you couldn't bear, for once, to be shut away from your precious business and society. It was as if you couldn't tolerate yourself, or us. Suddenly you jumped up and rushed out into the raging storm. That was the day you did your evil and killed your wife.

EDUFA. Great God! If you were not my father, I would call you——

KANKAM. Towards evening you returned. The rain had stopped,

and we of the household were sitting here, in this very place, to catch what warmth there was in the sickly sunset. You seemed brighter then, for which change we all expressed our thankfulness. In fact, contrarily, you were cheerful, though still a little restless. How could we have known you were carrying on you the hateful charm? How could we have suspected it, when your children were playing round you with joyful cries? How could we have known it was not a joke when you suddenly leaned back and asked which of us loved you well enough to die for you, throwing the question into the air with studied carelessness? Emancipated one, how could we have known of your treachery?

EDUFA *(rising)*. Incredible drivel! Incredible. Is this the man I have loved as father?

KANKAM. You had willed that some old wheezer like me should be the victim. And I was the first to speak. "Not me, my son," said I, joking. "Die your own death. I have mine to die." And we all laughed. Do you remember? My age was protecting me. *(Pause)* Then Ampoma spoke. *(Pause)* Yes, I see you wince in the same manner as you did when she spoke the fatal words that day and condemned her life. "I will die for you, Edufa," she said, and meant it too, poor doting woman.

EDUFA. Father, are you mad?

KANKAM *(shocked)*. *Nyame* above! To say father and call me mad! My *ntoro* within you shivers with the shock of it!

EDUFA *(aware that he has violated taboo)*. You provoked me.

KANKAM *(moving away)*. All right, stranger, I am mad! And madness is uncanny. Have you not noticed how many a time the mad seem to know things hidden from men in their right minds? *(Rounding up on EDUFA)* You know you killed your wife that day. I saw fear in your eyes when she spoke. I saw it, but I didn't understand.

I have learned that in your chamber that night you tried to make her forswear the oath she had innocently sworn. But the more you pleaded, the more emotionally she swore away her life for love of you; until, driven by your secret fear, you had to make plain to her the danger in which she stood. You showed her the charm. You confessed to her its power to kill whoever swore to die for you. Don't you remember how she wept? She had spoken and made herself the victim. Ampoma has lived with that danger ever since, in spite of all your extravagant efforts to counter the potency of the charm by washings and rites of purification. *(With great concern)* Edufa, I am here because I fear that time has come to claim that vow.

EDUFA. Leave me alone, will you? *(He sits miserably.)*

KANKAM. Confess it or deny it.

EDUFA. I owe you no such duty. Why don't you leave me alone?

KANKAM. To kill? Say to myself, Father, your son wants to murder, and go? All the world's real fathers would not wish a murderer for a son, my son. Yes, in spite of my rage there is still truth of father and son between us.

EDUFA. Rest. My wife, Ampoma, is not dying.

KANKAM. If she does not die, it will be by the intervention of some great power alone. An oath once sworn will always ride its swearer. But there might still be a chance to save her.

EDUFA. Indeed, in this age there are doctors with skill enough to sell for what's ailing her, and I can pay their fees.

KANKAM *(pleading)*. Confess and denounce your wrong. Bring out that evil charm. And before Ampoma and all of us whose souls are corporate in this household, denounce it. Burn it. The charm may not be irrevocably done if we raise the prayer of our souls together.

EDUFA. Will it help you if I swear that there is no ground for all your worry? And now will you let me go?

KANKAM *(with anguish)*. Hush! You swear? Oh, my son, I have finished. I can do no more. Have you sunk so low in cowardice? If you must lie, don't swear about it in a house in which death is skirmishing and the ancestral spirits stand expectantly by. A man may curse himself from his own lips. Do not curse the house in which your children have to grow.

Spirits around us, why don't you help him save himself? When he went to consult the diviner, he was already doing well. You could tell. If you looked at his new clothes, you could tell; if you looked at his well-appointed house in whose precincts hunger wouldn't dwell. Already, the town's pavements knew when it was he who was coming. Nudging announced him. Eyes pivoted to catch his smile. *(With disgust)* You could see all the ivory teeth and all the slimy way down the glowing gullets of those who were learning to call him sir. For he was doing well in the art of buying friends by street benevolence.

EDUFA *(seizing on a diversion)*. Now you betray yourself. It has taken me all these years to probe the core of your antagonism. From what you say, it is clear at last that you envied me. Oh! What lengths a man will go to hide his envy.

KANKAM. Pitiful.

EDUFA. Fathers are supposed to share with pride in their sons' good fortune. I was not so blessed. My father envied me and turned enemy—even while he ate the meat and salt of my good fortune.

KANKAM. Pitiful.

EDUFA. And there was I, thinking that enemies could only be encountered outside my gates.

KANKAM. Pitiful. At my age a man has learned to aim his envy at the stars. *(Suffering)* Pity him, you spirits. He grew greedy and insensitive, insane for gain, frantic for the fluff of flattery. And I cautioned him. Did I not warn him? I tried to make him stop at the point when we men must be content or let ourselves be lured on to our doom. But he wouldn't listen. He doesn't listen. It makes me ill. Violently ill. I vomit the meat and salt I ate out of ignorance from his hand.

I have finished. *(Pause)* It wouldn't be too much to ask to see the lady before I leave?

EDUFA. She mustn't be disturbed.

KANKAM *(picking up his umbrella from the seat)*. Well . . . as you wish, noble husband. There are enough women, I suppose, ready to fall for your glamour and line up to die for you. I am leaving. Forever now. *(He steps into the courtyard.)*

EDUFA. One moment. (KANKAM *turns to him hopefully.*) I hope you haven't talked like this to anyone. You could do so much harm. Unjustly.

KANKAM *(with a rage of disappointment).* Worm. Coward. You are afraid for your overblown reputation, aren't you? You are afraid that if the town got to know, they would topple you. No. I am tied by my fatherhood, even though I am not proud that my life water animated you. It is not my place to disillusion your friends. I'll let them bow to a worm. In time they are bound to know they're bowing too low for their comfort. Were this matter a simple case of crime, I would perhaps seek solution by bringing you to secular justice. As it is, to try still to save the woman's life, our remedy is more probable in the paths of prayer, which I now go to pursue away from your unhelpful presence. *(He leaves.)*

EDUFA.

Alone.

Tears within me that I haven't had the privilege to shed. Father!

Call him back that I may weep on his shoulder.

Why am I afraid of him? He would stand with me even though he rages so.

Call him back to bear me on the strength of his faith.

He knows it all. I can swear he is too true a man to play me foul. But I could not risk confirming it. I dread the power by which he knows, and it shall not gain admission here to energise that which all is set this day to exorcise.

No, a man needs to feel secure! But, oh, how I am stormed.

Don't ask me why I did it; I do not know the answer. If I must be condemned, let me not be charged for any will to kill, but for my failure to create a faith.

Who thought the charm made any sense? Not I. A mystic symbol by which to calm my fears—that was all I could concede it.

It still doesn't make any sense. And yet, how it frets me, until I'm a leaf blown frantic in a whirlwind.

If only I hadn't been so cynical. I bent my knee where I have no creed, and I'm constrained for my mockery.

Hush, O voice of innocence! Still your whining in the wind. Unsay it. Do not swear, for I am compromised.

She who lies there must recover if ever I'm to come to rest. I love my wife, I love her. My confidence is her hope and her faith in me, mine.

So are we locked.

ACT TWO

SCENE I

The CHORUS *is heard approaching* EDUFA's *house.*
CHORUS.

Ei! Ei—Ei!
We the orphans cry,
Our mother's dead,
O! O—O!
We the orphans cry.

They enter through the gate at a run. Their exuberance and gaiety would belie the solemn nature of their ritual observance. They stop below the courtyard steps.

CHORUS ONE *(calling).* May we enter? Are there no people in this beautiful house?

CHORUS TWO. In the house of the open gate?

CHORUS THREE. In the house of He-Whose-Hands-Are-Ever-Open?

CHORUS.

Open Face
Open Heart
Open Palm,
Edufa.

CHORUS FOUR. Come, scratch our palms with a golden coin.

CHORUS FIVE. With a golden nugget.

CHORUS. For luck and good fortune.

CHORUS ONE *(stepping up).* And Ampoma the beautiful; where is she? Woman of this house of fortune. Singing your husband's praise is singing your praises too. Tender heart who nurses him to his fortune. Stand side by side while we beat envious evil out of your house.

CHORUS. Are there no people in this beautiful house?

SEGUWA *(entering from the kitchen)*. Who let you in?

CHORUS *(cheerfully)*. The gate of this house is always open.

SEGUWA *(uneasily)*. Well . . . greeting . . .

CHORUS. We answer you.

SEGUWA *(still hesitating at the kitchen door)*. And you have come . . . ?

CHORUS ONE. We have come to drive evil away. Is the man of the house in? And the lady? We are driving evil out of town.

CHORUS.
From every home
From street and lane
From every corner of our town.
Ei! Ei—Ei!
We the orphans cry.

CHORUS TWO *(steps up, sniffing and trying to locate the scent)*. Incense.

SEGUWA *(moving quickly forward)*. Whose funeral sends you out in ceremony?

CHORUS. Another's, and our own. It's all the same. While we mourn another's death, it's our own death we also mourn.

SEGUWA *(touched)*. True. *(She wipes away a tear.)*

CHORUS *(crowding near her)*. Oh, don't let us sadden you.

SEGUWA. There is so much truth in what you say. I would say, Do your rite and go in peace, for it is most necessary here. I would say, Do your rite and do it most religiously, for it is necessary here. I would say it, but I am not owner of this house.

CHORUS ONE. Why do you hesitate? Is Edufa not in?

SEGUWA. I am trying to make up my mind whether he should be in or out.

CHORUS TWO. Well, if a man is in, he's in; and if he is out, he's out. Which is it?

CHORUS ONE. Make up your mind, for soon, noon will be handing over its power to the indulgent afternoon, and our ritual is timed with the rigours of high noon. Which is it? Is he in or out?

SEGUWA. For driving evil out, he is in, I suppose.

CHORUS. Aha! Then call him.

SEGUWA. I will do my best to bring him out.

CHORUS TWO. Do your best?

SEGUWA. Well . . . I mean . . . Ampoma, his wife, is lying down . . . and . . .

CHORUS ONE. And it is hard for him to tear himself away. . . . Aha!

SEGUWA. Yes . . . No . . . Well . . . let me go and find out. I can make up my mind better away from your questioning eyes. *(With a gesture of invitation as she makes for* EDUFA's *rooms.)* Wait.

CHORUS. We are waiting. *(They surge into the court.)*

CHORUS ONE. What's her trouble? There was a riot in her eyes.

CHORUS TWO. We haven't come to beat her. *(Showing her clappers)* These aren't cudgels to chastise our fellow men. These are for smacking the spirits of calamity.

CHORUS ONE *(snidely)*. Ampoma is lying down, she said.

CHORUS TWO *(laughing)*. Sick, or lying down in the natural way?

CHORUS THREE. I would say, Simply rich. Would you not do the same in her place? Let her enjoy her ease.

CHORUS FOUR. Imagine the fun of it. *(She goes to the seat, right, and mimes lying down luxuriously, much to the enjoyment of her friends.)* O lady, lady lying in a bed of silk! What kind of thighs, what kind of thighs must a woman have to earn a bed of silk? A bed of silk, O! If I had her life to live, I wouldn't be out of bed at eleven o'clock in the morning either. Never, O!

In the middle of this fun-making, EDUFA *rushes out. He stops short at the sight. But the mood of hilarity there compels him to a show of humour.*

CHORUS *(running up to crowd round him)*. Husband!

CHORUS ONE. Aha! The giver himself.

CHORUS. Greeting.

EDUFA. I answer. Well? . . . Well?

CHORUS ONE. We would not dream of passing up your house while we do our rite.

EDUFA. Whose death is it? Is the rite for a new funeral?

CHORUS ONE. No. It's for an old sorrow out of which time has dried the tears. You can say that we are doing what gives calamity and woe the final push in the back—which is a manner of speaking only, as you know——

EDUFA. And you have come here . . .

CHORUS ONE. To purge your house also in the same old manner, for calamity is for all mankind and none is free from woe.

EDUFA. Thank you. You may proceed.

CHORUS TWO *(in fun)*. Then cross our palms with the gleam of luck. And give us a welcome drink. *(EDUFA motions to SEGUWA, who goes to the kitchen to get drinks, taking the brazier away with her.)* And let the beautiful one, your wife, know that we are here.

EDUFA. She is not very well today.

CHORUS *(genuinely)*. Oh! Sorry.

EDUFA. Nothing serious. In fact she is getting better.

CHORUS *(relaxing)*. Good. We greet her and wish her well.

EDUFA. She thanks you. Welcome in her name, and from myself as well. *(He takes a big gold ring off his finger and touches the palm of each of the women with it, saying:)* Good luck and good fortune to you, friends. *(SEGUWA brings drinks on a tray, which she places on the seat near the kitchen.)* And here are your drinks.

CHORUS ONE *(solemnly)*. Come, friends. Let's do the ceremony for the benevolent one.

CHORUS *(becoming formal)*. Evil has no place here. Nor anywhere. Away, away. *(Moving rhythmically at a slow-running pace through the court and courtyard, they perform their ritual with solemnity. Chanting.)*

Our mother's dead,
Ei! Ei—Ei!
We the orphans cry,
O! O—O!
We the orphans cry.
    Speaking, at a halt.
Crying the death day of another
Is crying your own death day.

While we mourn for another,
We mourn for ourselves.
One's death is the death of all mankind.
Comfort! Comfort to us all,
Comfort!
Away evil, away.
Away all calamity,
Away!

Chanting, on the move.
Our mother's dead,
Ei! Ei—Ei!
We the orphans cry,
Our mother's dead,
O! O—O!
We the orphans cry.

During this ritual SEGUWA *stands attentively in the background.* EDUFA *remains just above the courtyard steps, intensely quiet, eyes shut in private prayer.* THE CHORUS *finish up on the steps below, facing him.*

CHORUS ONE. There now. We have done. Health to you. *(EDUFA is too removed to hear her.)* Health to you, Edufa, and to your wife and all your household. *(To her companions)* See how he is moved. We have done right to come to the house of one as pious as he.

CHORUS TWO. Such faith must surely bring him blessing.

EDUFA *(stirring)*. Your drinks await you.

The mood of the CHORUS *changes to lightheartedness again.*

CHORUS ONE *(as her companions collect their drinks, her own glass in hand)*. That's right. Tears and laughter. That's how it is. It isn't all tears and sorrow, my friends. Tears and laughter. It isn't all want and pain. With one hand we wipe away the unsweet water. And with the other we raise a cup of sweetness to our lips. It isn't all tears, my friends, this world of humankind.

CHORUS *(drinks in hand)*. May you be blessed, Edufa.

EDUFA *(hurrying them up nicely)*. Drink up. Day is piling up its hours, and you must be eager to attend the business of your own homes. It was good of you to come. *(He contrives to draw* SEGUWA *aside.)* Go in there. Ampoma was sleeping. It would not do for her to walk out into this. (SEGUWA *hurries into* EDUFA's *rooms.)* You did well to come. A man needs friendship. But it's late in the morning, and you are women . . . with homes to feed.

CHORUS ONE. We will come again to greet your wife.

EDUFA *(skilfully herding them out)*. Yes, yes——

CHORUS TWO. Would you sit us at your generous table? Eat with us?

CHORUS THREE. Charm us?

EDUFA. Yes. All in good time . . . some day soon.

SEGUWA *(running out happily)*. Edufa! Edufa! She has asked for food.

EDUFA *(excitedly)*. For food. She has?

SEGUWA *(making fast for the kitchen)*. For soup. She says, I would like some fresh fish soup. Thank God.

EDUFA. Thank God. Get it.

SEGUWA. After three days without interest——

EDUFA. Get it quickly.

SEGUWA. Thank God. *(She enters the kitchen.)*

EDUFA *(calling after her)*. Is there fish in the house? If not, send out instantly. Thank God. *(Stretching out his hands to the* CHORUS) Victory, my friends.

CHORUS ONE *(puzzled)*. So relieved. Ampoma must be more ill than he cared to let us know. Thank God.

CHORUS TWO. He is wise not to spill the troubles of his house in public.

EDUFA *(on his way in)*. Thank you, friends. I must leave you now.

SCENE II

As EDUFA *and the* CHORUS *are leaving,* SENCHI, *carrying a small battered leather case, swings in flamboyantly, whistling to announce himself.*

SENCHI. . . . and the wanderer . . . the wanderer . . . the wanderer comes home. *(Seeing the* CHORUS) Comes in the nick of time, when everything he loves is together in one place. Friends, women, bottles . . . *(His laughter is all-pervasive.)*

EDUFA *(thrilled)*. Senchi!

SENCHI *(airily to the* CHORUS*)*. Good afternoon. My name is Senchi, and I'm always lucky. I love women and always find myself right in the middle of them. Welcome me.

CHORUS FOUR *(quite pleased)*. He's quite a fellow.

SENCHI. She's right.

EDUFA. Senchi. What brings you here?

SENCHI *(stepping up to him)*. Life . . . brings me here. Welcome me.

EDUFA. Indeed. You've come in excellent time.

SENCHI. And what are you doing here? Practising polygamy? Or big-mammy? Or what? Anyone you choose to declare will be against the law. I'm in transit, as usual. May I spend the night with you?

EDUFA. But certainly. Do me the favour. It's very good to see you, and my privilege to house one as lucky as you obviously are.

SENCHI *(to* CHORUS*)*. Now he flatters.

EDUFA. I only wish we were better prepared to receive you.

SENCHI. Impossible *(His eyes on the* CHORUS*)* You couldn't improve on this welcome here. All good stock, by their looks. Local breed? They're not dressed for fun and games, though, are they? Pity.

CHORUS THREE *(approvingly)*. He's quite a fellow.

SENCHI *(sniffing)*. And I smell—what is that I smell? Incense? *(To* EDUFA*)* Say, have you changed your religion again? What are you practising now? Catholicism, spiritualism, neo-theosophy, or what? Last time I passed through here, you were an intellectual atheist or something in that category. I wouldn't be surprised to see you turned Buddhist monk next time. *(The* CHORUS *are leaving.)* Don't go when I've only just come. *(To* EDUFA*)* What are they going away for?

CHORUS. Our work is finished here.

EDUFA. They've been doing a ceremony here. Don't delay them any longer.

SENCHI. Why, I smelled something all right. What are they? Your acolytes? Wait a minute. They're in mourning. Is someone dead? *(To* EDUFA*)* None of your own, I hope.

EDUFA. No.

CHORUS. This was an old sorrow, friend.

SENCHI. Ah! I understand. One of those "condolences" rites. Why do you people prolong your sorrows so? *(To* CHORUS*)* Though, I must observe, you have a funny way of going about it—drinking and sniggering. *(Very playfully)* Come on, give me those confounded sticks. I'll show you what they are good for. *(He snatches the clappers from the* CHORUS, *and a mock chase follows, during which he tries to smack them. He flings the clappers in a heap below the steps near the kitchen.)* Now, embrace me, and be done with sorrow.

CHORUS *(delighted)*. Oh! Oh! We were on our way.

SENCHI. To me. *(*SEGUWA, *entering, sees the romping, and her single exclamation is both disapproving and full of anxiety.* SENCHI *turns to her.)* What's the matter with the mother pussy cat? Come over, lady, and join the fun.

EDUFA *(sensitive to* SEGUWA's *disapproval)*. Let the women go now, Senchi.

SENCHI. Why? That's no way to treat me.

SEGUWA *(ominously)*. Edufa.

EDUFA. They can come back some other time.

SENCHI. Tonight? All of them?

SEGUWA. Edufa.

EDUFA. Let them go now. Tonight? Very well, tonight.

CHORUS THREE *(eagerly)*. To eat?

SEGUWA. Edufa.

EDUFA. Yes. Why not?

SENCHI. You mean that?

EDUFA. A bit of a party, since my wife recovers . . . and——

SENCHI. Oh, how thoughtless of me. Has Ampoma been ill? And I haven't asked of her. . . . Though I've brought her a song. It's all your fault for distracting me. Sorry.

EDUFA. . . . and you too have come, my friend, and brought

us luck. It seems to me that we are permitted to celebrate my good fortune——

CHORUS ONE. Expect us.

CHORUS TWO. We will be glad to help you celebrate.

EDUFA *(to* CHORUS*)*. And to you also I owe my gratitude——

CHORUS. Expect us. *(They leave cheerfully through the gate.)*

SENCHI. Wonderful. *(He joins* EDUFA *in the court.)*

EDUFA *(with a great sigh)*. Oh, Senchi! This has been quite a day.

SENCHI *(suddenly serious)*. Tired? Between you and me, my friend, I'm downright weary in my b-o-n-e-s, myself. I've become quite a wanderer, you know, tramping out my life. It isn't as if I didn't know what I'm looking for. I do. But, oh, the bother and the dither. And the pushing and the jostling. Brother, if you meet one kind, loving person in this world who will permit a fellow to succeed at something good and clean, introduce me, for I would wish to be his devotedly and positively forever. Amen. But of that, more later. I'm worn out with travel. Lead me to a bed in a quiet corner for some sweet, friendly, uncomplicated sleep.

EDUFA. Won't you eat?

SENCHI. No food. Only peace, for a while.

EDUFA. As you wish. *(To* SEGUWA*)* Take my friend to the guest rooms overlooking the river. It's quiet there. We'll talk when you awake. No luggage?

SENCHI *(showing his battered leather case)*. This is all I care about.

EDUFA *(to* SEGUWA*)*. See that he has all he needs. And after, arrange a meal for tonight. Spare nothing. *(He hurries into his rooms.)*

SEGUWA *(grimly)*. This way. *(She strides ahead to the steps leading into the guest rooms.)*

SENCHI *(catching up with her)*. For the sake of a man's nerves, can't you smile? I can't stand gloom.

SEGUWA. You should have your fun another day.

SENCHI. What particular brand of fun is this you're recommending?

SEGUWA. The party tonight.

SENCHI. That? Don't call that a party, woman. Call it something like Senchi's Temporary Plan for the Prevention of Senchi from Thinking Too Hard. You don't grudge me a small relief like that, surely. (SEGUWA *wipes away a tear.*) Come on. Now what have I said? Are you one of those women who enjoy crying? I'll make a bargain with you, then. Allow me to have my rest. When I awake, I promise to make you cry to your heart's content—by singing, merely. I make songs, you know. (*Patting his leather case*) Songs for everything; songs for goodness, songs for badness; for strength, for weakness; for dimples and wrinkles; and, for making you cry. But I'll tell you a secret. I never make songs about ugliness, because I simply think it should not exist.

SEGUWA (*exasperated*). This way, please. (*She leads* SENCHI *up the steps.*)

ABENA *enters from the kitchen with a smart tray on which is a hot dish of soup. She is on her way to* EDUFA's *rooms, looking decidedly happy.*

ABENA (*stopping halfway up the steps, proudly smelling the soup*). She will like it. I used only aromatic peppers—the yellow—and the mint smells good. (EDUFA *comes out.*) Dear brother. (*She raises the tray for him to smell the soup.*)

EDUFA (*smelling*). Lovely. Little one, are you well? We haven't talked much of late.

ABENA. I'm glad she's better.

EDUFA. Oh . . . yes. You did your work well, it seems.

ABENA. My work?

EDUFA (*quickly changing the subject*). How is your young man? (*He takes the tray.*)

ABENA (*shyly*). I will see him today.

EDUFA. Good. You haven't had much of a chance lately, have you?

ABENA. No . . . er . . . Can't I take the soup in to her? I've had such thoughts. I miss her. We were so happy before all this began, stringing beads and looking through her clothes. She's going to let me wear her long golden chain of miniature barrels at my wedding—right down to my feet.

EDUFA. Let's get her up strong, then. You can see her tonight. We have guests.

ABENA *(appreciatively)*. Yes. I've heard him singing.

EDUFA. It's very good to have him here.

ABENA. He sings well.

EDUFA. Some women from town are coming to eat with us tonight.

ABENA *(with childlike joy)*. People here again. Laughter again.

EDUFA *(smiling, but compelling her down the steps)*. Sister, come. *(Intimately)* Did you mind staying up nights? Was it very hard?

ABENA *(unburdening)*. Not . . . too . . . hard. I didn't mind it inside the house, though it got so ghostly quiet at times, I almost saw my lonely thoughts taking shape before my eyes . . . becoming form in the empty air. And then, collecting the stream water . . . that . . . that in the night, and the forest such a crowd of unfamiliar presences.

EDUFA. Hush! It's over. All over. Thank you. Go out now. Enjoy yourself. Can you give us a nice meal tonight?

ABENA. Delighted.

As she goes through the kitchen door, SAM *enters through the gate, running, dodging, like one pursued. He carries a bird cage and a small tin box.*

SAM *(to an imaginary crowd towards the gate)*. Thank you. Thank you. *(Gloatingly)* They didn't get me. *(Speaking to no one in particular)* An idiot's life isn't so bad. There are always people to stop children throwing stones at us. They only do that for idiots, I find. *(To the cage)* Let us tell my master that. *(Paying tender attention to what is inside the cage, he walks up a step, crosses to left, and puts the cage and the box down.)*

SEGUWA *(entering from the kitchen)*. You're back.

SAM. Are you pleased to see me? *(Lifting up the cage)* Look, he is my bird.

SEGUWA *(horrified)*. Don't bring it near me. It's an owl.

SAM *(blithely)*. Of course. An owl is a bird.

SEGUWA. What's it doing here?

SAM. It came with me. It was an owl before; but now it's with me, it's no longer itself. It's the owl of an idiot. What we get, we possess. I caught it in a tree.

SEGUWA. Take it outside. *(SAM sulks, turning his back on her.)* Did everything go well? Did you find the place? Did you see the man? *(SAM, moving his bird cage aside, merely nods his affirmatives.)* And what's the news? *(SAM's back stiffens stubbornly.)* It's no good; he won't talk to me. I'll let your master know you're back. *(She goes into EDUFA's rooms, while SAM pays fussy attention to his owl. She returns with EDUFA, who is in a state of high expectancy.)* There he is . . . back.

EDUFA *(coaxingly)*. Sam, are you back?

SEGUWA. I don't know what he's doing with that thing. Let him take it away.

EDUFA. What is it, Sam?

SEGUWA. An owl.

EDUFA *(terrified)*. Take it out. *(SAM sulks.)* We would do well not to disturb him before we've heard what he has to say. He can get very stubborn. *(Sweetly)* Sam, come here. *(SAM doesn't budge.)* You may keep your bird. *(SAM turns to him, grinning broadly.)*

SAM *(pointing to the owl)*. My owl and I had a nice thought for you on the way. When you are born again, Master, why don't you come back as an idiot? There are always people to stop children throwing stones at us. They only do that for idiots, I find.

EDUFA *(smiling in spite of himself)*. All right. Now tell me quickly what I want to know. *(Anxiously)* Did you find the place?

SAM. It's an awful place. What do you send me to places like that for? Not the village itself. That is beautiful, floating in blue air on the mountain top, with a climbway in the mountain's belly going zig-zag-zig, like a game. *(He thoroughly enjoys his description.)*

SEGUWA *(impatiently)*. He's so tiresome with his rambling.

EDUFA *(trying to be patient).* Good, you found the village. And the man?

SAM. He is a nice man, tall as a god. And he fed me well. You don't give me chicken to eat, but he did. *(Thinks a bit)* What does such a nice man live in an awful house like that for? That's the awful part.

EDUFA *(very anxiously).* Never mind. What did he say?

SAM. Ah! *(Secretively)* Let me fetch my box of goods. *(He fetches the tin box and sets it down before EDUFA.)* First, three pebbles from the river. *(He takes out these pebbles.)* Catch them. *(He throws them one by one to EDUFA.)* One. Two. Three. (EDUFA *catches them all.)* Good! They didn't fall.

EDUFA *(intensely).* I understand that. We mustn't let Ampoma fall to the ground.

SAM *(taking out a ball of red stuff).* With this, make the sign of the sun on your doorstep where your spirit walks in and out with you. Come, I know you are not much of an artist. I'll do it for you the way the man showed me. *(He walks importantly to the steps leading to EDUFA's rooms, and as he draws a raying sun boldly on the riser of the first step:)* Rays! Everywhere . . . you . . . turn.

SEGUWA *(with awe).* Ampoma talks so much of the sun.

EDUFA. Yearningly.

SAM *(returning to the box).* And then came the part I didn't understand.

EDUFA *(hoarsely).* Yes . . . quickly, where is it?

SAM. Here it is in this bag. *(He produces an old leather pouch which is spectacularly designed and hung with small talismans.)*

EDUFA *(trembling).* Give it to me.

SAM. Now listen. He says burn it.

    EDUFA *snatches the pouch from him.*

EDUFA *(to SEGUWA).* Get fire—in the back courtyard. Quickly.

    SEGUWA *leaves in haste.*

SAM *(with emphasis).* The man says, Burn it with your own hands, before you bathe in the herbs for the last time.

EDUFA *(with eyes shut).* We're saved. *(Then he becomes aware again of the waiting SAM.)* Well done, Sam. You may go.

SAM. I won't go to that awful house again.

EDUFA. No. Get something to eat. And rest. You are tired. *(SAM picks up the box and walks eagerly to the bird cage.)* But . . . Sam. You must let that bird go.

SAM *(aggrieved).* My owl? Oh, Master, he is my friend. He's the bird of an idiot. He likes us. He and I had a nice thought for you on our way——

EDUFA *(threateningly).* Take it out of here! Out.

SAM. Oh . . . *(He picks up the bird cage and goes out of the gate muttering sulkily.)* We'll stay outside. . . . If they won't have us in, we won't eat. . . . We will starve ourselves. . . . We . . .

EDUFA *(gripping the pouch in his fists with violence).* This is the final act. I will turn chance to certainty. I will burn this horror charm and bury its ashes in the ground: the one act that was still hazard if left undone.

ACT THREE

SCENE I

A trestle table covered with a fresh white cloth is moved into the court, close to the central seat. So is a loaded drinks trolley. The seats left and right are shifted in. Wicker garden chairs provide additional seating.

ABENA and SEGUWA are preparing for the party, obviously enjoying doing it with some taste. They move in plates, cutlery, serviettes, wine glasses, etc., pursuing their work without paying more than momentary attention to any distractions.

SENCHI and EDUFA appear from the guest rooms. EDUFA is in evening dress but has yet to put on his jacket. SENCHI looks noticeably absurd in a suit that is not his size. He brings his leather case, which he soon places carefully against the trestle table.

SENCHI. I'm grateful to you for listening to all my talk.

EDUFA. If it helps, I'm happy to listen. What can I do more?

SENCHI. Every now and then I feel this urge to talk to somebody. It helps me to dispose of the dust of my experiences. And that's when I come here. There are not many people with enough concern to care about what accumulates inside a man. *(He indicates his heart.)* You and Ampoma both listen well, though I must say that you, being so solid and so unemotional, lack the rain of her sympathy.

EDUFA. That's your secret, then. I've never told you I admire you although you can't show a balance in the bank, have I?

SENCHI. No.

EDUFA. I do. You're so relaxed and normally so convincing with your laughter. Yet, you do puzzle me somewhat. Don't you think it is important to have solidity? Be something? Somebody? Is being merely alive not senseless?

SENCHI. What is this something, this somebody that you are? Give it name and value. I'm not being disparaging; I'm seeking.

EDUFA. I don't know. I thought I did until it got so confusing, I . . . Ask the town. They know who Edufa is and what he's worth. They can count you out my value in the homes that eat because I live. Yes, my enterprises feed them. They rise in deference from their chairs when they say my name. If that isn't something, what is? And can a man allow himself to lose grip on that? Let it go? A position like that? You want to maintain it with substance, protect it from ever-present envy with vigilance. And there's the strain that rips you apart! The pain of holding on to what you have. It gives birth to fears which pinch at the heart and dement the mind, until you needs must clutch at some other faith. . . . Oh, it has driven me close to horror . . . and I tell you, I don't know what to think now.

SENCHI *(who has been listening with concern).* We make an odd pair of friends, to be sure. You, with your machines growling at granite in your quarries to crumble and deliver to you their wealth; and I, trying to pay my way in the currency of my songs. But perhaps that, like many statements we are capable of expressing, is merely grasping at extremes of light and dark, and missing the subtle tones for which we haven't yet found words.

EDUFA. Yes, I do have my moments when I'm not quite as solid as you think, when solidity becomes illusory.

SENCHI. But you do give an impression of being settled and satisfied, which is what I'm not.

EDUFA. I wish I could, like you, dare to bare myself for scrutiny. *(Pause)* I'm being compelled to learn however, and the day will come, I suppose.

SENCHI. Ah, yes. We commit these thoughts to the wind and leave it to time to sift them. *(Snapping out of his serious mood)* I'm ready for immediacy which is this evening's light relief. Where are the ladies?

EDUFA. Don't worry; they will not miss this chance to dine at Edufa's house.

SENCHI *(preening)*. Do I look noticeable? *(Making much of his ill-fitting suit)* I've never gone hunting in fancy dress before.

EDUFA *(really laughing)*. Oh, Senchi, you're so refreshing, you ass.

SENCHI. Yes, call me ass. Always, it's "You're an ass!" Seldom does a man say, "I am an ass." That takes courage. But you're right. I am an ass, or I would be wearing my own suit.

EDUFA. Come on. You don't mind wearing my suit?

SENCHI. I do. It's the same as a borrowed song, to me. Singing other people's songs or wearing other people's suits, neither suits me.

EDUFA *(teasing)*. Well, you're in it now.

SENCHI. Being an ass, I am. However, it will serve for an evening of foolery. *(A flash of seriousness again)* Tell me, do you understand, though?

EDUFA. What, Senchi?

SENCHI *(earnestly)*. You see, it's like this. My own suit may be shabby, but its shabbiness is of my making. I understand it. It is a guide of self-evaluation. When I stand in it, I know where I stand and why. And that, strangely, means to me dignity and security.

EDUFA. There, you're getting very serious. Have a drink.

SENCHI. A drink. Ah, yes. *(Stopping short at the trolley)* Oh, no, not before I have greeted Ampoma with breath that I have freshened in my sleep.

He sits. EDUFA *serves himself a drink.*

SCENE II

EDUFA. Our guests will soon arrive. Before they do, I have an act of love that I must make tonight.

SENCHI. You surprise me. Can't you wait? You?

EDUFA. It is a gesture of pure pleasure such as my heart has never before requested.

SENCHI. I don't need telling about the pleasure of it. What I'm saying is, Can't you wait? You?

EDUFA. Just now you judged me unemotional.

SENCHI. Don't worry; after this confessional, I absolve you of the charge.

EDUFA. You see, I've never stinted in giving my wife gifts. Gold she has and much that money can buy. But tonight I'm a man lifted up by her love, and I know that nothing less than flowers will do for one such as she is.

SENCHI. Applause. Talk on.

EDUFA (*to* ABENA). Fetch the flowers, sister. (*She goes into the kitchen.*)

SENCHI (*watching her go*). You make me feel so unmarried, confusing Senchi's Plan for the Ruination of Women. You're driving me to sell my freedom to the next girl that comes too near me.

EDUFA. Don't do that. Learn to love, my friend.

    ABENA *returns with a beautiful bouquet of fresh flowers and hands it to* EDUFA.

SENCHI. Lovely.

EDUFA (*to* ABENA). Little one, you who are soon to marry, I'm giving you a chance to look at love. Take these flowers in to Ampoma. (*He speaks emotionally into the flowers.*) Tell her that I, her husband, send them, that it is she who has so matured my love. I would have presented them myself, but I have learned the magic of shyness and haven't the boldness to look into her eyes yet.

    ABENA *embraces him happily and takes the flowers from him.*

SENCHI. Applause! Standing ovation! This is the first graceful act I've ever seen you do. *(As* ABENA *walks away)* Keep the door open as you go, and let my song keep tune to this moment of nobility. *(He sings.)*

Nne [1]

Nne Nne

Nne

Nne Nne

O Mother

Nne

Nne Nne

    ABENA, *turning in appreciation of the song, drops the flowers, which fall on the step with the sign of the sun on it.*

ABENA. Oh! *(She quickly retrieves the flowers.)*

EDUFA *(becoming tense).* For God's sake, be careful.

SENCHI *(continuing after the incident).*

If I find you

Nne

Nne Nne

I'll have to worship you

Nne

Nne Nne

I must adore you

Nne

Nne Nne

O Mother

Nne

Nne Nne

    EDUFA, *enchanted by the song, attempts to join quietly in the refrain.*

She's wonderful

---

1. *Nne.* For the music to the following song, see page 386.

She's wonderful
O Mother
She's wonderful
Yes, if I find you
Nne
Nne Nne
I'll have to worship you
Nne
Nne Nne
I must adore you
Nne
Nne Nne
O Mother
Nne
Nne Nne

EDUFA. Very good, Senchi.

> SEGUWA *is so affected by the song that she is sobbing quietly behind the table.*

SENCHI *(noticing her).* That is the wettest-eyed woman I've ever seen. *(He goes to her.)* Oh, sorry; I promised to make you cry, didn't I? There now, are you happy?

SEGUWA. That's a song after my own heart.

SENCHI. After mine also.

> *There is a sudden ripple of laughter from* EDUFA's *rooms.*

EDUFA *(elatedly).* That is her laughter. That is Ampoma. I love her. *(ABENA returns.)* Is she happy?

ABENA. Radiant. She was standing before the mirror when I entered, looking at her image, her clothes laid out on the bed beside her. Seeing the flowers mirrored there with her, she turned to greet their brightness with her laughter. Then she listened to your song with her eyes shut and sighed a happy sigh. She listened to your message attentively and said, "Tell my husband that I understand."

EDUFA *(glowing).* She does. I know. She loves. I know.

ABENA. "Tell Senchi," she said, "that all will be left to those who dare to catch in song the comfort of this world."

SENCHI. That, I have understood.

ABENA. And she will join you later, she says.

EDUFA. Yes, she is able to, tonight. Great heart-beat of mine, it is good to be alive. *(Briskly)* Senchi, a drink now?

They go to the drinks.

ABENA. Everything is ready to serve, brother. And I am awaited.

EDUFA *(affectionately)*. Go; you have earned your moment.

ABENA *hurries out.*

SENCHI *(watching her approvingly)*. Little sister, buxom sister. I ought to think of marrying that girl.

EDUFA *(smiling)*. Too late. You have lost her to another.

SENCHI. Too bad. I'm always ending up blank. But, never mind now. *(Declaiming)* I will make do with ephemerals. Turn up the next page in Senchi's chronicle of uncertainties. *(He gets a drink.)*

SCENE III

SENCHI *(at the trolley, his back to the courtyard)*. They are coming.

EDUFA *(turning round and seeing nobody)*. How do you know?

SENCHI *(also turning round)*. I'm highly sensitised, that's all. I can feel women twenty miles away, minimum range.

The CHORUS *enter through the gate, talking. They are dressed, even overdressed, for the evening.*

CHORUS ONE. That was exciting, dodging those prying eyes in town.

EDUFA *(to* SENCHI*)*. You win. They are here.

CHORUS TWO. Won't they be surprised tomorrow when they learn that we too have been invited here.

CHORUS THREE. There they are, waiting for us.

SENCHI *(to* EDUFA, *meaning his suit)*. Do I look noticeable?

EDUFA *(sharing the fun)*. I don't stand a chance beside you.

CHORUS ONE. How do I look?

CHORUS FOUR. Fine. *(With relish)* Look at that table. It is good simply to see.

CHORUS TWO *(also impressed)*. Ei!

SENCHI. Is there a roadblock there? Come on; I never allow women to keep me waiting.

CHORUS *(in fun below the courtyard steps).* Is there anybody in this beautiful house?

SENCHI *(pleased).* A lively flock, eh? They have a sense of humour. That's a good beginning.

EDUFA *(coming forward).* Good evening.

CHORUS. We answer you.

SENCHI *(meeting them).* Embrace me.

CHORUS ONE *(flirtatiously).* Do you always do things in such a hurry?

SENCHI. That's a good one. That is a rollicking good one. Lady, for that much perkiness, I'm yours . . . momentarily.

EDUFA *(enjoying it).* Senchi. Ladies, it's very good of you to come, and thank you for this morning's kindness.

CHORUS ONE. We trust your wife keeps well. Shall we be seeing her this evening?

EDUFA. Certainly. She will join you presently.

CHORUS ONE. Accept this little gift for her from all of us here. *(She hands the gift to him.)*

CHORUS TWO. We were making so much noise here this morning; we hope we didn't disturb her in any serious way.

EDUFA. Oh, no. On her behalf, I thank you. Sit wherever you like. *(The* CHORUS *choose seats.* CHORUS FOUR *sits close to the set table, eyeing everything.)* This is indeed most pleasant. I'll get you drinks. *(He places the gift on the table and gets busy with drinks.)*

SENCHI *(startling* CHORUS FOUR *at the table).* We are not quite eating yet, you know.

CHORUS FOUR *(naïvely).* It looks so pretty.

SENCHI. You look prettier than forks and knives and stiffbacked serviettes; that is sure.

CHORUS FOUR *(uncomprehending).* Serviettes?

SENCHI. Yes, these things. *(Taking her by the hand to the seat near the kitchen)* Sit over here with me. I have other things I rather think it will be interesting to try to negotiate with you. May I hold your hand? Or is that considered adultery in these parts? *(They sit.)* I always try to get the local customs straight before I begin negotiations.

EDUFA *(handing out drinks)*. Senchi, give the lady a drink at least.

SENCHI *assists him*.

CHORUS FOUR. Lady! Ei, that's nice.

SENCHI *(pleased with her)*. She is positively c-u-t-e.

CHORUS TWO *(confidentially to CHORUS THREE)*. This is all as we imagined it. Better even.

CHORUS THREE *(full of curiosity)*. Who is his friend?

SENCHI *(at the trolley)*. Aha! I have ears like a hare, you know. Before a woman can say "Senchi," I come to the summons of her thought. I'm acutely sensitive. Edufa, she wants to know who I am. Tell her I'm a neo-millionaire in search of under-developed territories. *(The CHORUS respond with laughter.)* They applaud. They do have a sense of humour. Fine. *(Fussily)* Drinks all round, and who cares which is what. *(He hands a drink to CHORUS FOUR.)*

EDUFA. I do. Everyone gets exactly what she wants.

The drinks are settled. SENCHI sits in a central position.

SENCHI *(raising his glass ceremoniously)*. We have it in hand. *(A moment of awkward silence as people drink.)* Now, what's the silence for? This is a party. Shall we play games?

CHORUS ONE. What games?

SENCHI. Party games.

EDUFA. Excuse me. I'll see if Ampoma is ready. *(He goes to his rooms.)*

SENCHI *(rising promptly)*. That's kind of you, Edufa. *(To CHORUS)* He is a most considerate, kindhearted man when I'm around.

Let's make the best of our opportunities. Now, let me see. We will not play Musical Chairs; that, being a little colonial, is somewhat inappropriate here. But I'm open to suggestion . . . and . . . if you like, inspection too. *(CHORUS laugh heartily as he strikes poses.)* They merely laugh, which is no way to encourage me. Hm . . . *(He plays at thinking seriously.)* Do you like songs?

CHORUS *(enthusiastically)*. Yes.

SENCHI *(liking this)*. That means I can entertain you in songs, eh?

CHORUS. Yes.

SENCHI. Do you like stories?

CHORUS. Yes.

SENCHI. That means I must tell them, eh?

CHORUS. Yes.

SENCHI. What do I get for all of this, from you?

CHORUS ONE. We laugh for you.

SENCHI. And with me?

CHORUS. Oh, yes.

SENCHI. Yes. Yes. Do you never say No?

CHORUS. No.

SENCHI. Brilliant conversation. Senchi, you must make better headway. *(Pauses reflectively)* Oh, yes, you are. They say they don't ever say No.

CHORUS ONE. Isn't he funny!

> *She and the others have been enjoying a private joke centred on* SENCHI's *ill-fitting suit.*

SENCHI. Oh, madam, that's unkind.

CHORUS ONE. It's your suit . . . pardon me . . . but your suit . . .

SENCHI. That kind of joke should thoroughly frustrate a man. But I must admit it is most intelligent of you. I don't know whether you realise how positively brilliant your observation is. Well now, what next? I have an idea. I sing a bit, you know.

CHORUS *(eagerly)*. Ah!

SENCHI. Does that mean, Sing?

CHORUS. Yes.

SENCHI. Yes! We will all sing my song. Listen; it's easy.

> *He sings snatches of the song for* AMPOMA, *encouraging the* CHORUS *to participate. They try.*

CHORUS ONE. It's sad.

SENCHI. So it is. But, quickly before you start crying all over me, here is a rumpus song all right. We will have the foolery for which I'm fitly suited tonight. Here is the story of it. A traveller's tale. I'm a bit of a traveller, you know. *(He poses for effect.)*

And I came to this city called Bam, and there was this man; whether he is mad or simply stark raving poor, I couldn't ascertain. But he impressed me; I can tell you that. Wait a minute; I've written his story down. *(He takes some sheets of paper out of his leather case.)* I'm a bit of a writer, you know. *(The* CHORUS *nudge each other.)*

A man claimed insane walks through the city streets. No prophet nor priest costumed in fancy gown is he; but he too, afire with zeal, feels that men must heed his creed—or at the least applaud the wit with which he calls them sons of a bitch. *(He looks round for approval. The faces round him are getting blank with incomprehension. He becomes more declamatory.)*

He raves through the city streets at sane passers-by. And what does he say? He feels that heed ought to be given to his preaching, or at the least, applause must greet his singular screeching:

"Gentlemen,[1] show me a thought you've thought through, and I'll bow to you right low and grant you a master's due.

"Feather-fine ladies with hips that rhyme, who the blazes minds your children's manners at this time?

"Left, right, left, does not feed a nation. I'd rather have you roaring drunk at a harvest celebration."

Oh, he is a character, an absolute word-exhibitor. But, Ladies, where is your laughter? Aren't you amused?

CHORUS *(quite blank)*. We are listening.

SENCHI. Good. I thought myself that his words should sound good on a trumpet. *(He takes a small trumpet out of his leather case.)* Come on, procession! *(He begins to blow a tune to the words in quotation above. The* CHORUS *are swept into the fun. They are dancing round after him, procession style, when* EDUFA *enters, now in his jacket.)* Join up, Edufa. Procession.

EDUFA *complies.* SENCHI *alternates between the trumpet and singing the words. Presently, the whole group is singing to his accompaniment.* AMPOMA *appears unnoticed at the top of the steps. She is tastefully dressed in a delicate colour,*

---

1. *Gentlemen.* For the music to the following song, see page 387.

looking very much like a bride. She watches the romping scene briefly, with a mixture of sadness and amusement, before she descends at a point when the group is taking a turn in the courtyard.

EDUFA *(seeing her).* Ah, friends, my wife!

The singing and dancing comes to an abrupt halt.

SENCHI *(with profound admiration).* Ampoma. Mother.

CHORUS. Beautiful.

AMPOMA *(graciously).* I'm sorry I was not up to welcome you, Senchi.

SENCHI. You are here now, Ampoma, and well. I couldn't wish for more.

AMPOMA. That was your singing. It is a lovely song.

SENCHI. Yes, for such as you a man must sing. The song is yours, made in the strain of your name, my gift to you. *(He takes a sheet of music out of his pocket.)* Take it. *(She does.)* And accept me as yours, devotedly and positively forever. . . . Amen!

The CHORUS practically applaud.

CHORUS ONE. Isn't he a character!

AMPOMA *(to the CHORUS).* I didn't know about the women being here. Thank you for your company. I hope my husband is honouring your presence here.

CHORUS. We are most happy to be here.

EDUFA. There is a gift they brought for you.

AMPOMA. How kind. *(Pensively)* So many rays of kindness falling on me, each with its own intensity . . . *(Brightening)* I respond with warm heart . . . and hand. *(She shakes hands hurriedly and nervously with the CHORUS.)*

EDUFA *(whispering to her).* Your hand is trembling. You're sure you're not cold? I'll fetch you a wrap.

AMPOMA *(with cheerfulness).* No, I'm well wrapped in your affection, and that is warm enough. My friends, you see I have a most affectionate husband.

SENCHI. We will have to name this the night of fond declarations.

EDUFA *(a little nervously).* Had we better eat now?

AMPOMA. Yes, our friends must be hungry . . . and it is getting late.

SENCHI. Escort her to her chair there. *(He starts the* CHORUS *singing again and moving in mock procession into the court.* AMPOMA *joins in the game. Suddenly she loses her balance and barely avoids a fall. Only her hand touches the ground as she steadies herself.* SENCHI *springs to her support.)* Oh, sorry.

EDUFA *(worried).* Be careful with her. *(He escorts her to a chair by the pillar.)* Sit down, Ampoma, please. (SEGUWA, *who sees the fall as she is bringing in a dish of food, is frozen in her tracks. This so unnerves* EDUFA *that he speaks harshly to her.)* Where's the food? Why are you standing there? Bring it. *(He gives attention to* AMPOMA.*)*

AMPOMA. I'm all right. Please don't shout at her. She has nursed me well.

SENCHI. No, Edufa, don't. That woman's tears are too ready to fall.

From this stage, a strange mood develops in AMPOMA. *She frequently talks like one whose mind is straying.*

AMPOMA *(fast).* Friends, eat. My husband provides well. I hope you're happy here. Why am I sitting down? *(She rises.)* I must feed you. *(As she quickly passes plates of food served by* SEGUWA*)* Eat. We must eat to keep the body solidly on its feet. I wasn't able to cook for you myself. *(Pause)* That's sad. A woman must serve her husband well. But I'm sure the food is good. We never serve anything but the best to our friends. Eat. You don't know how good it was to hear you fill this house with merriment. Eat.

Everyone is served. AMPOMA *sits down and receives a plate from* EDUFA, *who has been watching her anxiously.*

SENCHI *(to* CHORUS FOUR*).* You may eat now. (EDUFA *sits down beside* AMPOMA, *but his mind is not on his food.)* Ampoma, I need your rare counsel. Which of these five women shall I take to wife, lawfully?

AMPOMA *(laughing gaily).* Oh, Senchi, bless you. Which one catches your eye everywhere you turn, like I catch Edufa's eye? That's the one you should have.

The women avert their eyes, eating busily.

SENCHI *(looking round)*. No hope.

EDUFA *(at the table)*. Here is wine. *(Like one about to propose a toast)* This evening is a celebration unpremeditated.

SENCHI *(sitting up)*. Speak, husband, speak.

EDUFA. There is nowhere I would rather be, nothing more than this I would rather be doing. Join with me in drinking to the health of my lovely wife, whom I publicly proclaim a woman among women and friend among friends.

SENCHI. Applause. Vote of thanks!

EDUFA. Drink. To her health.

CHORUS *and* SENCHI *(rising, each with glass in hand)*. To your health, Ampoma.

CHORUS ONE *(instinctively formal)*. In all directions we let our libation pour. Your husband is true and rare. Live together blessedly to the end of your days. Health to you.

CHORUS. Health to your children. Health to your house.

AMPOMA *(deeply shaken)*. I will have some wine now. Thank you, my friends.

EDUFA *(serving her)*. Here.

SENCHI. And enough of solemnity. You're making her pensive.
They all sit.

EDUFA *(with unconcealed concern)*. Ampoma.

AMPOMA. I'm all right. *(She rises. She is not all right.)* It is a moving thing to feel a prayer poured into your soul. But now it's over. *(Pause)* Give me some wine. *(Now straining for a diversion, she moves forward to gaze into the sky above the courtyard.)* The night is usually full of stars. Where are they all tonight? Senchi, can't you sing them out in a riot?

SENCHI *(beside her, parodying)*. Little stars; little, colossal, little stars. How I wonder where you are. How I wonder why you are. How I wonder which one of you is my star, and why you fizzle.

AMPOMA *(very pleased)*. That's good. Oh, Senchi.

CHORUS ONE. He is never at a loss for things to say.

CHORUS TWO. It's extraordinary.

EDUFA. If he could settle down, he could become a poet.

AMPOMA *(seriously)*. He is one already, no matter how he roams.

SENCHI *(touched)*. Thank you, Ampoma.

AMPOMA *(returning to her chair)*. Eat, friends, it's late.

CHORUS TWO. But you are not eating.

AMPOMA. I have fed all I need. And there is no time. Very soon I must embrace my husband before you all, answering the affection into which he draws me. *(She rises hastily and loses her balance again, just avoiding a fall, steadying herself with her hand.)*

EDUFA *(supporting her, and very disturbed)*. Don't trouble, I implore you.

SENCHI *(to AMPOMA)*. Sorry. *(Trying to relax the tensing atmosphere)* But, come on, Edufa. Let her embrace you. I haven't ever seen Ampoma breaking through her shyness. Besides, if she embraces you, then I can embrace all the others; and so the night makes progress swingingly.

AMPOMA *(embracing EDUFA)*. Women, I hope you don't think me without modesty. *(Taking up a position)* We spend most of our days preventing the heart from beating out its greatness. The things we would rather encourage lie choking among the weeds of our restrictions. And before we know it, time has eluded us. There is not much time allotted us, and half of that we sleep. While we are awake, we should allow our hearts to beat without shame of being seen living. *(She looks magnificent and quite aloof. Then she speaks more quietly.)* My husband, you have honoured me by your words and by your precious gift of flowers. I wish to honour you in return, in language equally unashamed. *(She beckons to SEGUWA, who, since AMPOMA's near fall, has been expressing her alarm in the background.)* Go to my room. On my bed there is a casket. Bring it to me.

> *(SEGUWA complies.)*

CHORUS TWO. Many women would like to be in a position to say what you have said here, Ampoma.

SENCHI. Therefore, I should not neglect to pay attention to my preliminary surveys which will prepare the way for such contracts to be signed. *(He eyes the CHORUS playfully.)* Shall we change seats? *(As he changes seats to sit by another woman)* I have been camping too long in one place and getting nowhere.

SEGUWA *returns with the casket.*

EDUFA *(confused and uncomfortable).* What's this?

AMPOMA *(opening the casket and taking out some smart waist beads).* Waist beads, bearing the breath of my tenderness.

CHORUS *(nonplussed, eyes popping, but laughing).* Oh! Oh!

EDUFA *(astounded, embarrassed, but not displeased).* Ampoma!

SENCHI *(beside himself).* Great! Whew!

AMPOMA *(inscrutable).* Women, you understand, don't you, that with this I mean to claim him mine? And you are witnesses. My husband, wear this with honour. *(She surprises EDUFA by slipping the beads round his neck. His first reaction is shock.)* With it I declare to earth and sky and water, and all things with which we shall soon be one, that I am slave to your flesh and happy so to be. Wear it proudly, this symbol of the union of our flesh.

The CHORUS *and* SENCHI *are making the best of a most astonishing situation by laughing at* EDUFA'*s discomfiture.*

EDUFA *(attempting to hide his embarrassment behind a smile).* Why, Ampoma . . . Well . . . what can I say . . . *(He removes the beads as soon as she lets go.)*

SENCHI. That's rich. Oh, Ampoma, you are the most terrific woman I have ever seen. Don't stand there so foolishly, Edufa. Do something. Say something. I would sweep her up in my arms, take wings, and be gone.

AMPOMA *(very abruptly).* Excuse me, friends, I must leave you. I hope you will tell the town what I have done without considering it gossip. If I had wished it not to be known, I would not have done it here before you. Take my hand in yours quickly. *(She shakes hands with the women in great haste.)* I am happy that you came. . . . I do not know you well, but you are women and you give me boldness to commit my deepest feelings to your understanding. *(She is hurrying away.)* Sleep well when you return to your own homes.

CHORUS *(chilled).* Good night, Ampoma. Good night.

EDUFA (*miserably*). I must see her in. (*He catches up with her before she reaches the steps.*) Are you all right?

AMPOMA (*brightly*). Oh, yes. It's such a relief to feel so well at last.

> *She takes his hand, looks round, and seems to be wanting to linger.* EDUFA *attempts to lead her away.*

SENCHI (*to* CHORUS). You have seen truth.

CHORUS ONE. I couldn't have believed it if my own eyes hadn't witnessed it. Ampoma?

SENCHI. Just do what she recommends, that's all.

> EDUFA *and* AMPOMA *are going up the steps.*

AMPOMA. Thank you, but don't leave our friends. I want to go in alone.

EDUFA. As you wish, my dear, but——

AMPOMA. I want to; please don't leave them now.

EDUFA (*reluctantly*). I'll make it very brief and join you presently. (*He comes down.*) Ah, Senchi, she's all but taken my breath away. (AMPOMA *falls on the step with the sign of the sun on it, causing* SEGUWA *to scream.* EDUFA *runs to his wife, yelling with horror.*) No! Ampoma! No!

SENCHI (*helping to lift up* AMPOMA). Why didn't you take her up the steps?

CHORUS TWO. She's been unsteady all the time. She's not recovered yet, is she?

EDUFA (*unaware of anyone else's presence*). There, Ampoma, there. You didn't fall all the way to the ground. I will not let you fall. No! No! No! Not to the ground. To the ground? No! Lean on me. You shouldn't have come out. I shouldn't have permitted it. Oh! No! (*He is taking her up.*)

SENCHI (*with great concern*). Take her in. It wasn't a big fall, fortunately. (*Helplessly*) Sleep well, Ampoma. (AMPOMA *turns to look at him with a wistful smile. He is left standing alone on the steps, deeply puzzled.*) That's strange. . . . (*He comes down.*) Well, sit down, ladies. (*Obviously trying to pretend the atmosphere of panic doesn't exist*) I don't blame Edufa for overdoing his concern. He's a man caught in the spell of high romance. Why, if I were in his shoes, I would be even more wildly solicitous. *(He thinks this over, forgetting the presence of the* CHORUS *meanwhile.)* In his shoes? No, not that. I'm wearing his suit, I openly confess, but his shoes I wouldn't wear. I, Senchi, must at all times maintain a genuine contact with the basic earth in my own shoes. *(Shaking himself out of his reflection)* Have a drink. *(But he cannot move.)* She didn't fall too badly, did she? Perhaps she shouldn't be up yet.

CHORUS ONE. I'm thinking the same, remembering her action here.

CHORUS TWO. You saw it? The tension beneath the smile?

CHORUS THREE. She was unhappy.

CHORUS ONE. But she was happy also, strangely.

> *It is now that* SEGUWA *is noticed wandering in the courtyard with gestures of desperation.*

SENCHI *(unnerved)*. Woman, you are too excitable. What are you fussing around for like a hen wanting somewhere to lay an egg? *(*SEGUWA *looks at him as if she's afraid he'll hit her.)* Control yourself.

SEGUWA. I cannot any more. She fell. Did you count? Oh! The thought! She fell three times, and each time she touched the ground. Oh! Oh!

> *The* CHORUS *converge on her.*

CHORUS ONE. What do you mean?

SENCHI. Oh, come off it. My goodness, she didn't break any bones. Ampoma wouldn't forgive you for making her seem so fragile.

SEGUWA. She fell off the sign of the sun; and the sun itself is blanked, and it is dark.

CHORUS *(with urgency)*. What sign?

SEGUWA *(out of control)*. Bad signs. They would pose no menace if no oath had been sworn and we were free to read in her present condition normal disabilities for which remedy is possible. As it is, the reality of that oath makes Edufa for all time guilty, no matter how or when she meets her end.

SENCHI. Don't talk to us in fragments, woman.

SEGUWA. I thought we could cancel out the memory. *(Rushing towards the steps)* But I see the sign of the three pebbles, and on the third fall she fell on the sign of the sun, to the ground. *(She points out the sign of the sun.)*

CHORUS *(crowding round)*. What is it?

SENCHI. What is this, woman?

SEGUWA *(hiding her face in her hands and turning away)*. It shouldn't be there to plague our memory, deluding us from the path of reason.

SENCHI. This woman is unstable. I wouldn't have her running about my house if I had one. But . . . what is this sign?

SEGUWA *(terrified)*. I don't know. I have told you nothing. Get out. I know nothing about it. Why did you come feasting here tonight? Get out! Get out, all of you. *(She rears up against the wall, pointing at the CHORUS.)* Or are you eager to take Ampoma's place? Can you pay the price of sharing Edufa's bed? Nothing less than your lives? Oh, he is most dangerous.

She dashes off into EDUFA's rooms. The CHORUS and SENCHI hover round the steps, staring at the sign of the sun.

CHORUS *(several voices)*. She's terrified.

SENCHI. So is Edufa. Does a fall call for these flights of terror? Such hysteria? *(He scrutinises the sign, and his distress increases.)* I should break in there and demand explanation.

CHORUS ONE. Do you remember this morning, at our ceremony, that woman's haunted look, her strangeness?

CHORUS TWO. Her fighting to say whether Edufa was in or out?

CHORUS ONE. And Edufa himself. If there wasn't something terribly wrong, would he have been so conspicuously relieved when Ampoma asked for food?

SENCHI. Do you mean that all this happened here?

CHORUS THREE. Yes, this morning, in our presence.

SENCHI *(grimly to himself)*. To me, also, he has shown some strange disturbances of spirit this day. . . . And then, Ampoma's wandering mind tonight, her . . . But let's not run on so. We know nothing until I go in there. *(He is about to force his way into EDUFA's rooms when SEGUWA rushes out. She cringes when she sees him and flees into the courtyard, her fist in her mouth as if to stifle an outcry.)* Where's Edufa? Woman, speak. What's happening here?

CHORUS. Talk to us. Tell us.

> *They and* SENCHI *press in on* SEGUWA *as she roams with her hand pressed against her mouth. She suddenly notices the clappers that the* CHORUS *used in the mourning rite, seizes them, and thrusts them impulsively at the* CHORUS.

SEGUWA *(bursting out).* Don't ask me to talk. Help me. You have come to do the rite, have you not? Do it quickly, I implore you.

SENCHI *(at the top of the step).* Edufa!

SEGUWA. What is there left of sacredness?

CHORUS. By the souls of our fathers, speak.

SEGUWA. It is that evil charm on which the oath was sworn. We cannot ever forget it. We cannot reason without it now.

SENCHI. What? Charms in Edufa's house?

CHORUS. What charm?

SENCHI. Edufa! It's Senchi.

SEGUWA. And yet he burned it. But the deed was done. He buried it, but it was her he buried.

CHORUS. Buried?

SEGUWA. Oh, speak, tongue! Women, you did your ceremony here, but you left the evil one himself behind you. Edufa. He is in there with his victim. This is the day when Edufa should have died. Another has died for him: his wife, Ampoma. She loved him, and she has died to spare his life.

CHORUS ONE. Died? For him? People don't die that kind of death.

CHORUS. Died? No. We have eaten here with her, laughed with her.

SENCHI *(helplessly).* Groans in there . . . like one who stifles agony lest he shed unmanly tears. I fear it is the worst, my friends.

SEGUWA. Coward! Coward! Coward! He is a cursed man. Go. Tell the town about the man who let his wife die for him. *(She breaks down.)* Then go and tell her mother. Oh, Mother! Will someone go and tell her mother, for I cannot look her in the face. I cannot look those motherless children in the face.

CHORUS. You lie. We will not believe you.

SEGUWA. Come, I'll show you where he buried it.

She strides ahead to take them to the back courtyard. Just at this point EDUFA *comes out, a man clearly going out of his mind. The* CHORUS *run up to crowd below the steps.*

CHORUS ONE. Oh, Edufa. Has this woman fed from your hand, who now maligns you so?

    SEGUWA *has fled at sight of* EDUFA.

CHORUS. We implore you, tell us she lies. We do not believe her, pious one. Tell us she lies.

SENCHI. Friend, what is this?

EDUFA *(dejectedly on the steps)*. If you see my father, call him back that I may weep on his shoulder.

CHORUS. Great God, is it true that she is dead?

SENCHI *(shaking him)*. Edufa. Friend. What's all this about charms?

EDUFA *(violent, his voice unnatural)*. I burned it. *(He slouches helplessly on the steps.)*

SENCHI. Stand up, man. What in the name of mystery is it all about?

CHORUS ONE. Do you hear him? He buried it, he says. There was something then? Edufa, is it true what this woman says? That Ampoma is dead, and in your place?

EDUFA. . . . and buried . . . *(Wildly)* I told her not to swear. I did not know that harm could be done. I did not know it. *(Looking belligerently at* SENCHI, *and not recognising him)* Who are you? Why are you looking at me?

SENCHI *(sadly)*. Senchi.

CHORUS ONE. He is raving.

EDUFA. I told her not to swear. I didn't know that harm could be done.

CHORUS. Not to swear, or harm could be done. Alas!

SENCHI *(seizing hold of him)*. Tell me all, Edufa.

    The owl hoots outside.

EDUFA *(wildly)*. Didn't he take that bird away? *(He looks at* SENCHI *dangerously.)* Who are you? Don't restrain me. *(Straining with more than natural strength)* Where is my leopard skin? I'll teach Death to steal my wives. *(So strong that* SENCHI *can no longer restrain him)* Death, I will lie closely at the grave again, and when you come gloating with your spoil, I'll grab you, unlock her from your grip, and bring her safely home to my bed. And until then, no woman's hand shall touch me.

CHORUS. She is dead. *(They rush into* EDUFA'S *rooms.)*

SENCHI *(with infinite sadness)*. There, Edufa, there . . . don't rave so. No . . . not this. *(He attempts to hold him again.)*

EDUFA *(wrenching himself free)*. The last laugh will be mine when I bring her home again. I will bring Ampoma back. Forward, to the grave. *(He moves in strength towards the back courtyard, roaring.)* I will do it. I am conqueror! *(His last word, however, comes as a great questioning lament.)* Conqueror . . . ?

> *He runs out by way of the back courtyard. The* CHORUS *return mournfully.* SENCHI *makes his way past them into* EDUFA'S *rooms.*

CHORUS *(several voices together, and a single voice every now and then, as they make their way out through the gate; rendered at a slow dirge tempo)*.

Calamity.

That we should be the witnesses.

Do not restrain your tears,

Let them stream,

Make a river of sorrow, for Ampoma is dead.

We do not know how,

We do not understand,

But she is dead.

Will someone go and tell her mother!

Edufa! Edufa!

How is it possible

That she is dead?

> *They can be heard beating their clappers after the chanting.* SENCHI *returns. He stands alone on the steps.*

SENCHI. Blank. I have ended up blank once again. All that is left, the laughter of the flowers in her lifeless arms and the lingering smell of incense. *(He descends.)*

And over me, the taut extension of the sky—to which I raise my song.

Will someone go and tell her mother? *(He sings.)*
And if I find you
I'll have to worship you
I must adore you
Nne
Nne Nne
O Mother
Nne
Nne Nne

The End.

Song 1

O, child of A - ma Why is she wan - der- ing,—

Why wan - der-ing, Why wan-d'ring in the night

Like the dy - ing?— Me - wuo!—

Song 2

♩.=80

Our moth-er's dead, Ei! Ei - Ei!

We the or-phans cry, Our moth-er's dead,

O! O - O! We the or-phans cry.

Song 3

Slowly, with feeling

(*mf*) Nne Nne Nne Nne Nne Nne 0, Mo-ther

Nne Nne Nne___ If I find you Nne Nne

Nne___ I'll have to wor-ship you Nne Nne Nne___

___ I must a - dore you Nne Nne Nne 0, Mo-ther

Nne Nne Nne She's won-der-ful She's won-der-ful 0,

Mo-ther She's won-der-ful Yes, if I find_you_

Nne Nne Nne_I'll have to wor-ship you Nne Nne Nne

I must a - dore you Nne Nne Nne 0, Mo-ther Nne Nne Nne.

Song 4

Alla marcia

[1] *(f)* Gen - tle-men, show me___ a thought you've thought through, and I'll bow to you right low and___ grant you a mas-ter's due. [2] Fea - ther-fine la - dies with hips that rhyme, who the blaz-es minds your child-ren's man-ners at this time? [3] Left, right, left, does___ not feed a na - tion. I'd ra-ther have you roar-ing drunk at a harv-est ce - le - bra-tion.

Tshakatumba / *Republic of the Congo*
(20th cent.)

MESSAGE TO MPUTU ANTOINETTE, GIRL OF THE BUSH, FRIEND OF MY CHILDHOOD

African sister black sister
you who do not know Damas or Mackay
you who must learn Césaire and Senghor [1]
you who are ignorant of the boundaries of your continent
5 and in the half-light go to draw water
like an ancient goddess
wearing an Edenic smile
at the only spring in the neighborhood
it is for you above all that I labor
10 it is for you that the cold benumbs me
sister of the sapodilla tree [2] loving sister
Africa will be the fruit of our accord.

"Message to Mputu Antoinette, Girl of the Bush, Friend of My Childhood" by Tshakatumba from THE AFRICAN ASSERTION. Copyright
© 1968 by The Odyssey Press.
1. *Damas . . . Mackay . . . Césaire . . . Senghor,* black poets who have
celebrated the beauty of black women. See the article on page 323. Claude
Mackay (1890–1948) is from the United States, Léon Damas (1912–   )
from French Guiana, Aimé Césaire (1913–   ) from the French West
Indies, and Léopold Sédar Senghor (1906–   ) from Senegal. **2.** *sapodilla
tree,* a tropical evergreen.

Tireless gazelle
who wanders at the close of day
15 through the hushed thickets of dead wood you gather
O black woman! guileless sister
your beauty touches me your beauty enchants me
like the blue wave simmering
in your unfathomable depths
20 To see moored beneath the intertwined lianas
a continent moored in a trance
where the tom-toms beat out the rhythm of life
O loving friend in the giant encrusted lokumé [3]:
Africa will be what together we make it.

3. *lokumé*, a Central African tree.

Amos Tutuola / *Nigeria*
(1920–   )

ANIMAL THAT DIED
BUT HIS EYES STILL ALIVE

> *The big gun that stops the voices of the sol-*
> *diers*
> *Animals are surplus in the town in which the*
> *people have no teeth*

As I (Adebisi, the African huntress) was travelling along in this jungle it was so I was killing all the wild animals that I was seeing on the way. When I saw that the night was approaching I shot one small animal to death. I made a big fire and I roasted this animal which was an antelope, in the fire. Before I ate it to my satisfaction it was about ten o'clock in the night. But anyhow I ate out of it as I could and I kept the rest of it near the fire which I would eat in the morning. After that I lay down near this fire and then I slept but there was nothing which was happened to me throughout this night.

When I woke up in the morning by the crying of birds and when the dove gave the sign of eight o'clock, then I ate the rest of that roasted animal. After that I hung my gun and hunting bag on my shoulder having checked the gun and saw that it was in good order. Then I started to look for the wild animals to be killed. And within three days I nearly killed the whole of the

Reprinted by permission of Faber and Faber Ltd., from THE BRAVE AFRICAN HUNTRESS.

wild animals of this jungle. It was very scarcely to see one or two and I was very happy about this, but it still remained three big troubles—how to drive away all the pigmies from this jungle as they used to detain hunters in their custody. How to kill the dangerous animals who had light on eyes and how to kill a very curious and dangerous boa constrictor which was very dangerous to the hunters as well.

After I nearly killed the whole of the wild animals, I did not travel more than seven days when I came across a big wild animal. It was as big as an elephant. I had never seen the kind of this animal before. Because he had a very big head. Several horns were on his forehead. Each of the horns was as long and thick and sharp as cows' horns. Very long black and brown hairs were full this head and they were fallen downward, they were also very dirty. All the horns were stood upright on his forehead as if a person carried a bunch of sticks vertically. His beard was so plenty and long that it covered his chest and belly as well. The teeth of his mouth were so plenty and long that whenever he was eating a person who was in two miles away would be hearing the noises which they were making. Even as the teeth and the horns of his mouth and head were so fearful many of the wild animals who saw him when he was coming to kill them with all these things were dying for themselves before he would reach them instead to kill them with his teeth and horns, because they were too fearful to them.

He had two curious eyes which were as accurate as full moon of the dry season. Both were on the right part of his head as the other animals did, but each was bigger and could see everywhere without moving head. The powerful light that these eyes were bringing out could not go far or straight but they were bringing out the clear and round light. The ray of this light was always round him and it could be seen clearly from a long distance.

He had a kind of a terrible shout with which he was frightening the animals and his humming was also terrible to hear. All the rest animals were so hated and feared him that they never went near the place that he travelled for one week.

There was none part of his body which was not terrible and

which was not frightened neither human being nor other creature of this world.

Immediately I saw this "super-animal" as I could call him, in that morning through the round clear light of his eyes, was that I stopped in one place and I first breathed out heavily with great fear. Because I could not escape again, I had already approached him too closely before I saw him. And at the same moment that he too saw me, although I was still quite aloof when he first saw me. He first sighted all his horns towards me and then he was running to me as fast as he could. But when I thought within myself that if I stood on the ground and shot him, he would kill me instantaneously, because my "shakabullah" gun would not be able to kill him in one shot, therefore I hastily climbed a tree to the top.

But when he ran to the place that I had stood before and he did not meet me there again. He was going round and round until when he saw me on top of this tree. As I was on top of this tree I thought that I was saved but not at all. Because at the same moment that he saw me on top of this tree, he started to bite the tree at the bottom. And to my fear within two minutes he had nearly bitten the whole bottom of this tree. When I saw that the tree was just toppling to the ground, just to save my life, I hastily jumped from there to the top of another mighty tree which was nearby. And when he saw me on top of this mighty tree again, he started to bite the bottom of it as well and he was in great anger this time because he wanted to eat me without much trouble as this.

And when I saw that this mighty tree was toppling down as well, then I hastily sold my "death," I said within myself that before this "super-animal" would kill me I must first defend myself perhaps I would be saved. Then without hesitation I shot him. But when the gun-shots hit him on the chest and hurt him as well on the hind legs. It was this time this "super-animal" became more powerful and more dangerous than ever. And it was this day that I believed that—the half-killed snake is the most dangerous. Because this animal was then shrieking and shouting and humming more terribly with angry voice than ever. His fearful humming was hearing all over the jungle.

He was jumping and dashing to the trees, rocks, etc. and within a few minutes he had broken down all the trees of that area and scattered everything in disorder with great anger. When he came back to the tree on top of which I was he started to bite the bottom of this tree until it fell down. This tree hardly fell down when he jumped on me, but I was so lucky that immediately this tree fell on hard ground, it sprang up again before it lay down quietly, I fell off from it to a little distance, so by that he missed me to grip with his paws. Of course I hit my back on another tree which was near that spot and that gave me much pain. And as I was hastily standing up he had jumped high up and as he was coming down just to cover the whole of me, I hastily lay flatly on the ground and then he simply rolled along on the ground instead. Before he stood up again I had taken my cutlass and I was waiting for him at once.

Within one second he had stood up, but he did not attempt to bite me this time, he wanted to hit me to death with his horns. But at the same moment that I saw what he wanted to do this time, I hastily leapt to my left when he was about to butt me with his horns and I cut him several times with my cutlass within this moment, so he simply butted a heavy rock instead when he missed me.

He hardly missed me when he turned to his back and as he was coming again with great anger, I hastily leaned my back on the stump of the big tree which he had cut down, and I exposed my chest and belly in such a deceived way that he believed that he would not miss me as before. So as he was running furiously towards me with all his power and when he was about to reach me, I hastily leapt again to my right unexpectedly and unfortunately he simply butted the stump of that tree. So all his horns pierced this stump of tree, he could not pull them out but he was held up there helplessly, except his hind legs with which he was scattering the ground very roughly.

After I rested for a few minutes then I started to beat him with my poisonous cudgel until when he was completely powerless and then he died after some minutes. It was like that I killed this "super-animal" as I could call him. But to my surprise was that as he had already died the light of his eyes was still shining clearly and thus it was when I left there.

After I had killed this animal I started to look about for the fearful boa constrictor which my father had told me about his news that he (boa) was also very dangerous. As I was looking for this boa constrictor it was so I was killing all the wild animals which I was seeing on the way. And in a few days' time I killed the whole of them. So this time there was no more the fear of the wild animals again in this jungle except the fears of this terrible boa constrictor and the pigmies. I roamed about for several days but I did not come across this boa until one day when I travelled back to the place where I had killed "super-animal" unnoticed. But it was still a great surprise to see that the light of the eyes of this animal was still shining clearly. The flesh of his body was already decayed and the bones were already scattered on the ground but the eyes which brought out this light was still alive, the light was as clear as when the animal was still alive. So the eyes and the long hairs which were covered the skull were still on this skull as well and all the horns were still on the skull but they were still pierced the stump of that tree since the day that the animal had butted it (stump) himself.

In the first instance that I came there unexpectedly and when I saw this head with the clear light I thought that the animal had become alive after I had left there the other day. I stood before this head and I started to think of what to do with it, because the clear light which came out from the eyes was very attractively. When I thought what to do with it for a few minutes and I did not know yet so I pulled the head out of the stump. I first trimmed the hairs of the head very short then I cut those long horns very short too after that I trimmed the inside of the skull very neatly. But to my surprise when I put this skull or head on my head it was to my exact size and it seemed on my head as a cock helmet. I was seeing clearly through the eyes and the light of the eyes travelled far away in the jungle but I was then so fearful that there was not any living creature which would see me would not run away for fear because I was exactly as when that animal was alive. So when I believed that it would help me in future I wrapped it with the skin of animal and I kept it in my hunting bag. As from that day I was using it in the night as my light and I was wearing it on the head whenever I was hunting. So this wonderful head became a very useful thing at last. ▶

DON'T PAY BAD FOR BAD

THERE ONCE LIVED two tight friends, named Dola and Babi. Both were ladies. Babi and Dola liked each other since when they were children. They wore the same kind of clothes and were always going everywhere together in their village and to several other villages as well. Because of this many people thought that they were twins.

Both were going everywhere together until they grew old enough to marry. But as they liked each other so much they decided to marry two men of the same family and who lived in the same house, so that they might be with each other always.

Luckily, a few days after they had thought to do so, they heard of two men who were born by the same father and mother and lived in the same house as well. So Babi married the one who was junior and Dola married to the second who was the senior. Now, Babi and Dola were very happy because they were living together in their husbands' house as when they had not married.

A few days after their marriage, Dola cleared a part of the front of the house very neatly. She sowed one kola-nut on that spot. After a few weeks the kola-nut shot out. Having seen this, she filled up one big jar with water and put it before her new kola-nut tree. Very early in the morning, Dola would go and kneel down before her tree and jar and then she would pray to the tree to help her to get a baby in time. Then after the prayer, she would drink some of the water which was inside the jar. Dola believed that there was a certain spirit who was coming and blessing the kola-nut tree and the water in the night. Having done all this then she would go back to her room before the rest of the people in the house would wake.

After some months, the kola-nut tree grew up to the height of about two feet. But unfortunately the animals of the village began to eat the leaves of the tree and this hindered its growth. One morning, Babi saw Dola, her friend, as she knelt down before the tree and jar praying. After the prayer, Babi asked: "Dola, what are you doing before that kola-nut tree and the jar?"

"Oh, this kola-nut tree is my god and I ask it always to help me to get a baby in time," Dola, pointing a finger to the tree and jar explained quietly.

But when Babi noticed that the animals had eaten the leaves of the tree, she went back to her room. She brought the head of her large pitcher from which the body had been broken away. She gave it to Dola and advised her to cover her tree with it so that the animals might not be able to eat the leaves of the tree again. Dola took it from her and thanked her greatly. Then she covered her tree with it and as from that morning the animals were unable to eat the leaves again and the tree then grew as quickly as possible in the centre of the head of the pitcher.

A few years after, the tree yielded the first kola-nuts. The nuts were of the best quality in the village. For this reason the kola-nut buyers bought them with a considerable amount of money. And when the tree yielded the second and third nuts, the buyers bought them with a large sum of money as before. So in selling these nuts, Dola became a wealthy woman.

Having seen this, Babi was so jealous that one day, she asked

— "Please, Dola, will you return the head of my pitcher this morning?" "What? The head of your pitcher?" Dola shouted with great shock.

"Yes, the head of my pitcher. I want it back this morning," Babi replied in a jealous voice.

"Well, the head of your pitcher cannot be returned this time unless I break it into pieces before it will be able to come out from my tree," Dola replied with a dead voice.

"The head of my pitcher must not break nor split in any part before you return it to me." Babi shouted without mercy.

"I say it cannot be taken away from the tree unless the tree is cut down!" Dola explained loudly.

"Yes, you may cut the tree down if you wish to do so, but at all costs, I want the head of my pitcher back!" Babi boomed on Dola.

"But, Babi, remember that both of us had become friends since when we were children. Therefore, do not attempt to destroy my kola-nut tree," Dola begged Babi.

"Yes, of course, I don't forget at any time that we are friends but at any rate, I want the head of my pitcher now!" Babi insisted with a great noise.

At last, when it was revealed to Dola that Babi simply wanted her tree to be destroyed so that she might not get kola-nuts to sell any more, she went to the court of law. She sued Babi for trying to destroy her tree. But when the judge failed to persuade Babi not to take the head of her pitcher back, he judged the case in favour of her, that Dola must return the head of the pitcher to her.

With great sorrow, the kola-nut tree was cut down and the head of the pitcher was taken away from the tree and returned to Babi. Babi was now very happy not because of her pitcher but of Dola's tree which was cut down. After that she and Dola entered the house and they continued their friendship as before. And Dola did not show her sorrow for her tree in her behaviour towards Babi.

A few months after the tree was cut down, Babi delivered a female baby. In the morning that Babi's baby would be named,

Dola gave her a fine brass ring as a present, to put on her baby's neck, because brass was one of the most precious metals in those days. Babi took the brass ring from Dola with great admiration and she put it on her baby's neck at the same time. This brass ring had been carefully moulded without any joint.

Ten years passed away, when one fine morning, as Babi's baby was celebrating her tenth birthday, Dola went to Babi, and asked gently—

"Babi, my good friend, I shall be very glad if you will return my brass ring this fine morning."

"Which brass ring!" Babi sprang up and shouted.

"My old brass ring which is now on your daughter's neck," Dola pointed a finger at the girl's neck as if she was simply joking with her.

"This very brass ring, on my daughter's neck?" Babi was trembling with fear.

"Yes, please," Dola replied quietly.

"Please, Dola, my good friend, don't try to take your brass ring back, as you know, before the ring can be taken away from my daughter's neck, her head must be cut off first because it is already bigger than the ring!" Babi begged with tears.

"I don't force you to cut off the head of your daughter but I want my brass ring back without cutting it!" Dola insisted.

At last when Babi failed to persuade Dola not to take her brass ring back from her, she went to the same court of law. She sued Dola for trying to kill her daughter. Unfortunately, the case was judged in favour of Dola when she had related the story of her kola-nut tree which was cut down when Babi insisted on taking the head of her pitcher back. The judge added that the head of Babi's daughter would be cut off in the palace of the king and in the presence of the whole people of the village so that everybody might learn that jealousy was bad. Then a special day was fixed to behead Babi's daughter so that the brass ring could be taken away from her neck.

When that day came the whole people of the village gathered in the front of the palace and the king sat in the middle of the prominent people. Then the king told Babi loudly to put her ten-year-old daughter in the centre of the crowd and she did so. She and her daughter stood and both were trembling with fear while the swordsman who was ready to behead her daughter stood at the back of the girl with the sword in hand and was just waiting to hear the order from the king and then to behead her. Then the king announced loudly to Babi—

"As Dola's kola-nut tree was cut down the other day when you insisted on taking the head of your pitcher back, so the head of your daughter will be cut off now, before Dola's brass ring will be taken away from your daughter's neck and given back to her."

The people were so quiet with mercy that it was a few minutes after the king had announced to Babi before they could talk to each other. And the people mumbled again with grief when the king gave the order to the swordsman to behead the daughter. But as the swordsman raised the sword up to cut the head off, Dola hastily stopped him and announced loudly—

"It will be a great pity if this ten-year-old daughter is killed, because she has not offended me but her jealous mother. And I believe, if we continue to pay bad for bad, bad will never finish on earth, therefore, I forgive what Babi has done to my kola-nut tree!"

The king and the rest of the people clapped loudly for Dola immediately after she pardoned Babi. Then everyone went back to his or her house with gladness. But Dola and Babi were still good friends throughout their lives' time. ▶

DISCUSSION QUESTIONS

Abrahams: THE BLACKS (*page 20*)

1. What does Abrahams mean by saying that "being black is a small matter in tribal Africa"? Why is he particularly aware of this condition? What is of paramount importance to the tribal African?

2. Kenyatta is pictured as a tragic figure in this essay. Explain the forces behind his personal tragedy.

3. In the last paragraph of the essay Abrahams voices a hope that in the Africa of the future "the finer qualities of the old ways" may be fused with the new. What might be considered among the best qualities of the old ways? What is good about the new ways?

4. Compare what you learn about tribal life in Abrahams' essay with that life as evidenced in such fiction as Ogot's "The Rain Came" (page 286) and Ekwensi's "The Law of the Grazing Fields" (page 155).

from TELL FREEDOM (*page 36*)

1. In German literature a novel that describes the growth of a child to maturity is called a *Bildungsroman*. Why might this term be an apt one to apply to this selection from Abrahams' autobiography? In what ways does the narrator grow? Is growth the principal content of the narrative?

2. Note the quotation from *Isaiah* that precedes the cutting. Establish its relation to the selection.

3. Discuss Lee's meeting with Joseph. Is this perhaps one of the most important events in the narrator's life?

4. Compare and contrast the first part of this selection (Lee's life with his uncle) with the second part (Lee's friendship with Joseph). Note the weather, Lee's activities, the attitudes of those with whom the boy comes in contact. What difference in atmosphere do you find between the two sections?

Adiko: THE DANCER (*page 54*)

1. Is this poem pictorial and descriptive of a dancer and his dance? Or is something beyond description intended?

2. What is the referent of *it* (line 17)? What is meant by ". . . of the dance,/He is the Phoenix/And the Giant"? How does a dance, a temporary burst of physical activity, mock and taunt death?

Anonymous: ANANSI'S FISHING EXPEDITION (*page 55*)

This folk tale joins a long tradition: among the most widespread of comedy situations is "the trickster tricked." Anansi himself belongs to the prototype of the pícaro of Spanish literature, the clever rogue who makes his way by his wits and who pulls outrageous pranks to guarantee his ascendancy over others. Hundreds of Anansi tales exist —more than about Paul Bunyan or John Henry in the United States, more than about Til Eulenspiegel in German folk literature. Many of them indirectly point a moral, though their primary purpose remains entertainment.

1. The bargain struck initially between Anansi and Anene is of course ridiculous. Trace the development of that bargain as it becomes increasingly humorous through repetition, and finally, by a "willing suspension of disbelief" (Coleridge's words) almost credible.

2. Discuss the dead pan manner in which Anene plays his way through the bargain as contributory to the developing humor of the situation. What modern comics do you know who use this device?

3. Has Anansi learned both the humor and the wisdom of the bargain with his final comment in the tale?

4. Is there a moral lesson or statement in this folk tale, as with fables generally?

5. In this tale Anansi is the trickster tricked, but in many Anansi stories he is the trickster. Read other tales of Anansi in collections of African folklore.

Anonymous: SONG OF A MOTHER TO HER FIRST-BORN (*page 60*)

There are no conventional questions on this poem. Such an affirmation of faith should not be reduced to the mechanics of analysis. (Do you agree?) Instead of questions we shall merely suggest some ideas, italicizing some chores for you.

1. We all have some idea of the hope, the incredibility, and the belief attendant in a nativity. *You can read of this hope in Luke* (the Bible) and get some idea of the feeling that is present in this poem.

2. This must be a very young and unsophisticated mother who creates such a tender poem. Her similes, as in line 3, reflect the limitations of her environment and experience. *Learn to watch similes —they betray a writer's interest and origins.*

3. This unknown author almost instinctively creates a striking system of contrasts. *Note lines 9–10.* The whole contrast, from the

weak tenderness of childhood to the man that will be, achieves personal dimension in lines 12–13. *Discuss.*

4. Stanza 6 changes mood and attention from the child to the mother, leaves "babyish" talk and centers on her who is author of this song. *Study this transfer.*

5. Stanza 8 begins with "You will tend his shrine when he is gone./With sacrifice and oblation . . ." The mother seems to indicate that she does not ask perpetual remembrance of herself by her son; that she has a full heart of happiness already. *Talk about this.*

Anonymous: JUSTICE (*page 63*)

With the statement, "not realizing he was deaf," this folk tale begins a comedy of misunderstanding that represents one of the oldest devices of humor. But not only in folk tales is this device used. Shakespeare, writing in a much more sophisticated genre, uses it in *A Comedy of Errors.*

1. After the initial misunderstanding, the entry of the chorus of villagers lends additional comedy. What does their participation tell you about the communal life of the native society? How does their bland acceptance of "justice" add to the humor?

2. If immediately after the first misunderstanding everything were cleared up, what would happen to the comedy of the situation? How is the further use of misunderstanding directly contributory to an increase in the comedy? As a cliché example, is the third repetition of the situation when someone slips on a banana peel funnier than the second instance? the first?

3. Do you consider the satire in this little tale kindly or sharp? Is anyone being laughed at? Or are you invited to laugh with the characters?

Anonymous: TALK (*page 65*)

The humor of this tale depends upon the involvement of more and more participants in an impossible but realized happening, and the nursery-rhyme-like repetition and increment with which these happenings are recounted (remember "This is the house that Jack built"?).

1. For a tale like this, is it necessary to have fully developed characters, or are tags such as "country man" and "fisherman" enough? Discuss.

2. Why do we enjoy the unself-conscious and detailed repeating of every statement, every thing said?

3. Why is it effective humor that the king's stool speaks only after the other participants have left his presence?

Anonymous: HOW HAWK LEARNED OF THE SHALLOW HEARTS OF MEN (*page 68*)

1. Comment on the attitude toward man displayed in this little tale: Is it bitter, or is it tinged with a wry humor? What might have inspired it? How accurate a portrayal of human nature does it provide?

2. Compare this tale to "The Gourd Full of Wisdom" (page 82), "Justice" (page 63), and "The Talking Skull" (page 74). Do they all have a purpose beyond mere entertainment? How do their narrative styles agree?

Anonymous: HOW THE WORLD CHANGED (*page 70*)

This is a creation myth. Creation myths try to explain how things came to be, or, to quote Paul Gauguin, who asks some of the questions in a painting of primitive life: "Who are we? Where do we come from? Where are we going?" Myths appear in every society and language and often resemble one another even when separated by oceans and continents; so, they become the material for fascinating comparative studies in literature and religion.

1. Compare this tale with *Genesis,* particularly the early idyll of the Garden of Eden. Edward Hicks painted several pictures entitled *The Peaceable Kingdom.* Look up one of them in a collection of American art.

2. Compare this myth of the advent of fire with the ancient Greek myth of Prometheus.

3. The disappearance of the sun (page 70)—what would you guess it explains?

4. How do biologists explain skin-color differences? Do you prefer the scientific explanation or that in the final paragraph of this tale?

Anonymous: SONG OF THE POOR MAN (*page 72*)

1. The poem begins with a paradox (stanza 1) and goes on to prove, suddenly and deftly at the end, that no paradox exists. The simple order makes for great structural strength and unity in the development of the poem. Discuss.

2. Are you surprised at finding the sound and structure of the verses Biblical? What reasons can you give that such sound and

structure are indeed perfectly natural to the people who created the poem?

3. There is gentle irony and humor in the description of the poor man, laughter that he doesn't even know how to eat a fish. Does this tone destroy or enrich the basic dignity of the poem?

Anonymous: THE TALKING SKULL (*page 74*)

1. Is the moral stated in this tale or left to the understanding of the hearer? What effect does the method have upon the impact?

2. Why does the skull refuse to speak until after the hunter has been executed?

3. This little tale in other times would have been called an *exemplum* ("The Pardoner's Tale" from Chaucer's *Canterbury Tales* is an example of this form). Find a definition of the exemplum in a dictionary of literary terms, and see how the characteristics defined there apply to "The Talking Skull."

Anonymous: FOUR TALES FROM TOGOLAND (*page 75*)

1. What phenomenon does "The Eye of the Giant" explain?

2. Compare "The Eye of the Giant" with Amos Tutuola's tale, "Animal That Died But His Eyes Still Alive" (page 390). Would you guess that Tutuola's narrative draws on this Togoland story or one similar to it in his own culture?

3. "The Singing Cloak" and "The Gourd Full of Wisdom" are both Anansi stories. (For some information on Anansi's role in African literature see page 55.) How does the figure of Anansi differ from one story to the next? Which is closer to the Anansi in "Anansi's Fishing Expedition" (page 55)? Judging from the tone of these tales, what do you think is the probable attitude toward Anansi of the people who tell the stories?

4. Is the Chameleon in "The Singing Cloak" an embodiment of the virtue we usually expect of the hero in this kind of story? Is the tale saying that virtue will be rewarded or is it saying something altogether different? Explain.

5. The supernatural fairy tale (and most of them are that) often uses substitutions of identity—in Grimm a frog turns out to be a prince; in "Sir Gawain and the Green Knight" a hideous old hag turns out to be the most beautiful woman in the kingdom. Usually the substitution of identity is a reward for virtue. Is this true in "The Hunter Who Hunts No More"?

Armattoe: THE LONELY SOUL (*page 85*)

People who walk along talking to themselves are viewed with suspicion in many societies. Armattoe has looked below the surface situation, though, and preaches us a little sermon.

1. Why would an older person be most apt to talk by himself "down a lonely road"?

2. Do you think the "child" addressed is actually a child? Explain your answer.

3. Does the repeated use of "laughing" suggest an imaginary dialogue? Discuss.

4. Discuss the swift achievement of identification in the two concluding lines.

Blay: FUNERAL OF A WHALE (*page 86*)

1. What is the color of mourning in Ghana?

2. What are the various social and religious roles of the old male members of Ghanaian society, of the young men, of the women?

3. What is included in the description that convinces us of the seriousness and importance of the ritual to the people of Missibi?

4. The immense and expensive effort put forth on this occasion must tax the community heavily. How might the effort be an economical one, however, in terms of national and ethnic unity?

5. In what respects is a funeral in many cultures, like this ceremony in Ghana, also a time of pleasure?

J. P. Clark: POEMS (*page 90*)

1. Often in poetry a storm is presented as threatening or violent, inspiring fear or awe. Is that true of the poem "Night Rain"?

2. Why might the poet speak of the "ample soothing hand" of the rain as "joined to that of the sea"?

3. As part of their program of rediscovery of authentic African culture, the French-speaking *Negritude* poets (see article, page 323) often take as their theme the beauty of black women. In the poem "Girl Bathing" the poet celebrates the beauty of a black woman. Is the poem more than celebration?

Dadié: MEN OF ALL CONTINENTS (*page 93*)

1. Who is addressing the "men of all continents"—a person or the spirit of the continent of Africa itself?

2. Who are the "you" and the "we" of the lines: "You who hold

heaven within reach/We/who seek ourselves in the false dawn of the streetlamps"? Is the speaker referring to different races of men or different conditions of mankind?

3. Is the dread of warfare and bloodshed the only thing that can bind men of various colors and races together?

4. What sort of hope is given out in the image: "But a star has always given a wink/On evenings of fires, in the hours drunk with gunpowder"? Reconcile this idea with the image presented in lines 14–15 and repeated in the last two lines.

Birago Diop: TRUTH AND FALSEHOOD (*page 95*)

Diop's closeness to his national folklore can be guessed at once by this one tale alone. This is an allegory, in the tradition of *Everyman,* but told with the humor, irreverence, and paradox that often accompany stories about the "little man." Often in world literature, the "little man" likes to puncture pretense, and show, as here, that morality may be worthy of veneration but may not always accomplish as much for the underling as cleverness, wit, and even duplicity.

1. What do we mean by *paradox,* and what is the paradox in this unequal contest between Truth and Falsehood?

2. Why does Falsehood say that "people no doubt *prefer* truth"? Does he mean that they'd like to be truthful only it doesn't always pay off—and is the author condoning this philosophy?

3. If you remember your fairy tales, events always happen in threes—someone gets three wishes, there are three bears, or a knight goes on three missions. Determine how this folkloric device fits this tale. What are the three events that determine the outcome of the narrative?

THE WAGES OF GOOD (*page 100*)

If "The wages of sin [evil] is death," as the Bible teaches, what are the wages of good? That is the proposition Diop examines in this fable.

1. In what way is the conflict between the boy and the alligator a struggle between the idealist and the realist? What conflict is implied between the expedient law of nature and the abstract good?

2. Do you feel sorry for Diassigue's sad plight at the conclusion of the story? Do you think that Leuk-the-Hare has arranged for real justice to be done?

3. How does this fable illustrate the common device of the trickster tricked?

4. In the English-speaking world a rabbit is not regarded as the most intelligent of beasts, and we prove it with a phrase, "hare-brained." What animals do we regard as symbols of wisdom?

5. What is a totem? Speculate on what alligators may have to do with blacksmiths.

6. Can a writer make his sermons more stinging when moving his anger out of the world of men and into the guise of animals? Why, or why not?

FOREFATHERS (*page 105*)

1. Why does the speaker tell his hearers to listen to "things rather than beings"?

2. Like Antaeus in Grecian thought, the poet seems to hold close to the earth for renewal. Find evidences of his sense of refreshment, courage, and strength.

3. The poet gives us a sense of the timelessness and unhurried pace of Africa, of a person who pauses silently listening and feeling the continuity of life. Would you say this attitude is primitive, or is it sophisticated in the full meaning of the word?

David Diop: POEMS (*page 107*)
    Africa

1. What image of Africa is Diop saluting in lines 1–4? Why does he say "I have never known you"?

2. There are bitterness and pessimism in the poem. Why is Diop justified in adding these notes of grief? Do they add passion to the song?

3. Why might the poet describe the flavor of freedom as "bitter"?
    Listen Comrades

1. Who are the comrades the poet is addressing? What is his tone as he speaks?

2. What does Diop mean in line 13, "I feel his mouth on my dreams"? Is the image metaphoric? Is this the actual dream of a sleeper or a dream of the ideal?

3. Who are they who attempt to control "The blood they hoped to snare in a circle of words"? Why is the word *circle* an apt choice?
    He Who Has Lost All

1. The first stanza of this poem sets up a series of contrasts with the material of the second stanza. Find the word in the first stanza which summarizes the idea developed? With which word in the second stanza is it contrasted?

2. What details does the poet use to flesh out the contrast on which the poem is built?

Your Presence

1. The loved one whose presence Diop celebrates is Africa. He uses the phenomenon of love to reveal the sense of Africa, the sense of his blackness, the sense of wholeness. Does the emphasis on Africa weaken Diop's tribute to love as understanding? Does it rob the phenomenon of some of its universality?

2. Discuss lines 11–12. What does Diop mean by "blood"? Is a metaphor contained in "necklaces of laughter"? If so, what are the various meanings it might imply?

Defiance Against Force

1. What does the word *that* (line 2) describe?

2. Against what is the "No!" to be shouted? Is the structure of the poem tight and controlled? In its few lines, does it have in it both the situation and the reaction?

3. In several of these poems by Diop most of the punctuation is omitted. What effect does the poet gain by this absence of breath stops?

4. What single idea pervades all five of these poems? Characterize the tone of each—which is the most militant, the most sorrowful? Would you agree that the speaker faces the future with hope?

Easmon: THE FEUD (*page 112*)

1. This passionate tale has much in common with Western literature, with overtones of *Romeo and Juliet*'s star-crossed lovers, with honor as fiercely sustained and avenged as anything in Spanish literature. What elements of the story belong particularly to Africa? Note particularly details of setting, customs, and way of life.

2. As in any good story, characters develop. What changes do you notice in Nenneh during the twenty years the story covers? What sort of man is Daimba Seisay? What is your final impression of each of these characters?

3. After Daimba's death the narrator comments that Nenneh was "feeling lost . . . now that the prop of her life was knocked away by her enemy's death" (page 143). What does this mean? Is this a tale of justice or of vengeance?

4. Throughout the story the author comments on people and society in general. Note the following:

a. Laconic and brutal as the information [of the raid] was, it was no worse than Nenneh had expected. It was the logic of the times. Her father had done the same thing to other tribes. Only she had never, never realised it had been so bad for the others as it was turning out for her . . .

b. Young though he [Daimba] was, both as man and as king, absolute power had corrupted him beyond redemption.

c. Poreh was made of sterner stuff than the princesses and parasites of Susu society.

Judging from such comments and from similar passages throughout the story, comment on the author's attitude.

Ekwensi: RITUAL MURDER (page 146)

1. The first scene takes place on the steps of a palace in a modern city; the second scene is in the dark corridor and the back room of that palace. Why do you think the author may have opened his story with this strong contrast?

2. Between the two scenes this passage occurs: "It was impossible to contemplate ancient evil beneath this façade of Western law and order. Surely no harm could come to Kofi." What is the function of this passage? Discuss its effectiveness.

3. Between the old Africa and the new one stand certain men ready to use old traditions unscrupulously to advance their position in the new world. How do these characters resemble the present-day Mafia?

4. The fetishman emerges from the old African culture. With keen psychology he uses the old magic methods to rebalance the system and make the guilty ones show their guilt. What psychological guilt factors stand active to aid the fetishman? How is his action right and appropriate to the action and atmosphere of the story?

5. Why does the fetishman feel he has betrayed eighty years of tradition by his actions even though through his efforts justice has been done? Does his taking the poison seem to you theatrical and unreal? If you feel so, is it because you are not tied to the culture that believes in the golden stool and human sacrifice?

6. Consider the title: "Ritual Murder." *What* is murdered; what people, ideas, and customs are destroyed? Is the fetishman a victim, or is he a murderer?

THE LAW OF THE GRAZING FIELDS (page 155)

1. Does this story sound as if the events were taking place in the Wild West of the United States rather than in Africa? What is there

about the landscape that is similar? What about the sense of property? The behavior of the men? The horse chase, pursuit?

2. What are the qualities one expects of a male in the glimpses the reader gets of this society? Do Amina's brothers conform to the masculine image that Ekwensi develops?

3. That remark of the brother as they all ride off at the end of the incident has the sound of a closing line from a television Western. Do you agree?

Fagunwa: THE FOREST OF THE LORD (*page 161*)

Probably the most fascinating aspect of this tale is its triple existence as *allegory,* as *folklore,* and as *epic.* Be prepared to discuss the tale as it fits into these three forms. Here are some helps.

1. As *allegory.* What might Fagunwa mean by using such place names as the Forest of the Lord, the Forest of Spirits, and the Wilderness of Silence? Why is the Forest of the Lord the most distant and the most formidable? How does the story of the fall of Lucifer correspond to the tale Little Devil tells of his arrival in the Wilderness of Silence? What resemblances do you find between Olowo-aiyé's wrestling match with Little Devil and Jacob's wrestling match with the angel (Genesis 32)? Is the dark forest through which the hero wanders an allegory of man's own journey through life? Adam was tempted by Eve in the garden of Eden. Is there similarity between this incident (and its location) and the hero's meeting with his future mate?

2. As *folktale.* A folktale is easily recognized by its real closeness to the people. One clue to this closeness may be found in the type of simile used by the author and his speaking characters; if the work is a folktale, the comparisons will be drawn from objects in the narrator's daily environment, not from literary allusions or artistic resemblances. Another clue to a folktale is the presence of proverbs and other homely sayings. Draw up a list of *as*'s and *like*'s with their reference points, and build yourself a picture of the environment and the life of the characters. Also draw up a list of proverbs and folk wisdom.

3. As *epic.* There will be some overlapping here with the aspects of the tale treated in question 1. Consider the hero. Notice the send-off he receives as the people's champion about to go out and do battle. As in epic, the hero battles not ordinary creatures but supernatural or mythical ones. Often he does so for no particular reason but to prove

his mettle. What are some of the hazards Olowo-aiyé is prepared to face? What adventures does he meet?

Hutchinson: ABOARD AN AFRICAN TRAIN (*page 178*)

1. In the first paragraph Hutchinson says of the migrant miners returning home: "They swaggered a bit and looked at us, the surface people, with contempt . . ." Who are "the surface people"? What causes the contempt the miners apparently feel? Why do they clout the recruits going to the mines?

2. The author tells how long each of the people in his compartment had been away from home. Why is this point important to him? Why have these people been away? What does the old man mean when he says, "A person only works for train fare" (page 181, paragraph 1)?

3. The author's tension throughout the narrative is caused by the fact that he has no passport. What echoes of this tension do you find in the lives of other passengers on the train?

4. Two statements recur throughout the excerpt: the mention of people who say the gramophone records take them back to Johannesburg "which they had probably never seen," and the comparison of the train's slow looping movements to "an African woman playing with her hips." What is the significance of each of these statements? Do you see any relationship between them?

Kalungano: DREAM OF THE BLACK MOTHER (*page 188*)

This poem is protest literature, but visionary and prophetic also— visionary, that is, until the final line, and then with total impact a protest poem.

1. Find other notes of protest besides the one mentioned above.

2. What is the effectiveness of the repeated, "Black mother/Rocks her son," that begins each stanza when combined with the following longer thoughts?

3. Discuss the suggestions implicit in "And in her black head/Covered with black hair/She keeps marvellous dreams."

4. Another poem dealing with the same subject matter is "Song of a Mother to her First-born" (page 60). Read and compare for treatment, attitude, impact.

Kenyatta: THE GENTLEMEN OF THE JUNGLE (*page 190*)

Kenyatta, the author of this tale, looked upon it as more than an animal fable. He says of it, "The relation between the Gikuyu [more often spelled *Kikuyu*] and the Europeans can well be illustrated by this Gikuyu story." Kenyatta's own words clearly indicate that the story can be read as an allegory. The *man,* whose name is the only one uncapitalized, may be taken to mean the average little man, the underprivileged person, the native.

1. What allegorically is the identity of the King of the Jungle? Who are Mr. Rhinoceros, Mr. Buffalo, Mr. Alligator, Mr. Leopard, and Rt. Hon. Mr. Fox, chairman?

2. What allegorical meaning can you attach to the Commission of Inquiry? Comment on the conduct of the inquiry. Is there any significance in the fact that Mr. Elephant and his wife serve a delicious meal to the Commission before the verdict is rendered?

3. What ironic borrowing from the history of government is there in the statement that the strong animals were "gentlemen chosen by God to look after the interests of races less adequately endowed with teeth and claws"? What is the real meaning behind the phrase "to turn the undeveloped space to a more economic use"?

4. Abraham Lincoln once said that you can fool all of the people some of the time, and some of the people all of the time, but that you can't fool all of the people all of the time. Find the same conclusion in this tale.

Laye: *from* THE AFRICAN CHILD (*page 194*)

Really brilliant works of literature are among the most difficult to discuss. Camara Laye's autobiography may well belong to this category; it is simple, direct, absolutely clear, warm, and human. No controversial statements are made; the author is well-adjusted and complete in his background. Because we meet such a narrative and such a person, we can therefore concentrate on elements in his life and story that reveal Africa, and a vanishing way of tribal life.

1. Ritual, as formality and protocol, is a way of life among the Malinke. Create a list of all the ritual uses that Laye notes. How do they parallel what we in the Western world call manners? How do they differ—for instance, is religion a part of some or all of the ritual observances?

2. What can you say about the nature of family life in this tribal community? Compare such ideas as respect for elders, position of women socially, religious equality and tolerance, justice, familial

closeness, respect for learning and teachers with similar concepts in Western life.

3. In the chapter on school life, what common denominators with the American way did you notice?

4. Uncle Lansana is one of the most fully realized characters in the autobiography, probably because he is a pivotal person in the family relationships we explored in question 2 above. Discuss his character as revealed by (a) his actions, (b) his statements, (c) Camara's reactions to him, and (d) his place in the community.

5. Discuss the purpose of the praise singer in Malinke life, and its ambivalent effects. Is the institution religious, or social?

Markwei: LIFE IN OUR VILLAGE (*page 251*)

1. What is the universal truth in this deft little poem? Do the elders know why hide and seek is a popular game?

2. Love just can't be kept down. For a comparative but serious situation, read Ekwensi, "The Law of the Grazing Fields," page 155.

Medhen: HOME-COMING SON (*page 252*)

1. Underdeveloped countries commonly delight in sending off to Europe or America their brightest sons, for university educations or for technical training. Are they welcomed back as blessings?

2. The word *black* is used throughout the poem to mean more than just a color. Trace the various ways of referring to *black* in the poem. Do you find it interesting that the opposite word, *white,* never appears? What does this omission tell you about the speaker, the culture?

3. It is to more than a country—it is to a *mystique* that the returning prodigal makes his entry. Explain, using all the examples you can find, why the poet feels that the home-coming son is returning not primarily to a nation but to a way of life.

Modisane: THE DIGNITY OF BEGGING (*page 254*)

1. "The Dignity of Begging" is a transplanting of the Spanish picaresque tale—a story of a rascal, usually from the lower classes of society, who makes his living by his wits and scorns the menial tasks he is supposedly engaged in. Why do you think stories of this type have been popular for centuries?

2. Analyze the tone of each of the following statements from the story:

(*a*) They use him to beg so they can balance the family budget. They never show him the comfort of love. Relentlessly they drive him, like an animal that has to work for its keep and feed (page 254, paragraph 2).

(*b*) I *must* uphold the dignity of begging. Professional ethics forbid all beggars from working (page 255, paragraph 6).

(*c*) To think the department wants to pin me behind a desk! The idea is criminal, to say the least (page 258, paragraph 6).

(*d*) He has wholly realized the separateness of good and evil and attained a purity in evil worthy of honest appraisal (page 263, paragraph 9).

(*e*) People who give alms to beggars do so to establish their superiority over the receiver . . . (page 264, line 3).

(*f*) Blushing Groom and the gullible public of Johannesburg will live in my mind forever. . . . I have to come back. I owe it to the profession (page 264, paragraph 7).

3. Although "The Dignity of Begging" is a humorous story, it evidences much real social concern. Give examples of such concern.

Mphahlele: THE MASTER OF DOORNVLEI (*page 265*)

1. In the second sentence of the story we read: "In the mud-and-grass church house a bird flitted from one rafter to another, trapped." Is there any significance in the content and position in the story of this sentence?

2. Why do you think the first character Mphahlele introduces is a nameless minor one? Do we know the boy well enough to establish sympathy with him? Does the author use him as a symbolic representative of the condition of his race, or as merely the center of a triggering event that causes the further action, or both?

3. What sort of man is Sarel Britz? Consider the changes in his thinking over the years as shown by his quotations from the thinking of his dead father, his memories from university days, his relationship with his mother, the episodes with Mfukeri.

4. In what way is Mfukeri the counterpart of Sarel Britz? Which is the more alienated character?

5. Allegorically, the battle between Kasper the horse and Donker the bull stands for more than a barnyard struggle. In what ways does each animal represent the owner and his attitudes? What is the role of the bystanders?

6. How many times do we seem to change protagonist in the

course of the action? Does the title of the story help you to determine the eventual protagonist and the resolution of the plot?

7. Discuss the ambivalent emotions of Sarel Britz as revealed in the two concluding paragraphs. What does the statement tell the reader about forces of change?

Abioseh Nicol: LIFE IS SWEET AT KUMANSENU (*page 276*)

1. What details does the author use to suggest that there is something uncanny in Meji's visit? Why does the author present these details in the same simple, factual manner in which he records other data of everyday village life?

2. Only Musa, the village magician, shares with the widow Bola the secret of her son Meji's death and reappearance. And yet he does not understand her. Characterize their differing views of life.

Nogar: POEM OF THE CONSCRIPTED WARRIOR (*page 284*)

1. This poem pays attention to the exploitation of subject races by their overlords. Do you consider it protest literature?

2. What do we mean by *conscript*? What does the term *warrior* usually connote? What is strange in the juxtaposition of *conscripted* and *warrior*?

3. Discuss "And the courage was not his own/And the hate was not his own."

4. What is the "irony" mentioned in line 23? What do you think happens to the central figure?

5. What do the following contribute to the impact of the poem: (*a*) minimal punctuation; (*b*) the interrupted prayer or litany, "Oh Our Lady of Anything," (and what bitterness is mirrored in the final word of the phrase?); the imagery of the final four lines?

Ogot: THE RAIN CAME (*page 286*)

It is easy to dismiss the situation of this tale as savage and primitive. We tend to forget that the Western world also has its tradition of human sacrifice: the admired Hellenic society sacrificed Iphigenia for a favorable wind; Abraham offered his son Isaac on the altar to God. In each of these stories a "scapegoat" takes the place of the human being, and the outcome is a happy one. So with Grace Ogot's story.

Remember also that we are reading here of a subsistence society, a small band or clan of individuals, with no science to explain natural phenomena such as rain, whose entire concern is keeping the group alive.

1. Labong'o functions as Chief and priest in his society. Why might these roles be associated in less well-developed societies? What is the importance of the ancestors? Why do you think they are given such importance?

2. Most warriors and chiefs concern themselves with a desire for sons to succeed them. Yet Labong'o was mocked because he had no daughter. What does this imply about the need and structure of the society in which Labong'o lives?

3. Oganda, as she walks to her death, makes up a song. What is the purpose of song in a "primitive" society such as this?

4. Consider the aftermath of this story: What sort of life will the young couple have, after violating the religious and social rules they have inherited? Will they be outcasts? Are they suited to each other—is Oganda as completely a rebel as Osinda? Can they ever rejoin their tribe? How, then, will they live—even keep alive?

Peters: POEMS (page 297)

1. While "Parachute" excites us with a new thrill, pays vivid attention to weightlessness, timeliness, and suspension, what is the poet really telling us? Is there anything new under the sun?

2. Rather than the glad song of return that its title might suggest, "Homecoming" is low-keyed and sad. Who might the one who has "paced the world" represent? Why does the house cast no shadow? Who are the new skeletons?

3. What similar theme appears in "Homecoming" and "Parachute"?

Rive: AFRICAN SONG (page 300)

1. The story line of "African Song" is slight. It is possibly not even a story about Muti. Maybe Rive's title explains a purpose other than narrative. Discuss.

2. If question 1 raises doubts about the genre of "African Song," we can still state that the work contains the essential of all plot— conflict. But not just one. How many forces within Muti are in conflict? How many forces within the subject, Africa? How many forces within the situation into which Muti is thrown?

3. Time becomes a flexible, variable continuum in the two spheres of activity which make up the tension. One sphere is in the movement

of a blue uniform; another sphere is in the pace, race, and movement of thought, which we only partially control. See whether, in your opinion, Rive manages an increasingly intense ratio building up to the inevitable, foregone conclusion. Does each sphere of activity increase relatedly in tempo and intensity?

4. Discuss elements of pride and doubt in Muti's reflections on his continent, "old in its youth, grey in its childhood." Is he a realist in his assessments? Is he ever an apologist?

NO ROOM AT SOLITAIRE (*page 309*)

We are all familiar with the Christmas story of the Nativity. Maybe we are too familiar with it, but only in its largest sense—filled with important event, Oriental kings, and troops of angels. Rive may be doing a good job here of focusing on its significance.

1. By introducing this motif into a new geographical setting, Africa, and by having it interrupt and intermingle with a host of trivial human hatreds, jealousies, and personalities, does Rive spoil or make more impressive our concept of the original event?

2. Considering the reasons we're given for Fanie's inn being empty, discuss the irony in the complexions of those who show up in his stable.

3. "How will we know Him when He comes again?"
"You are speaking dangerous things."
"What if He is not a White man?"
"He is a White man!"
"I know," Dawie said weakly.

—page 311, paragraph 26 ff.

Contrast this conversation with the behaviors of Fanie and Dawie in the last paragraph of the story. Have they been persuaded in spite of themselves? Is the whole matter just coincidence? Is Rive merely achieving a *tour de force* by certain resemblances between events? Do you think the two South Africans have achieved some racial tolerance as a result of their experience?

4. The quarrel between the two whites, and most of the Christmas Eve dialogue between Dawie and Fanie in the empty hotel, concerns whether black Africans are worth while and intelligent. Does the conclusion of this tale add any more information to what had been decided only by prejudice?

Rubadiri: STANLEY MEETS MUTESA (*page 318*)

Legend changes history into glamor; we read often of the achievements of glorious explorers and warriors, but seldom of their real discomforts as history was made.

1. Study the situation beginning in stanza 4, lines 29 and following, that make for the glamorizing of history.

2. Is the emphasis of this African poem on Stanley or on Mutesa?

3. How do you interpret "They bound for a kingdom" (line 6)?

4. What consequences follow the situation developed in the final two lines? What is the impact on the poem of this ending?

Segun: THE PIGEON-HOLE (*page 321*)

1. Mabel Segun chose free verse for her medium. How might it fit her subject matter, her message, better than more conventionally structured verse?

2. The constant change of identity may come as a shock to individuals who imagine a fixed moment at which a person suddenly knows who he is, what he wants, and what he has to do. Discuss the final stanza and see what ideas you can chip out of it. Once you have that stanza wrapped up, try the first stanza.

3. In what aspects has each one of us a "delinquent self"? Is this aspect of our personalities good or bad, or both? (See stanza 2.) Do you find the anecdote and the anecdotal form of stanza 2 effective or disruptive in viewing the poem as a whole?

CONFLICT (*page 322*)

1. This is, of course, a complaint from an emerging black nation, or a complaint from an emerging social class. How might the same complaint be applicable to you?

2. In what respects is each of us, growing up or already mature, an "infant overblown"?

3. What do you understand by "the middle way" (line 10)? What does Mabel Segun feel is wrong with it? Do you share her belief?

4. What contemporary poets and folk singers write ballads that echo the ideas voiced in "Conflict"?

Senghor: POEMS (*page 324*)

   Prayer to the Masks

As one of the *Negritude* poets (see page 323), Senghor believed strongly in rediscovering the cultural values of Africa. The masks he addresses in this poem are the guardian spirits of primeval ancestors.

1. Is this poem primarily tribal, or does it reveal a sense of identity

with all of Africa? What lines reveal some sense of identity with Europe? What lines reveal scorn of Europe?

2. Is the speaker ready for "the rebirth of the World" (line 15)? Explain the image of the leaven and the flour (line 16). Discuss its appropriateness.

3. What primitive forces does Senghor believe will enable the African to pass through the dying world into a new birth?

Night of Sine

At home in the peace of Sine, his tribe's home, Senghor remembers earlier members of the tribe who, like himself, had wandered far.

1. The poem moves from a world-weariness to the "lofty depths of sleep" in the final line. Trace this movement, the gradual quietness and peace that comes to the speaker.

2. Reread the poem carefully and determine what is essentially Senegalese or African—look for culture, religion, tradition. Then look for what is essentially common to all men—look for atmosphere, descriptions of nature, and emotions that all share.

Be Not Amazed

1. Why may the singer's song grow dark?

2. The drums are a symbol of Africa. Search out Senghor's references to the drums and explain each of them.

3. Senghor's poetry, like that of David Diop (see page 107), often voices nostalgia for an Africa that because of colonialism and changing cultures is rapidly disappearing. With this idea in mind what other meaning do you find in "Be Not Amazed"?

Soyinka: POETRY (page 328)

Fado Singer

We can enjoy music—sing with it, dance to it, even weep to it. But Soyinka says that music is also a drug, a habit, a menace, a spell from which man begs release.

1. Discuss the effect of music (total effect and total music) in the rapid, related images of these phrases: "pumiced skin," "hair roots," "fibre filters," and "tobacco nerve" (lines 1–3).

2. Discuss man's captivity to the power and suggestiveness of music as suggested in this series of images: "net" (line 4); "sitar strings" (line 4); "sutures of song" (line 8); "pluck" (line 10); "fingers" (line 17); "cosmic cord" (line 17).

3. Find interrelated images in these suggestions: "sutures" (line 8),

"pluck" (line 10), "midwife" (line 16), "cry of severance" (lines 16–17), "cord" (line 17).

Season

1. What is the season celebrated in this poem? What words suggest this time of year?

2. What are the analogies between rust and ripeness? What is the relationship between rust and "the germ's decay" (line 15)?

3. Imagery is crowded into this poem. Select the images clustered about the swallows or about the corn leaves, explain them, and develop the relationship between images.

I Think It Rains

1. Why does the speaker say he thinks it rains?

2. Explain the paradox of rain that is both yielding and unbending. What is the meaning of the last four lines?

Sutherland: EDUFA (*page 331*)

1. In the classical definition of tragedy, is Edufa the tragic hero of this play? That is, is his estate brought from high to low, from success to failure? Is this decline brought about by *hubris* (excessive pride), or ignorance, another form of pride? Does he reach a point where he understands the machinery that brings him into tragedy, acknowledges flaws in his character, and regrets the pitiable results on the lives of others around him?

2. Would Ampoma, who most easily enlists our sympathy, fit into the above description?

3. All through this drama the life of Ampoma seems to be preordained, fated by magic, by the convictions of those in her household and the village, and even by her own expectation or volition. If these statements are true, does it make her eventual death more, or less, tragic?

4. Africa is often described as a continent where the forces of tribal superstition and new education are still in delicate balance in their struggle. What events in Edufa's actions and statements would make him representative of this state?

5. Senchi, who seems to stand for the forces of mirth and life, says at the drama's end that he loses again. Discuss the value of Senchi in raising the action of the play to moments of emotional lightness that heighten the tragedy, as being one of the few who understand the need for music and gaiety, and as being a foil for his friend Edufa.

6. Compare the Greek legend of Admetus and Alcestis with the

story of Edufa and Ampoma. The legend is also the basis of Euripides' play *Alcestis*.

Tshakatumba: MESSAGE TO MPUTU ANTOINETTE (*page 388*)

1. This poem is a typical example of the verse of the *Negritude* school (see article, page 323). The poets mentioned in the first few lines founded the *Negritude* school as young students in Paris. What details suggest that this poet, too, is an exile?

2. The poet, writing on his childhood friend, dwells on her innocence. He describes her as "Edenic" and "guileless," but also as "ignorant" and as one "who must learn." How might one characterize the poet's attitude toward his friend and the Africa she represents?

Tutuola: ANIMAL THAT DIED BUT HIS EYES STILL ALIVE (*page 390*)

Tutuola's unusual use of language makes him one of the most interesting of African writers. His words are English, but the syntax is his own, originating perhaps in the subconscious or in a race memory of a forgotten original language. The semantics of his language—the meaning he attaches to words in differing contexts and placements—varies, kaleidoscopes, and as if he were writing poetry, effervesces into hundreds of new meanings.

1. Discuss the effectiveness of this "new language" in telling a tale that is probably impossible, or at least visionary.

2. Try rephrasing some of Tutuola's shorter paragraphs into Standard English. What have you gained or lost?

3. This little narrative might be called an archetype of a hunting narrative, one of the oldest kinds of story. It might remind you of *Beowulf*, or of Paul Bunyan. It may have something to say about legendary tales of creatures now disappeared from the earth: dragons or other fire-breathing monsters. Discuss these ideas.

DON'T PAY BAD FOR BAD (*page 395*)

1. As the tale approaches its climax, are you genuinely appalled and anxious about the decision that is to be reached? Is its justice clear to you? Does the resolution of the tale let you down?

2. Compare this parable with the Biblical tale of Solomon's decision as to the maternity of a child. What do they have in common? How do they differ?

BIOGRAPHIES OF AUTHORS

Peter Abrahams (1919–   )

Abrahams, born at Vrededorp, a slum of Johannesburg, South Africa, has given an account of his early life in his autobiography, *Tell Freedom*, which has been described as "the mirror of life in a tragic land." A refugee from apartheid, Abrahams left South Africa for good in the late 1940's. After living for some time in England, he moved to Jamaica, where he now makes his home. Abrahams is also the author of a number of novels, including *Mine Boy* and *A Wreath for Udomo*, and *Dark Testament*, a collection of short stories.

Assoi Adiko (20th cent.)

A native of Ghana, Adiko is a professor of history and geography. In addition to writing poetry, he is the author of a history of Africa.

R. E. G. Armattoe (1913–1953)

Before his death in Hamburg, Germany, in 1953, Raphael Ernest Grail Armattoe had led a wide and varied life. Born in Denu in the Gold Coast (now Ghana), he worked as a poet, anthropologist, historian, and physician. Educated in Europe, Dr. Armattoe practiced medicine during World War II in Northern Ireland, but in 1950 he returned to his native Ghana where he entered politics. While his poetry avoids bitterness and protest, Armattoe does proclaim the nobility of blackness; but he also recognizes the harsh realities of a life where dreams remain unfulfilled.

J. Benibengor Blay (1925–   )

Blay's numerous short stories and radio scripts are highly popular in his native Ghana. He has traveled in both Europe and the United States and has served as a member of parliament in Accra. In addition to several novels, Blay has published a collection of his early poetry, *Thoughts of Youth*.

J. P. Clark (1935–   )

John Pepper Clark's free spirit and abundant talent are evidenced in *America, their America* (1964), his autobiography. While studying at the University College, Ibadan, this Nigerian writer founded *Horn*, a poetry magazine that still continues to influence the direction of the poetic genre in his country. Clark has also studied at Princeton, published many poems, and a play, *Song of a Goat.*

Bernard Dadié (1916–   )

Dadié's strong loyalty to Africa is evident in both his poetry and his prose. Born near Abidjan, Ivory Coast, he was educated in Dakar, Senegal, where he worked for the Institut Français d'Afrique Noire for some years. Later he entered government service in his native Ivory Coast. He has published two volumes of poetry, *Afrique debout* and *La Ronde des Jours,* and a number of prose works.

Birago Diop (1906–   )

Senegalese born, Diop has lived for many years in Upper Volta, where he practices veterinary medicine. He is not a prolific writer, but all that he publishes is exquisitely wrought. Among his most charming works are his gently satirical retellings of African tales.

David Diop (1927–1960)

David Diop, no relation to Birago Diop, was born in Bordeaux, France, to a Cameroonian mother and a Senegalese father. Although he was in poor health and frequently hospitalized throughout his life, there is little indication of his physical weakness in his work. He wrote a stinging kind of protest which, paradoxically, often has about it a beauty that makes it seem to be pure art for art's sake. Diop was killed in a plane crash near Dakar in 1960.

R. Sarif Easmon (1913–   )

Born in Sierra Leone, Dr. Easmon practices medicine in Freetown. His literary output runs from adventure stories like *The Feud,* set in nineteenth-century Africa, to sophisticated comic treatments of contemporary life. Besides many short stories, he has published several plays, including *Dear Parent and Ogre* and *The New Patriots,* and a novel, *The Burnt-out Marriage.*

C. O. D. Ekwensi (1921–   )

Cyprian Ekwensi's short, well-structured fiction is a favorite of anthologists, and it has appeared in many collections. A member of the Ibo tribe, Ekwensi was born in the northernmost part of Nigeria. His background is varied: he has studied forestry and pharmacy, the latter both at home and in England; he has worked as a teacher, a pharmacist, a lecturer, and as Nigerian Director of Information.

D. O. Fagunwa (1900–1963)

Daniel Fagunwa, the most popular and most widely read of all Nigerian writers, produced four major novels, all in his native Yoruba language. Unfortunately, none of these works have yet been translated into English, with the exception of an extract, "The Forest of the Lord." His novels, written in the traditional Yoruba style and employing traditional Yoruba subject matter, have a fairy-tale atmosphere and usually point to a distinct moral. Before his death in 1963, Fagunwa was awarded the Margaret Wrong Memorial Prize "for an outstanding contribution to literature in Africa by a person of the African race."

Alfred Hutchinson (1924–)

Hutchinson's exciting, but difficult, life as a young man is vividly pictured in his autobiography, *Road to Ghana,* which was published in 1960 following his escape from South Africa to England via Zambia, Malawi, Tanganyika, and Ghana. Born in Hectorspruit, the East Transvaal, South Africa, Hutchinson was the grandson of a Swazi chief on his mother's side and an Englishman on his father's. He was educated in South Africa and taught for a while before he was arrested and imprisoned for his connection with the 1952 Defiance Campaign. In 1956 he was again arrested and charged with high treason. Jumping bail, Hutchinson escaped to Ghana where he married an Englishwoman, Hazel Slade. His autobiography is marked by a constant alternation of exhilaration and hope with futility and despair.

Kalungano (1929–)

Kalungano is a pseudonym for an elusive native of Mozambique. Almost nothing is known about the real identity of this poet.

Jomo Kenyatta (1891–)

Kenyatta, the son of a poor Kikuyu farmer, was born at Ichaweri, Kenya, and was educated at a Scottish mission school. He became active in politics at an early age and soon became leader of the first nationalist movement in Kenya. He traveled extensively in Europe and studied at both Moscow University and at the London School of

Economics. Returning to Kenya in 1946, he campaigned ceaselessly for African rights and independence for Kenya. In 1953 Kenyatta was sentenced to seven years' imprisonment by the British for "managing" the Mau Mau terrorist organization. Released from prison in 1961, Kenyatta saw his dream fulfilled in 1963 when Kenya became independent. Subsequently in 1964 he became President of the Republic of Kenya. In 1938 Kenyatta published *Facing Mount Kenya,* a book in which he tried to demonstrate how tribal life has been disrupted by the coming of the Europeans.

Camara Laye (c. 1924–   )

Novelist, short-story writer, and autobiographer, Camara Laye was born into the Malinke tribe in Guinea. At the age of eighteen he left western Africa for further schooling in France. He was working in a factory in Paris when he wrote his first book, *The African Child,* from which the selection in this anthology is taken.

Laye is one of those rare men who have had many different influences working upon them—from the tribal customs of his ancestors to the sophistication of a Paris education—and who has managed to make the best of these influences a part of himself and of his writing. There is no rancor in what he writes, only love.

Matei Markwei (c. 1923–   )

Born in Ghana, Markwei is an ordained minister who has spent a good deal of time studying theology in the United States, first at Lincoln University in Pennsylvania and then at Yale University.

Tsegaye Gabre Medhen (1935–   )

Medhen, a native Ethiopian, has served as the Director of Ethiopia's Haile Selassie Theatre and is best known for his play *The Oda-Oak Oracle.*

William (Bloke) Modisane (1923–   )

Modisane, born and raised in the slum Sophiatown, a suburb of Johannesburg, soon found life unbearable under the oppressive apartheid system of South Africa. Before his escape on foot from South Africa through Tanganyika and thence to Europe, Modisane remarked, upon looking at his newborn babe, that he felt remorseful, "for bringing such innocence into the world to perpetuate the work of the devil." This feeling is mirrored in much of his writing, including his autobiography, *Blame Me On History,* which was published in 1964 in England. While most of Modisane's writing centers upon a powerful protest theme, his first short story, "The Dignity of Begging," is satirical and free from the bitterness seen in his later work.

Ezekiel Mphahlele (1919–   )

Mphahlele is one of his continent's most respected educators. He was born in the slums of South Africa, and became a teacher in Johannesburg. But because he organized resistance against the country's policies toward educating Africans, he was banned from teaching there. He later taught at the University College of Idaban, Nigeria, and at University College, Nairobi, Kenya. He is the author of collections of short stories including *Man Must Live* and *The Living and the Dead;* an autobiography, *Down Second Avenue;* and essays on literature and politics, *The African Image.*

Abioseh (Davidson) Nicol (1920–   )

A distinguished and prominent Sierra Leonean physician, Dr. Davidson Nicol uses the pen name Abioseh Nicol when publishing his poetry and prose. Nicol was educated first in Nigeria and then in England, where he took a degree in Natural Sciences at Cambridge. In 1952 he was awarded the Margaret Wrong Prize and Medal for Literature in Africa. Nicol's robust prose is marked by a strong sense of the dramatic; and although it is characterized by a leisurely style, a distinct tone of sarcasm, irony, and cynicism can be found deep beneath the surface.

Rui Nogar (20th cent.)

Rui Nogar is a pseudonym for a Mozambiquan poet whose true identity is safely guarded by his pseudonym. Thus little is known about the man behind the poetry.

Grace A. Ogot (1930–   )

Mrs. Ogot, who began as a nurse and midwife in Uganda and Britain, went on to scriptwriting and announcing for the British Broadcasting Corporation, and now works as the public relations officer of a major African airline. The largest portion of her writing is in the short-story genre.

Lenrie Peters (1932–   )

Peters, born at Bathurst, Gambia, read medicine at Trinity College, Cambridge and was later trained as a surgeon in London. His first book, *Poems,* was published in 1964. Despite a sense of estrangement which pervades some of his poems, Dr. Peters voices a strong spirit of self-pride and personal dignity.

Richard Rive (1931–   )

Born in the slum quarter of Cape Town, South Africa, Richard Rive early discovered the fascination of Shakespeare and Dickens. He has never lost this interest, and on it he has built himself a secure reputation in Africa and abroad as teacher and writer. In 1962, under sponsorship of a foundation, he traveled throughout Africa and Europe studying current literary trends. His writing reflects his cosmopolitan understandings, yet remains innately African. Among his works are *African Songs,* a collection of short stories; *Quartet* and *Modern African Prose,* both anthologies; and *Emergency,* a novel.

James D. Rubadiri (1930–   )

Malawi, where Rubadiri teaches and writes, was once Nyasaland. After Nyasaland was united with the Rhodesias in 1953, Rubadiri stood with the African population who agitated against federation. In the rioting of the Nyasaland crisis of 1959, Rubadiri was arrested but not jailed. After his release he went to England, where he had studied earlier, to work for a time as a broadcaster. In his writing his aim is to interpret the thoughts and experiences of his people.

Mabel Segun (20th cent.)

A native Nigerian, Mabel Segun was educated in grammar school in Lagos and then attended University College in Ibadan. She has worked as a teacher, as editor of the Hansard of the Western Nigerian parliament, and has been in charge of overseas publicity in the Information Services of Western Nigeria. Characterized by a lively, connotative imagery, Miss Segun's verse becomes a vigorous protest medium, in which she sees Africans as "infants overblown,/poised between two civilizations." Her poetry has been published in the African journal *Black Orpheus* and in anthologies in Africa, Europe, and America.

Léopold Sédar Senghor (1906–   )

Léopold Senghor has won success as poet, linguist, teacher, and diplomat. He is very much a black poet, singing the beauty of his blackness, of his cultural heritage, of his people's closeness to nature. He makes much use of the night and the moon, the protective ancestral presences in his imagery. He was born a Catholic in Senegal, a land in which the majority are Moslems. He was the first West African to complete his degree at the Sorbonne in Paris. In 1960 he was installed as the first president of the Republic of Senegal.

Wole Soyinka (1935–   )

Soyinka—actor, playwright, musician, and producer as well as poet —has done much to give impetus to the Nigerian theater. He got his theatrical training in London, and that city saw the first production of his first play. Early he developed a good-humored, satirical style that was unique among African writers. His most recently published works, however, convey a more somber tone. A collection of plays which includes *The Trials of Brother Jero*, a wildly funny exposé of a religious hypocrite in the tradition of Molière's *Tartuffe*, has recently been published.

Efua T. Sutherland (1924–   )

Born in Ghana and educated in England, Mrs. Sutherland (nee Morgue) is married to an Afro-American civil servant; she and her husband make their home in Ghana. Mrs. Sutherland was the founder of the Ghana Drama Studio and of the Ghana Society of Writers. She also helped establish the magazine *Okyeame* to encourage new writers in Ghana. Mrs. Sutherland has written numerous short stories, poems, plays, and children's books. Her work, impressionistic in technique, is infused with passion, impatience, and the agony of her people.

Tshakatumba (20th cent.)

No biographical information available.

Amos Tutuola (1920–   )

The son of a Nigerian cocoa farmer, himself a blacksmith by trade, Tutuola fascinates readers with his unusual use of the English language. Somehow this language serves as a remarkable parallel to the Yoruba myths and legends he recreates in his work. His most popular work is *The Palm-Wine Drinkard*.

428   *Biographies of Authors*

PRONUNCIATION KEY

The pronunciation of each word is shown after the word, in this way: **ab bre vi ate** (ə brē′vē āt). The letters and signs used are pronounced as in the words below. The mark ′ is placed after a syllable with primary or strong accent, as in the example above. The mark ′ after a syllable shows a secondary or lighter accent, as in **ab bre vi a tion** (ə brē′vē ā′shən).

Some words, taken from foreign languages, are spoken with sounds that otherwise do not occur in English. Symbols for these sounds are given at the end of the table as "Foreign Sounds."

a	hat, cap	o	hot, rock	ə represents:	
ā	age, face	ō	open, go	a in about	
ä	father, far	ô	order, all	e in taken	
		oi	oil, voice	i in April	
b	bad, rob	ou	house, out	o in lemon	
ch	child, much			u in circus	
d	did, red				
		p	paper, cup		
e	let, best	r	run, try		
ē	equal, see	s	say, yes		
ėr	term, learn	sh	she, rush	**foreign sounds**	
		t	tell, it		
		th	thin, both		
f	fat, if	ŦH	then, smooth	Y as in French *du*. Pronounce ē with the lips rounded as for English ü in **rule**.	
g	go, bag				
h	he, how				
		u	cup, butter	œ as in French *peu*. Pronounce ā with the lips rounded as for ō.	
i	it, pin	ů	full, put		
ī	ice, five	ü	rule, move		
j	jam, enjoy			N as in French *bon*. The N is not pronounced, but shows that the vowel before it is nasal.	
k	kind, seek	v	very, save		
l	land, coal	w	will, woman		
m	me, am	y	young, yet		
n	no, in	z	zero, breeze	H as in German *ach*. Pronounce k without closing the breath passage.	
ng	long, bring	zh	measure, seizure		

The pronunciation key is from the *Thorndike-Barnhart High School Dictionary*, copyright 1968 by Scott, Foresman and Company.

INDEX OF AUTHORS AND TITLES

2 3 4 5 6 7 8 9 10 11 12 13 14 15 16 17 18 19 20 21 22 23 24 25   78 77 76 75 74 73 72